BRACKEN

Ecology, land use and control technology

BRACKEN

Ecology, land use and control technology

The proceedings of the International Conference – Bracken '85

Edited by R. T. Smith,
University of Leeds,

and

J. A. Taylor,
University College of Wales, Aberystwyth

Parthenon Publishing
THE PARTHENON PUBLISHING GROUP LIMITED

Published by
The Parthenon Publishing Group Limited
Casterton Hall
Carnforth
Lancs LA6 2LA
England

© Copyright 1986 The Parthenon Publishing Group
ISBN: 1-85070-128-8

Printed in Great Britain

Contents

6

C. Bracken Control   323

Names and Addresses of Contributors to this Volume

J W Aitchison, Department of Geography, University College of Wales, Aberystwyth, Dyfed SY23 3DB

Lesley Archibald, Department of Bioscience and Technology, University of Strathclyde, Glasgow G4 0NR

T P Atkinson, Geography Department, Goldsmiths' College, University of London, New Cross SE14 6NW

S M Attree, Department of Botany, University of Manchester, Manchester M13 9PL

D D Barber, Ministry of Agriculture Fisheries and Food (ADAS), Crown Building, Whitby Road, Pickering YO18 7HE

T J Bines, Nature Conservancy Council, South East Regional Office, Wye, Ashford, Kent

R V Birnie, Department of Peat and Forest Soils, Macaulay Institute for Soil Research, Craigiebuckler, Aberdeen AB9 2QJ

I W Brown, Planning Department, Clwyd County Council, County Hall, Mold, Clwyd

R W Brown, North York Moors National Park, The Old Vicarage, Helmsley, York YO6 5BP

M N Burge, Biology Division, Department of Bioscience and Technology, University of Strathclyde, Glasgow G1 1XW

T V Callaghan, Institute of Terrestrial Ecology, Merlewood Research Station, Grange-over-Sands, Cumbria LA11 6JW

J A Cooke, Department of Biology, The Polytechnic, Sunderland, Tyne and Wear SR2 7EE

P J Curran, Department of Geography, University of Sheffield, Western Bank, Sheffield S10 2TN

N A Davenhill, Forest Research Institute, Private Bag, Rotorua, New Zealand

M Davies, Green Crize Farm, Green Crize, Hereford HR2 8AA

A Dyer, Department of Botany, The King's Buildings, Mayfield Road, Edinburgh EH9 3JH

I A Evans, Department of Biochemistry and Soil Science, Memorial Buildings, UCNW Bangor, Gwynedd LL57 2UW

W C Evans, Department of Biochemistry and Soil Science, Memorial Buildings, UCNW Bangor, Gwynedd LL57 2UW

Nadezhda A Fetvadjieva, Higher Institute of Agriculture, "W Kolorov", Plovdiv, Bulgaria

O P Galpin, Llandudno General Hospital, Llandudno, Gwynedd LL30 1LB

B Gamblin, Office National des Forêts, 58 rue Bouquet, 76000 Rouen, France

Robyn E Gaskin, Forest Research Institute, Rotorua, New Zealand

P Hadfield, Department of Botany, The King's Buildings, Mayfield Road, Edinburgh EH9 3JH

L Hamilton, Department of Agriculture, Bairnsdale, Victoria, Australia

D A R Hannam, MAFF, Veterinary Investigation Centre, West House, Thirsk, North Yorkshire YO7 1PZ

R Hartnup, Soil Survey of England and Wales, Rothamsted Experimental Station, Harpenden AL5 2JQ

C H Haufler, Department of Botany, University of Kansas, USA

P A Heads, Department of Biology, University of York, Heslington, York YO1 5DD

D R Helliwell, Waterloo Mill, Wotton-under-Edge, Glos. GL12 7JN

M J Hicks, Institute of Terrestrial Ecology, Monks Wood Experimental Station, Abbots Ripton, Huntingdon PE17 2LS

G B Horsnail, May and Baker Ltd, Rose Cottage, Bagby, Thirsk, North Yorkshire

P J Hudson, North of England Grouse Research Project, The Game Conservancy, Askrigg, Leyburn, North Yorkshire DL8 3HG

Elizabeth J Hughes, Department of Geography, University College of
    Wales, Aberystwyth, Dyfed SY23 3DB

J A Irvine, Biology Division, Department of Bioscience and Technology,
    University of Strathclyde, Glasgow G1 1XW

J Johnson, ADAS, Government Buildings, Lawnswood, Leeds LS16 5PY

J M S Jubrael, Department of Botany, University of Manchester,
    Manchester M13 9PL

R C Kirkwood, Biology Division, Department of Bioscience and
    Technology, University of Strathclyde, Glasgow G4 0NR

P Lamontagne, Office National des Forêts, 58 rue Bouquet, 76000 Rouen,
    France

G J Lawson, Institute of Terrestrial Ecology, Merlewood Research
    Station, Grange-over-Sands, Cumbria LA11 6JU

J H Lawton, Department of Biology, University of York, Heslington,
    York YO1 5DD

J W Lea, Soil Survey of England and Wales, Rothamsted Experimental
    Station, Harpenden AL5 2JQ

H C Lee, Northern Ireland Plant Breeding Station, Manor House,
    Loughall, Co Armagh, Northern Ireland

J G Lockwood, School of Geography, University of Leeds, Leeds LS2 9JT

J E Lowday, Institute of Terrestrial Ecology, Monks Wood Experimental
    Station, Abbots Ripton, Huntingdon PE17 2LS

Deborah K Lyall, School of Geography, University of Leeds, Leeds
    LS2 9JT

M MacGarvin, Department of Biology, University of York, Heslington,
    York YO1 5DD

R H Marrs, Institute of Terrestrial Ecology, Monks Wood Experimental
    Station, Abbots Ripton, Huntingdon PE17 2LS

A T McDonald, School of Geography, University of Leeds, Leeds LS2 9JT

M McElwee, Biology Division, Department of Bioscience and Technology,
    University of Strathclyde, Glasgow G1 1XW

D R Miller, Macaulay Institute for Soil Research, Craigiebuckler,
    Aberdeen AB9 2QJ

D Moore, Department of Botany, University of Manchester, Manchester
    M13 9PL

A Morniche, Office National des Forets, 58 rue Bouquet, 7600 Rouen,
    France

Pamela S Naden, School of Geography, University of Leeds, Leeds
    LS2 9JT

A K Oswald, Long Ashton Research Station, Weed Research Division,
    Begbroke Hill, Yarnton OX5 1PF

C N Page, Royal Botanic Garden, Edinburgh

C G Palmer, Shell Chemicals UK Ltd, Woodview Cottage, Coddington,
    Ledbury, Herefordshire HR8 1JH

J I Pitman, Department of Geography, Kings College, University of
    London, London WC2R 2LS

R M Pitman, Department of Geography, Kings College, University of
    London, London WC2R 2LS

P I Petrov, Institute of Upland Stock Breeding and Agriculture, 5600
    Troyan, Bulgaria

D S Preest, Forest Research Institute, Private Bag, Rotorua, New
    Zealand

W G Richardson, Long Ashton Research Station, Weed Research Division,
    Begbroke Hill, Yarnton OX5 1PF

J Roberts, Institute of Hydrology, Wallingford, Oxfordshire OX10 8BB

R C Robinson, May and Baker Ltd, Ongar Research Station, Fyfield Road,
    Ongar, Essex CM5 0HW

C C Rudeforth, Soil Survey of England and Wales, Rothamsted
    Experimental Station, Harpenden AL5 2JQ

R Scott, Institute of Terrestrial Ecology, Merlewood Research Station,
    Grange-over-Sands, Cumbria LA11 6JU

C M Shearer, School of Biological Sciences, University of Sydney, NSW
    2006, Australia

Elizabeth Sheffield, Department of Botany, University of Manchester,
    Manchester M13 9PL

R M M Smith, Department of Biochemistry and Soil Science, University
    College of North Wales, Deiniol Road, Bangor, Gwynedd LL57 2UW

R T Smith, School of Geography, University of Leeds, Leeds LS2 9JT

D Soper, May and Baker Ltd, Ongar Research Station, Fyfield Road,
    Ongar, Essex CM5 0HW

Carole J Sparke, Department of Agriculture, University of Newcastle-Upon-
    Tyne, Newcastle-Upon-Tyne NE1 7RU

C Surman, May and Baker (New Zealand) Ltd, PO Box 35-060, Lower Hutt,
    Wellington, New Zealand

J A Taylor, Department of Geography, University College of Wales, Aberystwyth, Dyfed SY23 3DB

T R E Thompson, Soil and Survey of England and Wales, Rothamsted Experimental Station, Harpenden AL5 2JQ

J A Thomsom, School of Biological Sciences, University of Sydney, NSW 2006, Australia

P Wathern, Department of Agricultural Botany, University College of Wales, Aberystwyth, Dyfed

Ruth E Weaver, Department of Geography, University of Aberdeen, St Mary's, High Street, Old Aberdeen AB9 2UF

T M West, Long Ashton Research Station, Weed Research Division, Begbroke Hill, Yarnton OX5 1PF

G H Williams, Department of Botany, West of Scotland Agricultural College, Ayr KA6 5HW

C Willoughby, School of Biological Sciences, University of Sydney, NSW 2006, Australia

J Winkworth, May and Baker Australia Pty Ltd, 19-23 Paramount Road, West Footscray 3012, Victoria, Australia

P G Wolf, Department of Botany, University of Kansas, USA

P S Wright, Soil Survey of England and Wales, Rothamsted Experimental Station, Harpenden AL5 2JQ

J A Zabkiewicz, Forest Research Institute, Rotorua, New Zealand

List of those who attended "Bracken 85"

ADER   Miss K G   Glasgow University
ANDERSON   Mrs P   Consultant Ecologist
ATKINSON   Dr T P   Goldsmiths' College   London University
BARBER   Mr D D   ADAS   Pickering
BARKER   Mr A   Farmers Weekly
BIBBY   Dr C J   RSPB   Powys
BIRNIE   Dr R V   Macaulay Institute for Soil Research
BLOOMFIELD   Mr J R G   May and Baker Ltd   Essex
BROWN   Dr I W   Clwyd County Council
BROWN   Dr R W   North Yorkshire Moors National Park   Helmsley
BURGE   Dr M N   Strathclyde University
BURN   Miss A M   Nature Conservancy Council   Bangor
CALDWELL   Dr N E   The National Trust (South Wales)   Dyfed
CAMERON   Mr G   Union Carbide Europe
CHENE   Mr G   Office National des Forêts   France
CHRZANOWSKA   Ms K   Water Research Centre   Bucks
COOKE   Dr J A   Sunderland Polytechnic
COOKE   Mr K   May and Baker Ltd   Ilkley
COX   Mr T W   May and Baker Ltd   Glos.
CURRAN   Dr P J   University of Sheffield
DAVIES   Dr D H K   Edinburgh School of Agriculture
DAVIES   Mr M D   MDA Services
DRUMMOND   Mr J M   May and Baker   Scotland
DYER   Dr A F   University of Edinburgh
EVANS   Em. Prof W C   University College of North Wales
FETVADJIEVA   Prof N   Agronomic Institute of Plovdiv   Bulgaria
FISH   Ms E A   Suffolk Trust for Nature Conservation
FITZGERALD   Mr C J   Suffolk Trust for Nature Conservation
GALPIN   Dr O P   Llandudno General Hospital
GAMBLIN   Mr B   Office National des Forêts   France
GARLAND   Mr P   Union Carbide UK Ltd
GASKIN   Mrs R E   Forest Research Institute New Zealand
GOODMAN   Mr N H   May and Baker Agrochemicals   Essex
GRAHAM   Mr A J   ADAS   Cumbria
HADFIELD   Mr P R H   Edinburgh University
HAGGER   Dr R J   Long Ashton Research Station   Oxford
HANNAM   Mr D A R   MAFF   Thirsk
HARTINGTON   Mr P   Bolton Abbey Estate   Skipton
HAYES   Lt Col J P R   Ministry of Defence

13

HEADS Mr P A	University of York
HEARN Miss K A	National Trust Glos.
HELLIWELL Mr D R	Wotton-Under-Edge Glos.
HORSNAIL Mr G B	May and Baker Thirsk
HUDSON Dr P J	The Game Conservancy Leyburn
INGLEBY Vis M R	Snilesworth Northallerton
JOHNSON Mr J	ADAS Leeds
KIRKWOOD Dr R C	University of Strathclyde
KNEALE Dr P E	Leeds University
LAMONTAGNE Mr P	Office National des Forêts France
LAWSON Mr G J	Inst of Terrestrial Ecology Cumbria
LAWTON Dr J H	University of York
LEE Dr H C	Northern Ireland Plant Breeding Station
LOCKWOOD Dr J G	University of Leeds
LOVEGROVE Mr R R	RSPB Powys
LOWDAY Mr J E	Institute of Terrestrial Ecology
LYALL Ms D K	University of Leeds
MACLEOD Mr S H C	Silica Sand Company Otley
MARRS Dr R H	Institute for Terrestrial Ecology
MAYALL Mr J L	Commonwealth Bureau of Pastures & Field Crops
MILLER Mr D R	Macaulay Institute for Soil Research
MORLEY Mr J D	Whitby
MORTON Dr A J	Imperial College Berks
NADEN Dr P S	University of Leeds
O'CONNER Mr B L	MAFF Northallerton
OGDEN Mr P A	Snowdonia National Park Authority
OSWALD Mr A K	Long Ashton Research Station Oxford
PAGE Dr C N	Royal Botanic Garden Edinburgh
PALMER Mr C G	Shell Chemicals Ltd
PANDOV Mr K	Bulpharma Bulgaria
PETROV Mr P	Inst. Upland Stock Breeding, Troyan, Bulgaria
PITMAN Mrs R M	King's College London
PREEST Dr D S	Forest Research Institute New Zealand
QUEST Mr P C	North Yorkshire Moors National Park
RADLEY Dr G P	Nature Conservancy Council Norwich
REES Mr D I	Nature Conservancy Council Cardiff
RICHARDSON Mr W G	Long Ashton Research Station Oxford
ROBERTS Mr H W	Welsh Office Agriculture Department
ROBERTS Dr J M	Institute of Hydrology Oxfordshire
ROBERTS Ms L J	ADAS Dyfed
ROBINSON Dr R C	May and Baker Ltd Essex
SHEARER Ms C M	University of Sydney
SHEFFIELD Dr E	University of Manchester
SMITH Mr P A	Wath Estate
SMITH Mr R M M	University College of North Wales
SMITH Dr R T	University of Leeds
SOPER Mr D	May and Baker Ltd Essex
SPARKE Dr C J	University of Keele
SURMAN Mr C	May and Baker (New Zealand) Ltd
SWANN Mr N B	Du Pont (UK) Ltd Stevenage
TAYLOR Prof J A	University College of Wales Aberystwyth
THOMPSON Ms A R	Dow Chemicals Co Ltd Herts
THOMPSON Mr T R E	Soil Survey of England and Wales
THOMSON Prof J A	University of Sydney Australia
TURNER Dr A K	Glasgow University
TURNER Dr D J	Oxford Plant Science Ltd
VAN SCHOUBROECK Miss M E P	University College of Wales, Aberystwyth
WARD Miss S	Dartmoor National Park Authority
WEAVER Miss R E	University of Aberdeen
WILDRIDGE Mr S M	May and Baker Essex
WILLIAMS Dr G H	West of Scotland Agricultural College
WILLIAMS Mr J L L	Welsh Office Agricultural Dept
WILLIAMS Mr R	Nature Conservancy Council

Preface

Bracken research is enormously indebted to the work of Alexander Stuart Watt (1892 - 1985) whose publications spanned more than 60 years. Watt was very much a pioneer ecologist concentrating originally on woodland communities then later, in his work on the Breckland, upon factors determining the spatial arrangement of plant communities, their changes in time and the effects of grazing. In continuous field recording over many years, much of it concerned with bracken, such dynamic ecological questions were addressed and have formed the basis for updated material presented in this volume. In 1976 Alex Watt had, in collaboration with other bracken specialists, been instrumental in convening the Linnaean Society's Symposium on 'The Biology of Bracken' in London. Subsequently the Royal Society of Edinburgh arranged a regional Conference in 1981 to focus on 'Bracken in Scotland'.

'Bracken-85', on which this volume is based, took place from 1-5 July 1985 at the University of Leeds. Attended by over 100 delegates (see list), some 50 papers were offered at the conference by an unusually wide range of specialists representing the United Kingdom and a number of overseas countries. All but one of the papers which were presented appear in this book. Some are little altered from original papers submitted, while others have undergone varying degrees of surgery by the authors and editors. The latter hope that the final outcome of this exercise has been a more balanced and readable volume. The book contains three sections, A. The Bracken Problem: Nature, Extent and Origins, B. Biology and Environmental Relationships of Bracken Communities and C. Bracken Control. These represent a re-arrangement of material under broader headings than were adopted at the original Conference. With so many contributions, a breakdown under different headings was clearly desirable but has its limitations in view of the subject range of each paper. The book represents a state-of-the art review of progress in our understanding of bracken as a plant and the land use and environmental problems it now poses. A distinctive and essential component of the volume is therefore the section on bracken control in which varying solutions to what has

15

become known as "the bracken problem" are offered.

Bracken emerges as one of the most successful and versatile plants in the world. It ranges from sub-Polar latitudes to the Equator and from sea level to 3000 m in the Tropics. Characteristically, it awaits woodland clearance or agricultural decline before advancing and, once established, is aggressive and supremely competitive. It can adapt to the open, from its earlier, shaded habitats. Through its toxic effects it is hostile to many other plants and to many animals, generating carcinogens and creating an extensive form of biological pollution which affects grazing animals and possibly humans. The combination of health-hazard and land loss has created for the bracken plant a reputation which is both unique and sinister. World-wide, the plant is spreading on to underused or abandoned agricultural land which it is very difficult and expensive to reclaim. It has also spread where burning has been practiced both in range and forest management. In Britain alone, land losses this century to bracken encroachment are in the same league as the more publicised losses to urbanisation and forestry. Moreover, the encroachment rates of between 1 and 3% per annum would appear to be unprecedented in the historic and prehistoric records.

Bracken itself is responding to the changing situation created by its advancement. It is possibly evolving to new and even wider environmental tolerances and more subtle survival strategies as may be indicated by its propensity for polymorphism. Most significantly it offers a permanent, aggressive challenge to any control technology. Biological control may be the solution, provided suitable predators can be identified and successfully released. Alternatively, the perception of bracken as a major and accessible energy crop for conversion to a competitive biofuel provides a coming-to-terms with the plant, as happened in earlier centuries, and a conservational form of control which could be introduced alongside eradication schemes and afforestation programmes. Remote, steep bracken banks could be left as they are, for these often claim attention for their picturesque changes of colour with the seasons. The gentler, warmer bracken slopes could be converted back to pastures, occasionally to arable cropping, provided enclosure and controlled grazing are practicable. The latter, incorporating cattle as well as sheep, forms a suitable recipe for avoiding periodic and costly cash injections for hill pasture rehabilitation. Such multi-purpose, ecologically perceptive land use strategies applied to the management of existing bracken lands, are the best long-term solution to the general problem of countryside planning.

It is hoped that the progress revealed and stimulated by BRACKEN '85 will be maintained and strengthened not least because, as the bracken problem becomes larger in scale, it will become increasingly difficult and costly to solve. Again, once solutions - permanent ones - have been found, an equally formidable task faces their dissemination and implementation. The bracken problem is as much an educational and political challenge as it is a scientific and technical one.

R T Smith
J A Taylor

January 1986

An International Bracken Group

The need for continuing national and international communication in bracken research and bracken land problems led to the establishment, at a meeting at the University of Leeds on November 14th 1985 of the <u>International Bracken Group</u>. The following terms of reference were agreed.

(i) To provide a continuing scientific and technical liaison regarding research developments in bracken and the environmental problems posed by it; to provide guidelines, as required or requested for research and land development strategies.

(2) To communicate the results and the needs of bracken research to both local and national authorities, including the media; to promote the funding of bracken research and bracken land development programmes.

Whilst recognizing that many valuable initiatives have been achieved on an individual basis it is hoped that the formation of the Group will help bring the problem of bracken more into the public eye as well as helping lone workers feel less isolated in their endeavours. Any readers who wish to be kept in touch with the activities of the Group are invited to communicate with Professor J A Taylor.

Acknowledgements

The editors would like to record their grateful thanks to all those who contributed to the success of the Conference on which this publication is based. Special mention is due to May and Baker Ltd, MAFF and Shell Chemicals UK for important contributions to a final excursion day in the North York Moors at Bracken '85, not reported elsewhere in this volume. Thanks are also due to the typist, Miss Judith Allison at Superscript, 18a Otley Road, Leeds 6, for the production of word-processed copy.

The Bracken Problem:

Nature, Extent and Origins

The Bracken Problem: A Local Hazard and Global Issue

J A Taylor

INTRODUCTION

Estimating bracken areas

Let us begin by paying a tribute to the vision and energy of Sir George Stapledon[1], first Director of the Welsh Plant Breeding Station at Aberystwyth, who personally mapped the vegetation of northern Ceredigion in 1913 in great detail and later, in 1936, in collaboration with William Davies[2], produced a generalised vegetation map for the whole of Wales. Dense bracken areas were delineated quite precisely on the Ceredigion map which was presented on the same scale (1;10560 or 6" to the mile) as that adopted for the second vegetation survey of Wales, organised from the Geography Department, UCW, Aberystwyth under the direction of the author in the period 1961-66[3]. A detailed cartographic analysis by Dowrick[4] revealed that the total area under dense bracken cover in northern Ceredigion, Dyfed, had virtually doubled from 6.4 km^2 to 14.3 km^2, an average increase of 1.91% per annum over 65 years, ie. almost within the average life-expectancy of the individual (Table 1). The author[5] attempted a comparison of the vegetation records of the Stapledon and Taylor surveys (Fig.1) of Wales and concluded that the total area of dense bracken cover in the Principality has increased from 3.0% in 1936 to 5.8% in 1966. This is equivalent to a virtual doubling in a period of 30 years or so. Table 2 presents estimated bracken areas for Wales (precisely measured from maps), England (reported in MAFF leaflet, No 190[6]) and Scotland (entirely hypothetical and extrapolated from the statistics for Wales, on the basis of two assumptions: (i) that the currently available figures for Scotland are not only variable but underestimates and (ii) that the scale of the bracken problem in Scotland is unlikely to be less, proportionately, than that for Wales). The results of current work to estimate the actual extent of the bracken cover of Scotland, by Birnie (herein), which will test these two assumptions, is eagerly awaited. It should be concluded here that some parts of Scotland appear to have

21

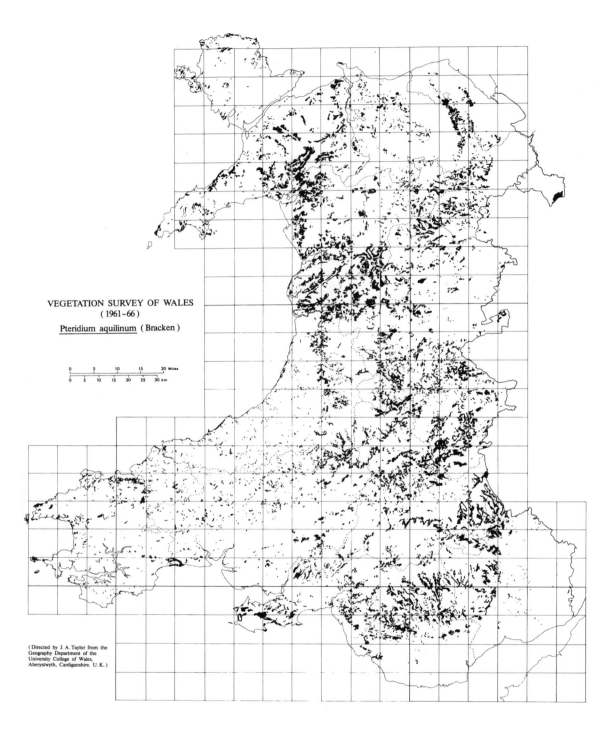

VEGETATION SURVEY OF WALES
(1961–66)

Pteridium aquilinum (Bracken)

(Directed by J. A. Taylor from the
Geography Department of the
University College of Wales,
Aberystwyth, Cardiganshire. U. K.)

Figure 1   Wales: distribution of bracken (Pteridium aquilinum) 1963
(after Vegetation Survey of Wales[3])

Table 1. Local mean percentage rates of bracken expansion per annum in Britain

Locality	Bracken area	Date	Bracken area	Date	% Annual area increase
North Ceredigion	6.39 km²	1913	14.34 km²	1978	+1.91%
East Dartmoor	5.88 km²	1969	6.37 km²	1976	+1.19%
Western Powys (a)	76.5 km²	1962	116.6 km²	1978	+3.28%
(b)	231.5 km²	1962	139.6 km²	1978	-3.77%
S.E. Clwyd	74 ha	1966	87 ha	1980	+1.14%
Mid Glamorgan	103 ha	1960	113 ha	1978	+0.54%
Menteith Hills (South Central Highlands)	8 ha	1946	17 ha	1980	+3.3%
Poltalloch site					
South	1201 ha	1947	1202 ha	1967	+0.0% (net)
Centre	929 ha	1947	1313 ha	1967	+2.2% (net)
North	2205 ha	1947	2543 ha	1967	+1.0% (net)
Total	4335 ha	1947	5058 ha	1967	+1.0% (net)
Brynffynnon					
Moel Arthur (Clwyd)	n.a.	1948	n.a.	1984	+2.6%
North York Moors	[A generalised average over recent years]				+1.0%

(a) Common land
(b) Enclosed land

Sources: North Ceredigion (Dowrick, 1976); East Dartmoor (Dowrick, 1977); Western Powys (a) + (b) (Lloyd, 1979); S.E. Clwyd (Hughes, 1981); Mid Glamorgan (Cornish, 1979); Menteith Hills (Birnie, 1984); Poltalloch site (Birnie and Miller, 1985, herein); Brynffynnon (Brown and Wathern,1985, herein); North York Moors (Brown, 1985, herein).

only a thin bracken cover, eg. the Central Lowlands and the North Eastern Lowlands, which would detract from the national 'averaged' figure in contrast to regionally dense covers in Argyllshire and Southwest Scotland.

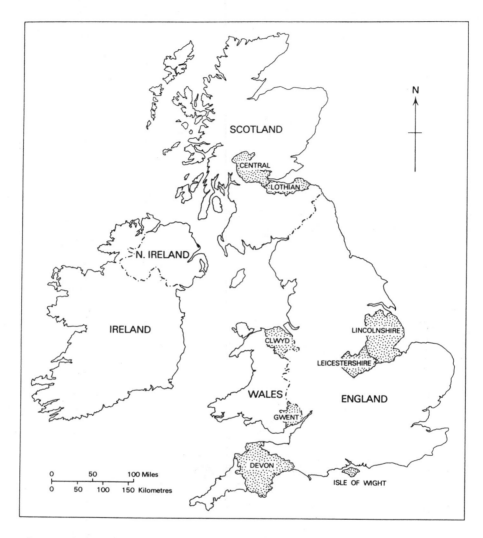

Figure 2   British Isles: national areal equivalents lost to bracken encroachment (see Table 2)

Encroachment rates

A series of independent measurements[5,8-17] of bracken encroachment rates for widely dispersed sites throughout Britain show a remarkable degree of accord (Table 2). The source material for these estimates is, exclusively, summer aerial photography or imagery. With the outstanding exception of enclosed land in western Powys, which records a reduction in bracken area of 3.77% per annum (eradication schemes have been intense and clearly successful in this

24

Table 2. Bracken Statistics and Estimates

Country	Area	Bracken Area	Bracken Encroachment Rate
A. WALES	20,761 Km²	1241 Km² (= 5.8% of land area: = GWENT) approx. = TILLAGE) approx. (140,000 ha.)	20.7 Km² p.a. = 2072 ha. p.a. = 5120 ac. p.a. = 1 to 3% land loss p.a.
B. SCOTLAND (a) (Taylor, 1978)[16]	78,762 Km²	4720 Km² (= 6.0% of land area; = CENTRAL & LOTHIAN (approx.)	
(b) (Bunce, et al., 1980)[15]		981 Km² (= 1.2% of land area)	3% p.a. land-loss in Kincardineshire (Birnie, 1984)[14]
(c) (Hendre, 1958)[7]		1820 Km² (= 2.3% of land area)	
C. ENGLAND	130,357 Km²	404 Km² = 40,400 ha. = 0.3% of the land = ISLE OF WIGHT	1.0% p.a. land-loss in North York Moors (Brown herein)[8] 1.19% p.a. land-loss in East Dartmoor
D. U.K.	243,363 Km²	6720 Km² (est. from G.B. figures) (= DEVON)	2880 Km² = 1.3% land-loss p.a. (Bunce, et al., 1980)[15]
E. GREAT BRITAIN	229,880 Km²	6361 Km² (= LINCOLNSHIRE)	103.6 Km² (25,600 ac. land-loss p.a. = 2.8% land-loss p.a. (Taylor, 1978)[16]

area), all average annual encroachment rates are positive, ranging from 0.65% to 3.3%. Significantly, the highest rates recorded so far are on the common lands of western Powys, (+3.28%) (see Hughes and Aitchison, herein) and in the Monteith Hills of Southern Central Highlands[14]. In Table 2, land losses to bracken expansion are expressed in terms of the more familiar county units. For example, the bracken cover of Wales (1,241 km^2), if consolidated, would obliterate Gwent or an area nor far below total tillage within the Principality (Figure 2).

Similarly, England has lost the equivalent of the Isle of Wight (c 400 km^2) to the weed, and Scotland (hypothetically, assuming a 6.0% cover) has lost 4720 km^2, which would account for the combined area of Central and Lothian. Incorporating the same assumptions for Scotland as above, Great Britain has lost 6361 km^2 (= Lincolnshire) and the UK has lost 6720 km^2, (= Devon) to bracken encroachment (Figure 1).

On two grounds, all these calculations are underestimates. First, the initial data base is 1961-66, since when it may confidently be assumed that bracken has been advancing at an annual rate of from 1% to 3% in round figures and varying from region to region. Secondly, the vast majority of bracken occurs on slopes of considerable steepness (Table 3), and the recording areas, as shown on maps, photographs or imagery, incorporate predictable errors which increase with the angle of the slope. For example, for a 10° slope the error is -1.5% but for a 30° slope, the error is as much as -15.5% (Figure 3). However, assuming that the data presented in Figure 3 apply to 1985, then the estimated average annual land loss to bracken, of 103.6 km^2 (= c 10,000 ha) by the year 2000, represents an area equivalent to either the county of Gwent or the county of Surrey, which will additionally have been obliterated by the weed, if the eradication programmes remain as small and ineffective as they have been in recent decades.

Land losses to urban development[18] and afforestation[19] are well documented and well known. The former were averaged for the early 1970s at 15,000 to 20,000 ha per annum. The latter, for the period 1966 to 1976, averaged at a loss of 13,379 ha per annum, but ranged from 5000 to 20,000 ha in individual years. This latter rate has declined a great deal since 1976 with the Forestry Commission being forced to cut land acquisition costs and seek sources of cash revenue, while private forestry has been less able than previously to maintain benefits to investors through tax concessions. It is also probable that the rate of urbanisation has tended to decelerate since 1976, as the British economy has undergone a net decline. Bracken, in contrast, marches on. Accepting the above rates of land loss, it may be concluded that, in the recent past, <u>for every two hectares of farming land lost each year to urban development and forestry, from 0.5 to 1.0 ha is being lost to bracken encroachment</u>. This is a very serious state of affairs locally, regionally and nationally, and not least on a farm scale[20], (Table 4), a point which will be developed later in the paper.

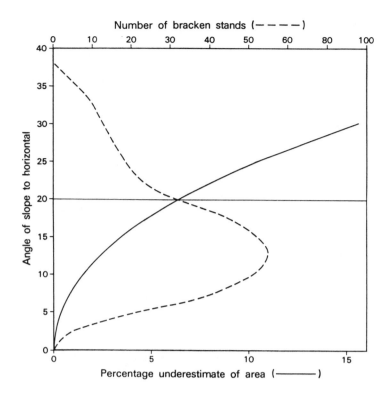

Figure 3 The relationship between angle of slope and the underestimation of slope-area on maps. The formula used is $A = a \div \cos \alpha$ where A is the length of the slope on the ground, a is the length of the slope on the map, and α is the angle of the slope.

Table 3.   Selected point locations in west central Wales : the number of stands of bracken from the map analysis in relation to the angle of slope upon which they were sited (after Platt and Taylor, 1985)[20].

Angle of slope	Number of stands	%	Cumulative %	Inverse cumulative %
	5	2.45	2.45	99.99
5.5 - 10°	40	19.61	22.06	97.54
10.5 - 15°	55	26.96	49.02	77.93
15.5 - 20°	45	22.06	71.08	50.97
20.5 - 25°	22	10.78	81.86	28.91
25.5 - 30°	25	12.25	94.11	18.13
30.5 - 35°	11	5.39	99.5	5.88
35.5 - 40°	1	0.49	99.99	0.49
	204	99.99	99.99	99.99

Table 4. Percentage area in bracken on a selection of farms in west central Wales (after Platt and Taylor, 1985).[20]

% bracken cover	No. of farms	Continuous cover <10% sward	Patchy cover <10% sward	Continuous cover >80% sward	Patchy cover >80% sward	Continuous cover 100% sward	Patchy cover 100% sward
0-10	8	2	1	-	2	-	3
11-20	7	2	1	1	2	-	1
21-30	6	3	-	1	2	-	-
31-40	5	-	-	3	2	-	-
41-50	3	-	-	2	1	-	-
51-60	0	-	-	-	-	-	-
61-70	1	-	-	1	-	-	-

THE BRACKEN PROBLEM

Bracken, the natural environment and land use

Aside from man-controlled domestication, weeds represent the positive response of the plant kingdom to the impact of man's land use. Commonly, plants which are recessive in their natural habitats are released from competition from superior species, eg. trees, removed by man, and expand within limits dictated by biotic pressures. Less commonly, some plants which become weeds, also have the capacity to dominate in natural ecosystems, or more precisely, the capacity to adapt, long-term, to varying states of competition with other plants and with animals. The bracken fern is a prime example of such versatility, longevity and persistence, and, moreover, it plies its successful strategies in a wide variation of climates, altitudes and latitudes, except for the polar regions[21,22].

Defining the 'bracken problem'

The bracken problem is therefore fundamentally a loss of land to a weed which is very difficult to control. Bracken expands or retreats (i) on its own terms, in the absence of human interference, (ii) in relation to man-induced changes in land use and (iii) in response to natural environmental changes, again in the absence of man. These three sets of relationships often coincide over space and time in a complex manner and compete for supremacy. They are summarised in Tables 5A, 5B and 5C which are self-explanatory. In essence, the bracken fern may (i) pioneer new habitats but, more usually, (ii) assert after natural deforestation or burning, or natural reduction of predators, or (iii) very commonly and internationally, it accompanies the pioneer fringe of agricultural colonisations, awaiting its chance to encroach just as soon as those

28

BRACKEN RETREAT

(A1) Natural degeneration as litter gain exceeds loss. (This is rarely observed, at present, in Britain). Other vegetation resurges, including tree regeneration, which may be checked if bracken readvances, as commonly occurs in Britain.

(A2) Fauna recover in numbers and diversity.

(A3) Soil freed eventually from rhizome systems but tends away from 'brown podzolic' towards either a more podzolized or a more gleyed profile.

(A4) Nutrient cycle reduced and nutrient status lowered somewhat, e.g. potassium, but pHs may rise, e.g. to 5.0 to 6.0.

(A5) Microclimate gradually adjusts to mesoclimate; increased exposure and increased frost susceptibility.

(A6) Decrease in toxins present and reduced health risks for animals and humans.

(A7) Decreased biomass (if used as a resource) but increased agricultural potential.

(A8) Increase in animal predator populations.

Table 5A contd.

BRACKEN EXPANSION

(A1) Other vegetation out-competed; tree regeneration prevented; bracken in equilibrium with its environment but at a high phytosociological status.

(A2) Fauna restricted but some shelter provided.

(A3) Soil monopolised by intensive rhizome development but soil profile tends towards 'brown podzolic' i.e. a podzolised 'brown earth'.

(A4) Nutrient cycle enhanced compared with adjacent habitats; high potassium levels but relatively low pH levels e.g. 4.0-5.5

(A5) Microclimate more strongly developed: reduced and retarded temperature ranges, reduced frost susceptibility, higher humidities, increased shelter.

(A6) More toxins generated: health risks increased for animals and humans.

(A7) Increased biomass (if used as a resource) but reduced agricultural potential.

(A8) Reduction in animal predator populations.

(A) BRACKEN-INDUCED CHANGES

Table 5A. Consequences of the expansion or retreat of bracken in relation to changes induced by bracken itself.

29

BRACKEN RETREAT

(B1) Minimal or no interference with expanding woodland cover.

(B2) Infrequency or absence of forest burning.

(B3) Creation of large pastures (with widely spaced boundaries), heavily grazed by large herds, e.g. a predominance of cattle.

(B4) Primary arable cycles, but bracken may survive in shaded boundary zones or hedges.

(B5) Agricultural expansion and intensification, e.g. new enclosures and innovations. Agricultural change, from grass to arable or from sheep to cattle, for example.

(B6) Introduction of schemes for bracken control and eradication.

(B7) Adequate maintenance of soil pH levels e.g. above 5.5-6.0.

(B8) Inadequate drainage schemes permit high water tables.

(B9) Non-operation of acid rain (deposition) hazard: soil pH levels maintained at above 5.5.

Table 5B. contd.

BRACKEN EXPANSION

(B) MAN-INDUCED CHANGES

(B1) Forest thinning and removal either directly for settlement, agriculture, charcoal, or indirectly via animal hunting and herding.

(B2) Forest burning (re B1) scorches buds and promotes spore release and germination.

(B3) Creation of small pastures (with closely spaced hedges or walls giving shade and shelter), lightly grazed by small herds, e.g. a predominance of sheep.

(B4) Reduced use of arable land, especially its eventual abandonment, when bracken becomes a major coloniser.

(B5) Agricultural decline or underuse. Agricultural change, from arable to grass or from cattle to sheep, for example.

(B6) Absence of schemes for bracken control and eradication.

(B7) Inadequate maintenance of soil pH levels e.g. falling below 5.5.

(B8) Drainage schemes, lowering water tables.

(B9) Acid rain (deposition) lowers soil pH to less than 5.5.

Table 5B. Factors affecting the expansion or retreat of bracken in relation to changes induced by human activities.

BRACKEN RETREAT

(C1) Close-canopied, dense woodland with excessive shading and very few clearings.

(C2) Infrequency or absence of natural forest fires.

(C3) Climatic cooling with shorter growing season and increased frost risk.

(C4) Trend towards an 'Atlantic' type of maritime climate with increased altitudinal lapse rates, increased wind exposure and increased susceptibility to frost at the higher altitudinal limit of bracken.

(C5) Soil compaction, panning or shallowing due to freezing, drying, drainage impedence or erosion.

(C6) Increased trampling by larger fauna e.g. aurochs, deer, etc.

(C7) Improvement of calcium levels in the soils, e.g. through colluviation.

(C8) Increase in animal predator populations.

Table 5C. contd.

BRACKEN EXPANSION

(C1) Open-type woodlands, with abundant semi-shaded habitats in clearings and at woodland edge.

(C2) Natural forest fires scorch buds and promote spore release and germination.

(C3) Climatic warming with longer growing season and reduced frost risk.

(C4) Trend towards a 'Boreal' type of continental climate with reduced altitudinal lapse rates, reduced wind exposure and reduced frost susceptibility at the higher altitudinal limit of bracken.

(C5) Soil 'loosening', mixing or deepening due to winter frosts, earthworm activity or tree root development.

(C6) Reduced trampling by larger fauna e.g. aurochs, deer, etc.

(C7) Soil acidification, through long-term depletion or acid rain (deposition).

(C8) Reduction in animal predator populations.

(C) ENVIRONMENTALLY-INDUCED CHANGES

Table 5C. Factors affecting the expansion or retreat of bracken in relation to changes induced by the natural environment.

colonizations slow down, and especially when they retreat or are abandoned.

HISTORY OF BRACKEN IN BRITAIN

These themes are well demonstrated in Pteridium spore records gleaned from pollen diagrams for sites in Wales[23,24] and Northern England[25] (Figure 4A). The curves for the past 10,000 years give precise context to the reviews provided by Rymer[26], and Huntley and Birks[27], the latter source being an isopoll atlas of European vegetation history in general. Bearing in mind the diversity of sites, authors and dating methods used, the two curves for Wales and Northern England are remarkably parallel, if deviating in the timing of the first mid-Holocene peak. The latter is about 2000 years later for Northern England compared with Wales. The two curves are divisible into alternating plateaux and peaks. For Wales, the period from 10 ka to 7 ka, and, for Northern England, from 10 ka to 5 ka, was one of relative stability, with bracken accompanying the development of extensive woodlands and being confined to shaded clearings and woodland edges. It had a minority and localised role at this stage. By the period 7 ka to 5 ka in Wales, and 5 ka to 3 ka in Northern England, the bracken curves peak as the Neolithic Revolution led to the first large-scale deforestations and the first permanent farms, fields and settlements. The period from 5 ka to 2 ka in Wales, and 3 ka to 1 ka in Northern England witnessed a second plateau, indicating some degree of net, but complex, balance between bracken survival and the impact of Bronze Age and Iron Age agriculture, the latter in particular being adapted to the lower slopes and valleys. Finally, in the historic period, but again peaking later in Northern England, a second and greater bracken expansion occurred, possibly resulting from a combination of factors, including the medieval climatic optimum, the enclosure of upland heaths[28], population movement and farm establishment upslope in the nineteenth century, depopulation and evacuation downslope in the twentieth century, and the increasing dominance of sheep in upland grazing systems over the past 50 years or more. Within these four-fold cycles, deviations occurred with respect to elevation (Figure 4B). The 'upland' sites (bottom-left) display least variation over time for both regions. 'Coastal' or 'lowland' sites for Northern England are similarly conservative but the analogous curve for Wales has a much greater amplitude. However, it is the 'intermediate' site-curves which are not only parallel to each other but also exert a strong influence on the 'mean' curves (bottom-right). Moreover, both curves take off sharply in the historic period and are still rising today, whereas the curves for the other sites show a recent decline. The 'intermediate' sites are the upper slopes and plateau shoulders, between 200 m and 350 m OD, where the current concentrations of dense bracken occur and where most variations in the bracken cover and land-use pressures are expressed.

AN INTERNATIONAL WEED
Global range

Page[21] has indicated, through his taxonomic and phytogeographical studues of Pteridium species, that their global

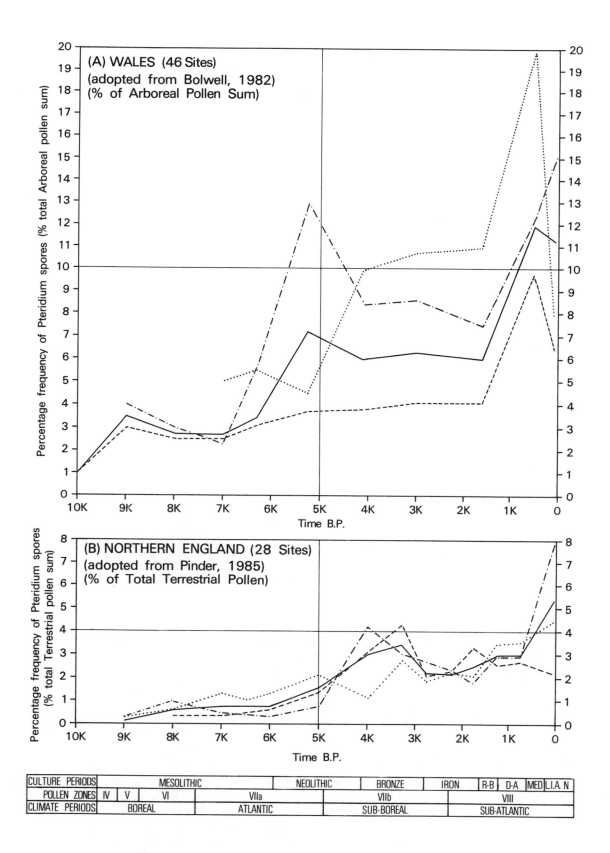

CULTURE PERIODS		MESOLITHIC				NEOLITHIC	BRONZE	IRON	R-B	D-A	MED	L.I.A. N
POLLEN ZONES	IV	V	VI	VIIa			VIIb			VIII		
CLIMATE PERIODS		BOREAL		ATLANTIC			SUB-BOREAL			SUB-ATLANTIC		

Figure 4A   Percentage frequency of Pteridium spores, 10,000 − 0 BP

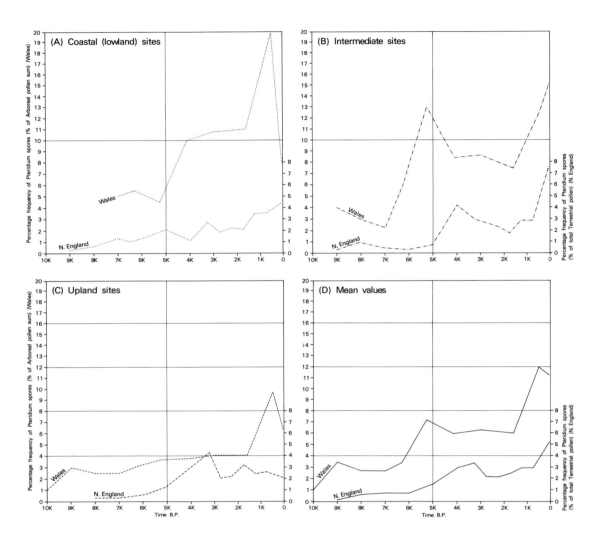

Figure 4B   Bracken spore frequency curves 10,000 - 0 BP, by site groups

distribution approximates to ubiquity, with the major exclusions of those parts of Eurasia and North America north of the Arctic Circle, and the continent of Antarctica, where, significantly, agriculture is, by conventional experience, a non-starter. Again, the temperate mountains, above c 600-1000 m, and the tropical mountains above c 3000 m, are in the same category. The author has recently recorded Pteridium aquilinum (i) at 510 m OD on the slopes of Cader Idris in west central Wales, where the average annual rainfall is c 2000 mm and the temperatute regime is approaching periglacial (it also occurs in the Breckland in eastern England at 35 m OD where the rainfall is c 700 mm), (ii) on the north-facing coast of the island of Corfu in a characteristically Mediterranean climate of long summer drought and warm wet winters, (iii) on the volcanic peaks of Gran Canaria, at 500 m in a dry, sub-tropical climate with runs of 5 to 6 years, for example, without any precipitation except for cloud and mist and (iv) in burned 'galeria' (gallery forest) at 1100 m near Brasilia in the

Brazilian 'cerrados' which experience a typically wet/dry seasonal 'savannah' climate. Flenley[29] has recorded <u>Pteridium esculentum</u> (Forst.f.) Cockayne at elevations between 2100 m and 2700 m in the highlands of New Guinea and at, and just above 3000 m on Mount Ruwenzori in East Africa. These individual observations are testimony to the enormous latitudinal and altitudinal range of the bracken fern which appears to be able to adapt and survive all climatic limitations and constraints except frost and severe wind exposure, the latter being more precisely defined as fast-moving cold air at freezing temperatures (see Smith R T, herein).

International questionnaire

A questionnaire was circulated in early 1985 to all countries in the world via the British Embassies or the equivalent. Although only 30 valid replies have been received from the 164 countries orginally circulated (excluding the UK), 27 (=90%) reported the presence of Pteridium and only 3 (=10%) did not. The view was expressed by 23 that the country had a 'bracken problem', often localised and regional, but 20 (87%) perceived this problem as 'negligible' or 'minor' and only 3 (13%) as 'major' or 'serious'. This rather limited sample of information does indicate the global dispersion of Pteridium, the widespread awareness that it is a 'problem' but only in specific environments eg. agriculturally underused or abandoned areas, forested zones, in upland grazings (more especially in the tropics) and along the sides of fields, forests and valley bottoms.

Case studies

Three case studies are of especial interest. Firstly, Professor Robert Mount[30] of Auburn University, Alabama regards the bracken problem in the southeast of the USA as 'serious'. The use of fire in forest management, prior to 1960, was accidental, or due to arson or lightning, but, since 1960, prescribed burns have been used extensively as part of forest management in the pursuit of uniformity of stands. This policy has clearly favoured bracken which is becoming the dominant ground flora on many soil types, suppressing other species eg. <u>Aristida stricta</u> (wire grass) which used to be very prominant in coastal areas of the South. The scale of the encroachment, according to Mount[30] is vast yet unappreciated, as is the health risk to animals, goats and the white-tailed deer. Forest management policies in central Ontario, Canada, have also produced similar results. (R T Smith, pers comm).

A second case study is reported by Dr Walter Lang[31], who is in charge of one of the State District Offices of the Black Forest in Bavaria, West Germany. Again, bracken has encroached aggressively in recent years, out-competing other species, including berry-bearing bilberry etc. that normally provides food for birds and animals, including the wood grouse and the red deer - which, as a result, have declined in numbers. This region has suffered severely from acid deposition, receiving pollution from many directions and, under the effects of continental anticyclones in winter, this becomes concentrated, cumulative and has caused, in many areas, irreparable damage to forest stands. This again gives the semi-shaded canopies ideal for bracken expansion. Moreover, the eventual acidificaion of soil also favours the weed. The application of manure and fertilisers to correct calcium deficiencies is less common now than it used to be, so with soil pHs decreasing to less than 3.0 and even to 2.5 in places, the acid-tolerant bracken fern is favoured. The same process is probably operating in the British uplands, and elsewhere, as well.

A third case-study presents a new bracken map of New Zealand (Figure 5)[32]. The widespread distribution in North Island is reminiscent of the pattern presented for Wales, but in South Island two major concentrations occur, in the far north and extreme south. As in Britain, it is the medium altitudes rather than the high or low altitudes which are mainly affected but the dominant land use involved is forestry, not agriculture. Bracken control is therefore mainly associated with afforestation projects and forest management. It is possible that the traditional intensity of New Zealand farming has been instrumental in checking the encroachment rates of the weed onto grazed areas.

These three case-studies encapsulate the bracken problem and its twin origins: land management practices, and environmental changes, part natural, part man-induced.

A HEALTH HAZARD

A series of papers herein, by W C Evans, I A Evans, Galpin and Smith, Hannam, and Hudson, indicate the stage reached in research into bracken-induced diseases in animals and man. It has been unequivocally shown (i) that direct consumption of bracken fronds or spores can induce cancers in animals and, on the basis of Japanese evidence, in humans[33] and (ii) that bracken generates, via frond drip, rhizome exudates and spore release, several toxins and carcinogens which, successively diluted, enter local hydrological cycles and are available for consumption anywhere along a series of biogeochemical pathways. In addition to water, another important vector is milk. Although Galpin and Smith herein have found no correlations between high cancer mortality rates in humans in parts of north-west Wales and the density of bracken cover per administrative area or catchment, the aggregated nature of the mortality data and the variability of size and shape of the areas to which they refer were bound to disguise whatever relationships may exist in high-risk areas. The latter include valley heads, farms and hamlets within dense, arcuate bracken zones, and taking local, not mains, water supplies off the slopes, and milk from cattle grazing on bracken-infested pastures. Here the pathways are short, direct, and regularly used. By now, however, only a small minority (less than 1.0%) of farms are not on the mains but small-scale dairying and keeping a cow or two for domestic milk supply still persists. Again, the old producer-retailer system has been extensively replaced by the milk-lorry, and bulking at the local creamery. Pasteurization etc. has also buffered public milk supplies against infections. Similarly, bulking has occurred in public water supplies via the reservoir system. In addition to valley-head 'risk-areas' there are also 'risk-times', in particular when spore-release occurs, which is normally in late summer or early autumn, ie. late September to October, when, as I A Evans recommends

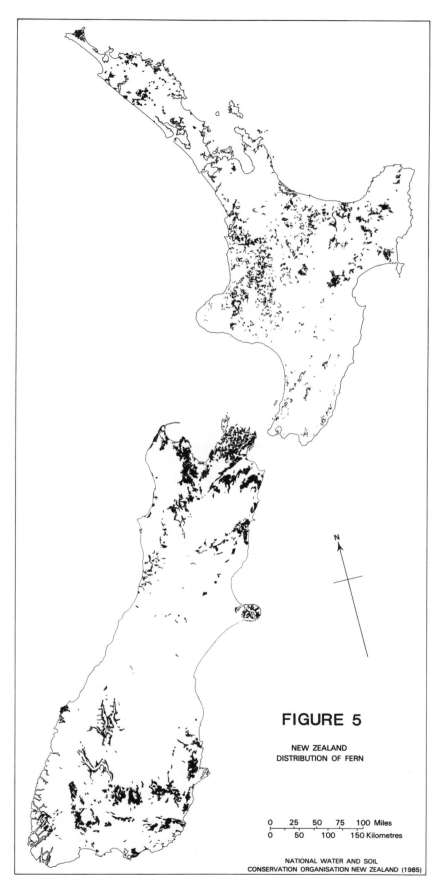

FIGURE 5

NEW ZEALAND
DISTRIBUTION OF FERN

0	25	50	75	100 Miles
0	50	100		150 Kilometres

NATIONAL WATER AND SOIL
CONSERVATION ORGANISATION NEW ZEALAND (1985)

herein, people working in or near bracken should wear face-masks. Under no circumstances should bracken fronds ever be eaten unless they have been thoroughly boiled in alkaline water. Bracken can form part of Japanese coleslaw, not only in Japan but in Japanese restaurants. The experimental evidence published by Hirayama[33] showed, statistically, that regular bracken-eating Japanese population groups developed three times as many cancers as non-bracken-eating, control groups.

The health risks to cattle and sheep are severe, especially in bracken-infested, enclosed fields, when, under certain weather or management constraints, the grazing options available to the animals may be reduced. For example, drought may check grass growth, inclement weather may force sheep into bracken for shelter, bits of bracken are cut with the hay and may be eaten, sooner or later. Other environmental factors[34] may operate in upland Britain to induce disorders in the digestive system. Siliceous rocks and blanket peats induce soft but very acid water supplies. Locally, such rock formations as the Silurian and Ordovician include lead and cadmium ores, which are, cumulatively, toxic. To these documented hazards must now be added the bracken fern which is proven to generate such carcinogens as shikimic acid, and others not yet biochemically identified.

More research is urgently needed to study 'risk-areas' and 'risk-times' on a local medical, and local environmental scale where the cancer-bracken relationship must be more sharply focussed. Not only is land being lost to bracken encroachment at an alarming and unprecedented rate in Britain (and, indeed, elsewhere), but such land is also being polluted by a toxic and carcinogenic plant.

BRACKEN CONTROL

Finding the Achilles heel

A large number of papers in this volume deal with the many and varied aspects of bracken control, ranging from cutting and rolling, to aerially-applied selective herbicides, soil-acting herbicides, tractor-mounted weed-wipes and biological control by the release of selective predators like the South African moth, Parthenodes angularis, but, as Page (herein) points out, successful eradication or control of the bracken fern will come not from an aggressive, frontal attack but from a subtle discovery of, and coming to terms with, its Achilles heel, if it is ever found to possess one! Lawton, herein, is sanguine that the search for the right predators from the right hemisphere, continent or subcontinent will eventually win more success.

Eradication strategy

Experience, technology, competition, inertia, information, perception and bureaucracy all tend to confound the evaluation of different methods of bracken control and create entrenched views rather than the right answers for each individual manifestation of the problem on a local or farm scale[20]. Underlying this complex situation are certain principles which may be regarded as constants amid the variables.

The first principle is that each individual bracken stand is unique in location, topography and accessibility. Secondly, its taxonomy, age and growth stage will also be characteristic as related to any eradication programme. Thirdly, the type of land, be it enclosed or unenclosed, and its tenure, whether rented or owned, common or crown land, will predetermine any proposed control programme. Fourthly, the availability of access for tractors, Land Rovers etc. and any proposal to provide or improve vehicular access will be most relevant. Fifthly, and most important, the intended land use of the area to be cleared of bracken should be an integral part of the control programme. The usual intention is grassland but it should be enclosed and grazed as soon as possible by store cattle rather than sheep - or both. However, on the less steep slopes, arable cropping is quite feasible and, in special cases, forestry.

Multi-purpose land use strategies

A flexible, multi-purpose land-use programme, adapted to the varying potentials of the different bracken areas within any particular farm[20], is likely to be more successful than the Micawber-like assumption that a step-by-step conversion from bracken to pasture will result from using sheep alone, without any enclosure. Experimental work is also needed on the introduction of small-scale forestry developments on farms (Helliwell, herein) and on the harvesting of bracken for local conversion into biofuels, preferably at mobile pelletization plants (see Lawson et al herein). In these contexts, conservational issues can be reconciled not only in the preservation of selected bracken stands (which, ideally, will not be accessible to grazing animals), but also in the creation of diverse land-use patterns on farms which will help preserve some local flora and fauna and also attract new species to the farm and its environs. It follows that the ideal way forward is for particular farms to have their own land-use development programmes, forming a constructive after-care to bracken eradication schemes which will in turn be successful in attracting improvement grants. The current availability of grants is restricted, uneven and unfair and needs drastic rationalisation - on the basis, for example, of the comprehensive, farm-based, land-use strategies outlined here.

THE CASE FOR A NATIONAL CAMPAIGN FOR BRACKEN CONTROL IN BRITAIN

There is at present in Britain an increasing divergence between the escalating rates of land loss and land pollution to bracken encroachment and the diminishing resources available to stem the tide of deterioration. Indeed, if a national campaign were to be launched for bracken control in the near future it would probably take until the end of the century merely to begin to contain the advancing weed in a constant area. To achieve a national hold on the bracken fern by the year 2000, (assuming an average annual increase in the national bracken area of 1% is to be prevented over the next fifteen years) a total area of 1554 km^2 (= 150,000 ha) of bracken will need to be eradicated. This area is approximately equal to the size of the County of Gwent or the County of Surrey. Assuming an average cost of reclaiming bracken land at £40 per ha[35], it can be estimated that total national reclamation costs, at current prices, to prevent the continuing 1% pa encroachment of bracken in Britain, would be £40 x 150,000 = £6,000,000. The recent sales value of the type of forestry or farm land which includes bracken slopes approximates to £1,000 per hectare[36,37]. This means that the agricultural land that would be retained in agriculture by 2,000 AD would be valued at £150,000,000, a truly phenomenal restoration and reinvestment. The cost-benefit per hectare is 25:1. On this evidence, it may be confidently postulated that it would be more cost-beneficial to the farmer and to the nation to reclaim one hectare of bracken land rather than one hectare of heathland or one hectare of wetland. Yet, current improvement grants go mostly to heathland and wetland reclamation rather than to bracken eradication, much to the chagrin, surely, of all conservationists.

Additionally, the health risks to animals and, in risk-areas already discussed, to humans, would be checked and eventually reduced, further enhancing the cost-benefit argument.

It should also be pointed out that the bracken-infested lands under discussion are within the marginal lands of Britain and within the 'Less Favoured Areas' designation of the EEC where farms and communities are under economic and social pressures in addition to the limitations of the climate and soil of the British uplands. These regions and communities are subsidised in many ways at present. As 'Less Favoured Areas' they qualify for higher levels of grant aid. What better form of investment could there be for our hills and uplands than a comprehensive and generous system of grant aid for bracken control, thereby reclaiming vast areas of potentially valuable grazings and, in effect, adding a large land area, and quality slopes at that, to our national heritage? Land is a long-term and largely renewable resource, regardless of the contemporary and localised context of EEC food surpluses. The global food requirement will continue to rise, and its challenges will be met more effectively in policies of land protection and reclamation rather than technology-based increases in agricultural productivity alone.

ACKNOWLEDGEMENT

The constructive comments of Dr Richard Smith on an earlier draft of this paper are gratefully acknowledged.

REFERENCES

1) Stapledon R G (1913) Land use and vegetation map of northern Ceredigion : scale 1/10560. Presented in wall map form; housed at Welsh Plant Breeding Station, Aberystwyth

2) Stapledon R G and Davies W (1936) A survey of the agricultural and wastelands of Wales, London, Faber and Faber

3) Taylor J A (1968) Reconnaissance vegetation surveys and maps. In, Bowen E G, Carter H and Taylor J A (eds) Geography at Aberystwyth, Ch 6, 87-110, University of Wales Press, Cardiff

4) Dowrick S J (1976) Twentieth-century vegetation change in North Ceredigion. BSc Project Essay, UCW Aberystwyth, Dept. of Geography

5) Taylor J A (1974) Marginal physical environments. In Jenkins D A

(ed) <u>Marginal land use : integration or competition?</u> Potassium Institute, Colloquium Proceedings, No 4, UCN Wales, Bangor, 10-29

6) MAFF (1983) <u>Bracken and its control.</u> Leaflet 190. HMSO

7) Hendre G F (1958) The size of Scotland's bracken problem. <u>Scot. Agric. Econ.</u> 9, 21-28

8) Dowrick S J (1977) <u>A biogeographic study of aspects of bracken distribution and growth in the Heytor-Rippontor area of E Dartmoor.</u> BSc Dissertation, UCW Aberystwyth, Department of Geography

9) Lloyd S (1979) <u>The changing pattern of bracken in central Montgomeryshire, (1962-78).</u> BSc Dissertation UCW Aberystwyth, Department of Geography

10) Hughes S A (1981) <u>Ecological factors and the changing distribution of bracken on Eglwyseg Mountain, Clwyd.</u> BSc Dissertation UCW Aberystwyth, Department of Geography

11) Cornish I D (1979) <u>A study of the changes in bracken distribution on Caerphilly Common, (1960-78) and the factors governing its present distribution.</u> BSc Dissertation, UCW Aberystwyth, Dept of Geography

12) Brown I W and Wathern P (1985) Bracken control and land management in the Moel Famau County Park, Clwyd, North Wales, In Smith R T and Taylor J A (eds) <u>Proceedings of BRACKEN '85 Conference</u> (This volume)

13) Brown R W (1985) Bracken in the North York Moors : its ecological and amenity implications, In Smith R T and Taylor J A (eds) <u>Proceedings of BRACKEN '85 Conference</u> (This volume)

14) Birnie R V (1985) Mapping bracken (<u>Pteridium aquilinum</u>) infestation in Scotland : an assessment of remote sensing-based mapping techniques, In Robertson R A (ed) <u>Remote sensing in peat and terrain resource surveys</u>, Proc. Symp. IPS Commission I, Aberdeen, 87-101

15) Bunce R G H, Barr C J and Whittaker H A (1980) <u>An integrated system of land classification.</u> NERC, ITE, Annual Report, 28-34

16) Taylor J A (1978) The British upland environment and its management. <u>Geog.</u> 63 (4), 338-353

17) Birnie R V and Miller D R (1985) The bracken problem in Scotland: a new assessment using remotely sensed data, In Smith R T and Taylor J A (eds) <u>Proceedings of BRACKEN '85 Conference,</u> (This volume)

18) Best R H (1976) The extent and growth of urban land <u>The Planner</u> 62, 8-11

19) Forestry Commission : <u>Annual Reports</u>

20) Platt A and Taylor J A (1985) <u>Research investigation into bracken</u>

41

encroachment rates and reclamation strategies in West Central Wales.
Final Report : Department of Geography, UCW Aberystwyth

21) Page C N (1976) The taxonomy and phytogeography of bracken - a review. Bot. J. Linn. Soc. 73, 1-34

22) Taylor J A (1980) Bracken : an increasing problem and a threat to health. Outlook on Agriculture, 10 (6), 298-304

23) Bolwell J M (1982) The development of bracken (Pteridium aquilinum) through the Flandrian. BSc Project Essay, UCW Aberystwyth, Department of Geography

24) Taylor J A (1985) The relationship between land-use change and variations in bracken encroachment rates in Britain. In Smith R T (ed) The biogeographical impact of land use change, Biogrographical Monographs 2, 19-28; BSG/Geo Books, Norwich

25) Pinder C (1985) The changing distribution and development of bracken in the Pennines during the Flandrian. BSc Project Essay; Deparament of Geography, UCW Aberystwyth

26) Rymer L (1976) The history and ethnobotany of bracken. Bot. J. Linn. Soc., 73, 151-176

27) Huntley G and Birks H J B (1983) An atlas of past and present pollen maps for Europe : 0-13,000 years ago. CUP

28) Parry M L (1978) Climatic change, agriculture and settlement. Dawson : Archon Books, Folkestone

29) Flenley J R (1984) Private Communication

30) Mount R (1985) Private Communication

31) Lang W (1985) Private Communication

32) Map prepared by G Eyles and L Russ from data in the New Zealand Land Resource Inventory. NWASCA 1975-79. Soil Conservation Centre, Ministry of Works and Development, Palmerston North, New Zealand.

33) Hirayama T (1979) Diet and Cancer. Nutr. Cancer, 1, 67-81

34) Howe G M (1963) National atlas of disease mortality in the United Kingdom. Nelson, London

35) Williams G H (1980) Bracken control : a review of progress 1974-1979. Res and Dev Publications No 12 West of Scotland Agricultural College

36) MAFF (1985) Agricultural land prices in England and Wales. Booklet 2320 (84)

37) Inland Revenue (1984) Property valuation office. Market Report. Spring 1984. No 41, 18

42

The Bracken Problem in Scotland: A new assessment using remotely sensed data

R V Birnie and D R Miller

INTRODUCTION

The aim of this paper is to present a progress report on a programme to map the extent and rate of spread of bracken on Scottish hill land. This programme is based partly upon the use of remotely sensed data. In the first section, the methods and results of a pilot study conducted in 1981/82 are outlined. The conclusions from this study are then linked to the development of a survey methodology for a national mapping programme which commenced in September, 1984. Some recent results from this programme are presented to illustrate the initial application of the survey methods.

BACKGROUND

During the 1940s and early 1950s, bracken clearance, mainly by cutting, was a common feature of Scottish hill farming practice. By 1952, some 8,000 ha of hill pasture were being treated annually under Department of Agriculture and Fisheries for Scotland (DAFS) grant-aid schemes[1], but by 1970 the increasing costs of labour and other factors had resulted in a dramatic decline in bracken control measures, only 200 ha being recorded as being treated that year. Following a report[2] in 1970 on the effectiveness of asulam in bracken control, a resurgence in control took place with some 3,500 ha being treated in 1974. This upsurge was, however, short-lived and by 1977 only 1,500 ha were treated. At the present time, some 1,200-1,400 ha/year are being treated with DAFS aid, this low figure being attributed to the cost of application and the conditions associated with grant-aid, although the latter have recently been reviewed[3].

The trend towards a reduction in bracken clearance schemes has to be seen against a background of extensive bracken infestation in Scotland. In 1958 it was estimated that 182,000 ha, or approximately 5%, of permanent grass and rough grazings were affected[4]. With the reduction in control, bracken is likely to have spread significantly.

43

Estimates[5] suggest that bracken now infests 470,000 ha, or 11%, of Scottish hill land. If true, this represents a considerable waste of resources. So far, however, little attempt has been made to establish either the extent to which bracken has spread during the post-war period or its current distribution. One of the main reasons for this has been the lack of a convenient mapping base to carry out such an extensive survey. Recognising the potential of remote sensing for this purpose, DAFS approached the Macaulay Institute in 1981 with a request that a pilot study on the use of remote-sensing techniques for mapping bracken be conducted.

DAFS PILOT STUDY

The objective of the pilot study was to compare air photo and satellite image-based techniques for mapping bracken and to establish a mapping strategy for the rapid and accurate assessment of bracken infestation throughout Scotland. A subsidiary objective was to determine whether the rate of bracken spread could be determined by photogrammetric analysis of historical air photo cover. The results of the pilot project have been presented elsewhere[6,7] and are only summarised here. The project was carried out in three phases between September, 1981 and December, 1982.

In the first phase, all available aerial photography and satellite imagery of a 50 km-square test area in the southern central Highlands was obtained. This area, extending from Loch Tay in the north to the Menteith Hills in the south, was chosen after consultation with DAFS staff. The second phase of the project involved both field mapping and laboratory analysis. Ground survey was used to establish actual bracken distribution in selected areas. This provided accurate boundary information against which those interpreted from aerial photography or satellite imagery could be compared. The laboratory analysis involved the use of a Bausch and Lomb Zoom Transferscope and a Wild B8S photogrammetric plotter for air photo mapping. Satellite image analysis was accomplished using the Macaulay facility, MAPIPS[8] and the GEMS image processing system at RAE Farnborough. The final part of the study involved the development of a method for rapid field assessment of the accuracy of interpreted, bracken boundaries.

The study utilised one LANDSAT image (Path 222 Row 20 24/8/76). Comparison between interpreted bracken distribution and actual bracken distribution indicated that the major bracken infestations could be identified. Where only an indication of bracken presence or absence was desired, the satellite interpretation was approximately 78% accurate. However, for boundary information only 30% accuracy was achieved using Landsat MSS data (Table 1).

Utilising panchromatic aerial photography, bracken boundaries could be successfully identified at a scale of 1:10,000 or larger. At scales smaller than than 1:25,000, it proved difficult to identify bracken consistently. The date of photography also proved crucial. Photogrammetric plotting of a small test area in the eastern Grampians also indicated that changes in bracken distribution could be identified by analysis of historical photo cover. Using 1946 RAF photography and 1980 Clyde Surveys coverage it was shown that bracken infestation had increased by 112% since 1946 or an average rate of

TABLE 1   Summary of field check results

Cases	Sites 1	2	3	4	5	6	7	8	9
1 Present not mapped			X					X	
2 Present mapped incorrectly	X		X	X			X		
3 Present mapped correctly						X		X	X
4 Absent but mapped		X			X				X
5 Absent not mapped						X	X		
Presence/absence only	X	-	X	X	-	X	X	X	X

2.2% per annum (see Taylor, herein).

The major conclusion drawn from the pilot study was that LANDSAT MSS imagery alone could not provide an accurate base for bracken mapping. Aerial photography at scales of 1:25,000 and larger was required before bracken boundaries could be reliably identified. Aerial photography also provided a suitable medium for assessing post-war changes in bracken cover.

THE PRESENT SURVEY AND ITS METHODOLOGY

The results of the pilot project proved counter to initial expectations. Although it did prove possible to map bracken accurately on 1:25,000 or larger scale aerial photography, to perform a national mapping programme on such a base would be a major task. Alternatively the more suitable base, satellite imagery, had provided inaccurate results.

Utilising the results of the pilot study, the methodology of the present survey, commenced in September 1984, represents an amalgam of techniques. Recognising the value of aerial photography, the initial objective was to establish accurately the extent of bracken cover in a number of test areas around Scotland and to determine how bracken infestation has changed during the post-war period. Some preliminary results of this work are presented below. The second objective of the survey was to extrapolate from these local results and derive regional estimates of bracken infestation. It is hoped that this extrapolation will be achieved using land cover information derived from LANDSAT Thematic Mapper (TM) images combined with information on soil types and topography. The accuracy of these regional estimates will be tested with reference to air photo analysis and ground checks. It is also intended to repeat the statistical estimation of Hendry[4] by including a question on bracken in the June 1986 Agricultural Returns. The survey methodology is outlined below, in five stages.

1   Test site selection

Test sites had to be selected to study the rate of spread of bracken in different environments. The criteria used to determine likely areas were:

    a) known bracken occurrence, based on Hendry's map[4] and on Land Capability mapping by the Soil Survey of Scotland.

    b) available aerial photography, providing a range of dates of coverage from the 1940s and 1960s to as recent as possible, with scales of 1:25,000 or larger[6].

    c) a range of climatic, topographic, soil type and management conditions, across Scotland, based on OS topographic maps, Soil Survey of Scotland maps and a bioclimatic map[9].

Ten sites were chosen for study (Fig.1 and Table 2).

TABLE 2   Test sites

Detail sites	OS Grid references	
1 Glensaugh	NO 368000E	698000N
2 Sourhope	NT 386000E	620000N
3 Poltalloch	NR 181000E	698000N
4 Gatehouse	NX 259000E	561000N
Comparison sites		
Loth	NC 297000E	992000N
Fearnoch	NM 292000E	728000N
Moorfoot Hills	NT 648000E	330000N
Dunkeld	NO 304000E	748000N
Strathfillan	NN 236000E	730000N
Conic Hill	NS 242000E	692000N

    These sites provide a range in eastings of 211 km and northings of 350 km; altitudes vary from sea-level at Poltalloch to 500 m OD at Strathfillan. At the four main test sites, open hillside slopes range from level to about 50°. Glensaugh and Sourhope are both Hill Farming Research Organisation (HFRO) stations, with controlled burning and grazing regimes and appropriate records. Sourhope and Conic Hill were both studied by Joan Mitchell[10], and so historical information is available to compare with present-day bracken boundaries. None of the area has been sprayed or cut. For all sites, except Sourhope, low oblique panchromatic photography was taken by the RAF between 1946 and 1954 at a scale of c 1:9,900. All are covered by OS 1:25,000-1:27,000 vertical panchromatic photography, giving data for the 1960s or 1970s. Four sites have 1:10,000 photography between 1981-1984 with other coverage in the late 1970s at 1:10,000-1:15,000 (also panchromatic). The dates of photography range from April to September. Four of these sites are being studied in greater detail, two in the west (Poltalloch and Gatehouse) and two in the east (Glensaugh and Sourhope). Here, in addition to photogrammetric mapping, land survey techniques are being used to map the current bracken boundaries. These sites are also being monitored in the course of a detailed ecological study of bracken by the Department of Geography, University of Glasgow.

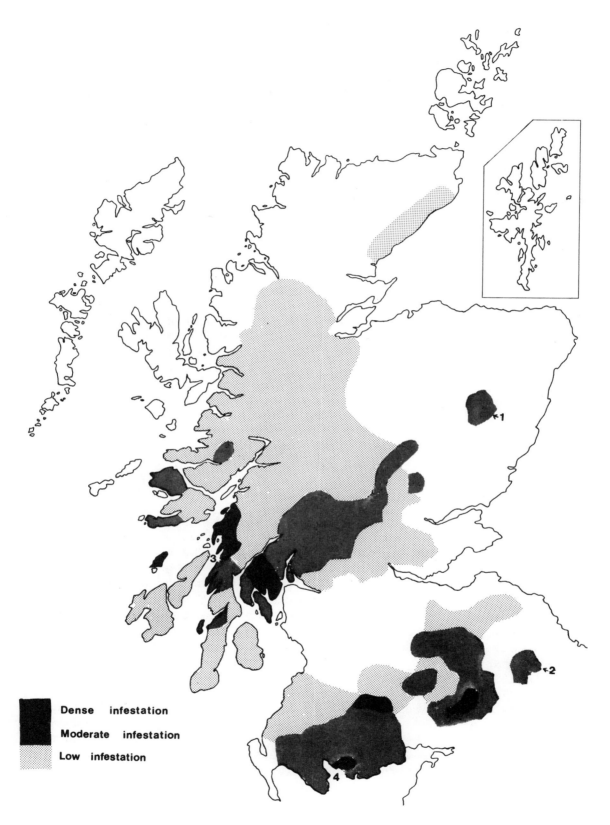

Figure 1   The distribution of bracken in Scotland based on the map of
Hendry (1958).   The four main test sites are indicated.   Comparison
sites have been omitted for clarity - see Table 2).

2 Land survey

At each of the four primary test sites, selected bracken stands are being delineated by land survey techniques. Of these, only Poltalloch has so far been completed. This will be used as an example (Fig.2). The survey was carried out in the first week of September 1984. The equipment used was a Wild T1, 6" theodolite and DI4 electronic distance meter (EDM) with a prism and pogo. The theodolite angles were estimated to 3" precision, and the EDM had an accuracy of 5 mm 5 ppm. Control was calculated from three nearby OS trigonometric pillars so that comparison with photogrammetric plots of the area was possible. In total, 483 detail points were measured along the bracken fronts in this area. There are two reasons for this approach. One is to locate the fronts to a high degree of accuracy; the second, is to position pegs along the main and diffuse bracken fronts. It will then be possible on subsequent visits to measure precisely the movement of the bracken fronts.

The value of the above method depends upon the definition of the bracken fronts. Typically, two fronts may be identified - the "main" front, which is the extent of 100% bracken coverage, and the "diffuse" front, which is the furthest extent of bracken fronds. The diffuse front, when it exists, is comparatively easy to define, but the main front is less clear and is considered to be where bracken forms a closed canopy with litter beneath. Check observations on points of detail such as walls show that the potential accuracy of the plot is of the order of 27cm. The bracken fronts observed were bordering on heather, rushes and pasture grasses. A variety of discrete bracken stands were also pegged.

3 Historical plot, 1947

To assess the rates of bracken spread over a longer period of time, an historical record of bracken distribution is required, the best source of which is aerial photography. The oldest available is RAF fan photography. As this is low oblique photography, taken using a 20" focal length camera, the Wild B8S photogrammetric plotter cannot be used to map the bracken distribution. Thus, use has to be made of a Bausch and Lomb Zoom Transferscope and a Sketchmaster. This means that relief displacement in the projected photographs is not eliminated. OS 1:10,000 map sheets and photogrammetrically-produced supplementary control are used to control the plots in planimetry. In addition, some topographic features were surveyed so that as small an area as possible is uncontrolled. Thus, on the steepest slopes, accuracies of the order of a few metres should still be expected. Photo-interpretation is a more serious source of error. To ensure as accurate an interpretation as possible, field overlays are done of each photograph, or a section of it, and each area is inspected using a zoom stereoscope before plotting. On the August 1947 photographs, the bracken is easily delimited through tonal differences with surrounding pasture land. It is less clear in areas of heather, where textural differences are often more important. Where the bracken fronds are diffuse, the furthest extent cannot be identified, and only the main boundary is plotted (Figure 3).

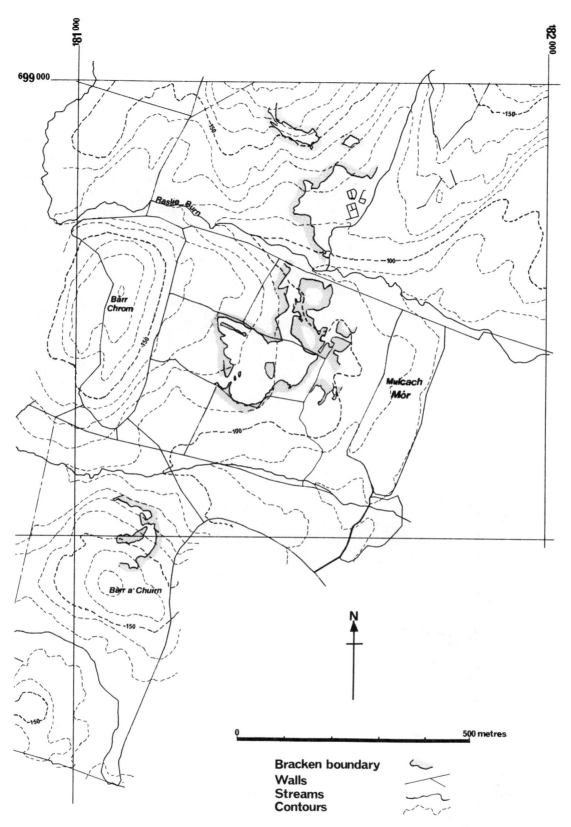

Figure 2 The Poltalloch test site showing the bracken boundaries as surveyed in September 1984. The Raslie Burn (stream) is the southern limit of the northern section, while the burn to the north of Barr a'Chuirn is the northern limit of the southern section. The central section lies between these two burns.

49

Figure 3   Bracken distribution at Poltalloch in 1947

4 Interpretation of recent photography

The 1967 OS 1:25,000 photography was the largest scale available. This was obtained using a 152 mm focal length camera, and is suitable for photogrammetric plotting, thus eliminating relief displacement as an error source (Figure 4). This photography was flown in May, which is the reason for the reversal in air-photo interpretation guides compared with the 1947 photography. An additional consequence of using May photography is that the areas mapped are litter-covered and therefore effectively identify the previous year's main boundary (as explained above). From this photography, contours at 5 metre intervals can also be plotted, enabling bracken distribution to be related to altitude and slope. The planimetric accuracy of the plots is also better because the plot is done on a cross-slide table. Air photo interpretation is the most likely source of error. At the smaller scale and at this time of year, tone is the most important aid to bracken identification, particularly in heather surroundings. In the grass-dominated areas, the textural differences are more important.

5 Analysis of photogrammetric plots: Poltalloch results

The areas where bracken has either increased or decreased were identified by comparison of the 1947 and 1967 distribution maps (Figs. 5a and 5b). The total area of bracken infestation, the area of bracken increase, and the area of bracken decrease, were then computed using a digitising system, linked to a PET microcomputer. In order to reveal the relative rates of bracken spread in different ecological settings, the Poltalloch site was subdivided into three sections: north, centre and south, the two east-west burns (streams) forming the boundaries. The relevant results are presented in Table 3.

Table 3   Changes in bracken coverage 1947 to 1967 at Poltalloch site

Site	1947 (m^2)	1967 (m^2)	Increase (m^2)	Decrease (m^2)	Total section areas (m^2)	Gross annual increase %	Net annual increase %
South	120,074	120,218	24,036	23,892	302,525	1.1	0.0
Centre	92,854	131,345	53,114	14,623	280,525	3.0	2.2
North	220,542	254,275	50,199	6,466	343,253	1.2	1.0
Total	433,470	515,838	127,349	44,981	926,303	1.5	1.0

The north section comprises steep slopes with rocky outcrops and shallow soils which support an unimproved grassland sward. Here, bracken increase has on average been 1.1% per annum, only a relatively

51

Figure 4   Photogrammetrically-derived plot showing the bracken
distribution at Poltalloch in 1967

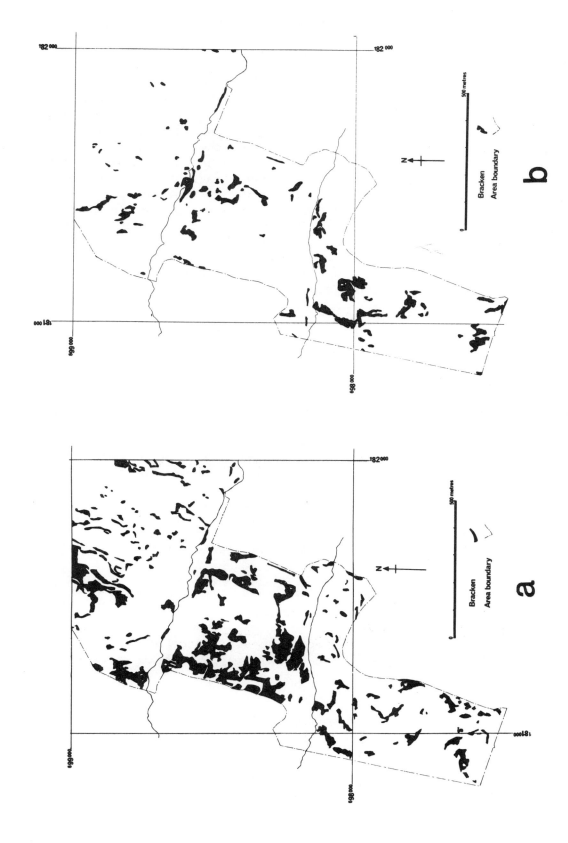

Figure 5   a) Increase in bracken cover at the Poltalloch site over the period 1947-67, b) Decrease in bracken cover over the same period

53

small area losing its bracken cover during the period (Table 3). The central area is less steep, with deeper soils and an improved grassland sward. There is evidence, in the form of run rigs, that this area was formerly cultivated. Here, the pattern of bracken infestation during the period 1947-67, has been complex, with both increase and decrease, but the overall effect has been for the bracken-infested area to increase rapidly. The average rate of increase has been 3.0% per annum but this is offset by a decrease of some 0.8% per annum, giving a net increase of 2.2% per annum. The southern section is characterised by steep slopes and abundant rocky outcrops. The vegetation is dominated by heather. Here, there has been little change in the absolute levels of bracken infestation but the increase/decrease columns in Table 3 reveal a rather more dynamic situation with a 20% change in both during the 19 year-period covered by the survey. When the 1984 land survey observations are considered, the bracken still appears to be spreading in the north and central sections (Figure 2); the central field still displays a complex pattern of spread with further areas of decrease evident. In the heather-dominated communities to the south, the bracken distribution has stabilised with little significant change from the 1967 boundaries.

CONCLUSIONS

The full implications of the Poltalloch work have yet to be assessed from an ecological and land management viewpoint. Several interesting questions can be posed. Why are the bracken changes in the central section so complex? Can they be related to progressive restriction of available grazing area? Why has the interaction of bracken with heather and grass in the south been so dynamic? The answers to these questions will benefit from consideration of results from other study sites, when these are completed. From a methodological viewpoint, the Poltalloch survey has demonstrated that historical photo-analysis does provide useful data, confirming the results of the original pilot study. It still remains to be seen how successfully such local observations can be extended to provide regional estimates of bracken infestation.

ACKNOWLEDGEMENTS

The authors wish to acknowledge the assistance of Jane Morrice and Paula Horne in the preparation of this paper, and to thank Robin Malcolm for kind permission for access to his land.

REFERENCES

1) Mackay J T (1984) Grants for hill land improvements. Abstract of paper presented to Symposium on "The Economics of Hill Farming and the Benefits of Bracken Clearance", organised by May & Baker Ltd, Edinburgh, 5th April, 1984

2) Holroyd J, Parker C and Rowlands A (1970) Asulam for the control

of bracken (Pteridium aquilinum (L.) Kuhn). Proceedings 10th British Weed Control Conference, 371-376

3) Birnie R V (1985) An assessment of the bracken problem in relation to hill farming in Scotland. J. Soil Use and Management, 1, (2)

4) Hendry G F (1958) The size of Scotland's bracken problem. Scot. Agric. Econ., 9 (2), 21-58

5) Taylor J A (1985) Bracken encroachment rates in Britain J Soil Use and Management, 1 (2), 53-56

6) Birnie R V (1983) Mapping bracken (Pteridium aquilinum) infestation in Scotland: an assessment of remotely sensed mapping techniques. Proceedings of the Symposium of the IPS Commission 1, Aberdeen, Sept 12-15, 1983, 115-126

7) Birnie R V (1984) The extent of bracken encroachment in Scotland. Abstract of paper presented to Symposium on "The Economics of Hill Farming and Benefits of Bracken Clearance", organised by May and Baker Ltd, Edinburgh, 5th April, 1984

8) Stove G C and Ritchie P F S (1982) A hybrid photogrammetric and image processing system. Photogrammetric Record, 10 (60), 629-644

9) Birse E L (1971) Assessment of climatic conditions in Scotland. 3. The Bioclimatic Sub-Regions. The Macaulay Institute for Soil Research, Aberdeen

10) Mitchell J (1977) The effect of bracken distribution on Moorland vegetation and soils. Unpublished PhD Thesis, University of Glasgow

The use of small-format, light aircraft photography to estimate the green leaf area index of pteridium

P J Curran

INTRODUCTION

When using remotely-sensed data to estimate the green leaf area index (one-sided area of green leaves to a given land area), there is a trade-off between cost and accuracy. At one extreme, there is a low-cost, small format, light aircraft photography[1,2], and at the other extreme, there is high cost multispectral scanner data[2-4]. As ecological research is likely to remain a fairly low-cost activity, this paper will aim to determine the accuracy with which small-format, light aircraft photography can be used to estimate GLAI.

The use of remote sensing to estimate GLAI is made possible by the causal relationship between GLAI and red and near infrared reflectance. Under the majority of conditions, GLAI has a negative relationship with red reflectance and a positive relationship with near infrared reflectance. There are many factors that influence reflectance independently of GLAI. These factors include soil colour, the presence of senescent vegetation, the geometric relationships of the sun to the sensor and canopy, and the phenological stage of the canopy at the time of imaging[5,6]. When the effects of these factors are minimised, previous workers have obtained very high correlations between GLAI and both red and near infrared reflectance. These correlations have been high enough to encourage researchers to invert these relationships in order to estimate GLAI from remotely-sensed reflectance data[7-10].

STUDY AREA

The study area (Figure 1) was Snelsmore Common, a heathland in Berkshire, UK. The heath is the largest area of its kind in Berkshire and is underlain by lowland plateau gravels of late Tertiary and Quaternary age. The heath vegetation is primarily ling, <u>Calluna</u>

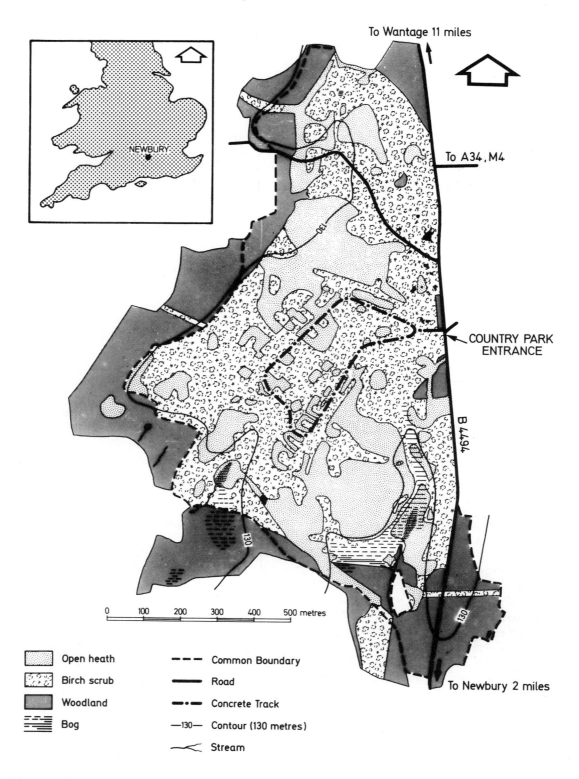

To Wantage 11 miles

To A34, M4

COUNTRY PARK
ENTRANCE

B 4494

To Newbury 2 miles

0   100   200   300   400   500 metres

	Open heath		--- --- Common Boundary
	Birch scrub		——— Road
	Woodland		—·—·— Concrete Track
	Bog		—130— Contour (130 metres)
			—⌁— Stream

Figure 1   The study area: Snelsmore Common, Berkshire, UK.

vulgaris, with some Erica species in both the drier and wetter sites.
Due to frequent burning, the heather is of mixed age, and has been
invaded on the drier and often more badly burnt sites by bracken,

Pteridium aquilinum.   The soil is a thin humus podzol with a surface layer composed of compact, dark humus with bleached sand grains and flint fragments[11].

EXPERIMENTAL METHOD

The experiment was based upon a three-stage procedure: (i) the relationships between reflectance and GLAI were derived using ground-based measurements of reflectance (Figure 2, Graph A); (ii) inversion and estimation used airborne measurements of reflectance; and (iii) accuracy assessment involved a comparison of estimated and measured GLAI (Figure 3, Graph B).

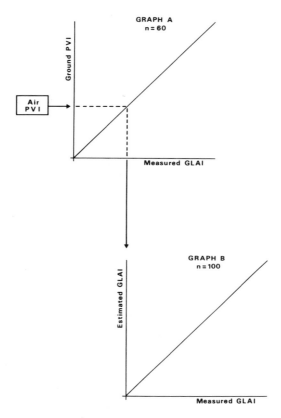

Figure 2   The experimental method in graphical form. Ground measurements of PVI were plotted against GLAI, (Graph A), this calibration relationship was used to estimate GLAI from airborne measurements of PVI (Air PVI). The estimated GLAI was then plotted against measured GLAI (Graph B).

Collection of ground data to derive the relationship between reflectance and GLAI

Snelsmore Common was visited on twelve occasions over a period of 14 months during 1980 and 1981. At each of five random sample points within areas of (i) Pteridium, (ii) Pteridium/Calluna and (iii) bare ground, respectively, radiometric red and infrared reflectance measurements[12], photographic red and near infrared reflectance measurements, or both, were taken[13]. At these same points in the

59

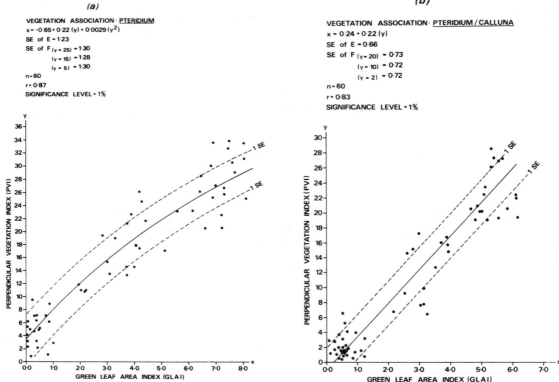

Figure 3 Relationships between PVI calculated from ground reflectance data and GLAI of (a) Pteridium and (b) Pteridium/Calluna. SE = standard error, E = estimate, F = forecast.

Pteridium and Pteridium/Calluna canopies, $0.2m^2$ vegetation samples were collected and GLAI was determined using the method discussed by Curran[14]. These data were expressed as a single mean red reflectance value, one mean near infrared reflectance value and one mean GLAI value per random sample point.

The derived relationship between reflectance and solar elevation was determined for the two canopies. There was no significant deviation in red reflectance from the mean red reflectance. However, because the near infrared reflectance did decrease markedly with solar elevation, the near infrared reflectance data were standardized to a constant solar elevation[14,15].

The corrected data were used to calculate a reflectance index, termed the Perpendicular Vegetation Index (PVI)[16]:

$$PVI = \sqrt{(\rho S_R - \rho V_R)^2 + (\rho S_{IR} - \rho V_{IR})^2}$$

Where: ρS = soil reflectance,
         ρV = vegetation reflectance,
subscript R = red wavelengths,
subscript IR = near infrared wavelengths.

This reflectance index was positively related to GLAI for both the Pteridium and Pteridium/Calluna surfaces (Figure 3).

Collection of multispectral aerial photography and the measurement of GLAI

Near vertical, 35 mm format aerial photography was taken from a light aircraft at around 11.00 hours local time, on 20 dates, from June 1980 to August 1981. The camera had the same film-filter combination as used for ground photography. At each of five 36 m^2 random sample points within the Pteridium, Pteridium/Calluna and bare ground, red and near infrared reflectance was measured[15]. At each of five 0.2 m^2 random sample points within both the Pteridium and Pteridium/Calluna, the vegetation was harvested and the GLAI determined[14]. The results were presented as the mean GLAI for each of the two vegetation canopies.

For each flight, the aerial photographic red and near infrared reflectance data were transformed to PVI values. The PVI values were then used to estimate the GLAI of Pteridium and Pteridium/Calluna via the calibration relationships (Figure 3). The mean of the estimated GLAI range was plotted against the measured GLAI for the Pteridium and Pteridium/Calluna. This estimated GLAI was linearly related to the measured GLAI (Figure 4).

ACCURACY ASSESSMENT AND DISCUSSION

The accuracy of GLAI estimation is dependent upon the acceptable error of the estimate, the type of vegetation and the season. If only very low errors are acceptable for each estimate, then accuracies will be near to 0%. If very high errors are acceptable for each estimate, then accuracies will be near to 100%. Between these two extremes the actual error will be directly related to the initial standard error of the forecast and the accuracy with which GLAI can be measured[4,14]. In practice, a user will wish to estimate a wide range of GLAI values at a predetermined range of acceptable error. In this experiment, at a low error of ± 0.5 GLAI, the accuracy of GLAI estimation averaged 46%, with 39% for the Pteridium and 53% for the Pteridium/Calluna; at a medium error of ± 1.0 GLAI, the accuracy of GLAI estimation averaged 81%, with 73% for the Pteridium and 89% for the Pteridium/Calluna, while at a high error of ± 2.0 GLAI, the accuracy of GLAI estimation averaged 99%, with 100% for the Pteridium and 98% for the Pteridium/Calluna.

The accuracy of GLAI estimation also varies with season[14]. It was highest in spring and summer when the canopy was growing rapidly or was stable, and was lowest during the early spring and autumn when the canopy contained a mixture of brown and green vegetation. If GLAI estimation was restricted to the spring and summer months, the accuracy of GLAI estimation, at an error of ± 1.0 GLAI, increased by 3% to an average of 84% for the Pteridium and Pteridium/Calluna.

CONCLUSIONS

(1) Small-format, light aircraft photography has been successfully used to estimate the GLAI of Pteridium and Pteridium/Calluna.

(2) With an error of ± 1.0 GLAI the accuracy of GLAI estimation was 73% for Pteridium and 89% for Pteridium/Calluna.

61

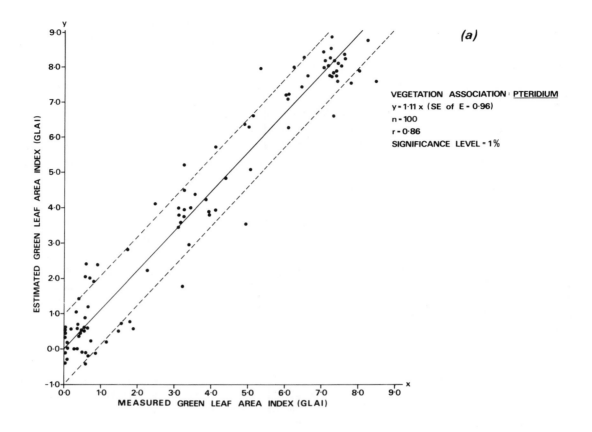

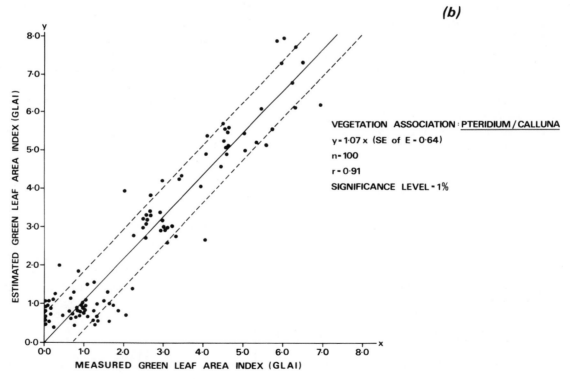

Figure 4   Relationships between estimated and measured GLAI of (a)
Pteridium   and   (b)   Pteridium/Calluna.   SE of E = standard error of
estimate.

(3) The accuracy of GLAI estimation was highest during the late spring and early summer when there was no brown, senescent bracken within the canopy.

ACKNOWLEDGEMENTS

The author wishes to acknowledge the financial support of the Natural Environment Research Council under research grant GR3/4076 and to thank Dawn Williamson for her comments on a draft of this paper.

REFERENCES

1) Curran P J (1981) Remote Sensing: The Role of Small Format, Light Aircraft Photography. Reading: Geographical Papers

2) Curran P J (1985) Principles of Remote Sensing. London: Longman

3) Wardley N W and Curran P J (1984) The estimation of green leaf area index from remotely sensed airborne multispectral scanner data. International Journal of Remote Sensing, 5, 671-680

4) Curran P J and Williamson H D (1985) The accuracy of ground data used in remote sensing investigations. International Journal of Remote Sensing, 6. (In press)

5) Curran P J (1980) Multispectral remote sensing of vegetation amount. Progress in Physical Geography, 4, 315-341

6) Curran P J (1983) Problems in the remote sensing of vegetation canopies for biomass estimation. In R M Fuller (ed) Ecological Mapping from Ground, Air and Space, 84-100 Cambridge: Institute of Terrestrial Ecology

7) Pollock R B and Kanemasu E T (1979) Estimating leaf area index of wheat with Landsat data. Remote Sensing of Environment, 8, 307-312

8) Bartlett D S and Klemas V (1980) Quantitative assessment of tidal wetlands using remote sensing. Environmental Management, 4, 337-345

9) Hardisky M A, Daiber F C, Roman C T and Klemas V (1984) Remote sensing of biomass and annual net productivity of a salt marsh. Remote Sensing of Environment, 16, 91-106

10) Hatfield J L, Kanemasu E T, Asrar G, Jackson R D, Pinter P J, Reginato R J and Idso S B (1985) Leaf area estimates from spectral measurements over various planting dates of wheat. International Journal of Remote Sensing, 6, 167-175

11) Curran P J (1981) The estimation of the surface soil moisture of a vegetated soil using aerial infrared photography. International Journal of Remote Sensing, 2, 369-378

12) Milton E J (1980) A portable multiband radiometer for ground data collection in remote sensing. International Journal of Remote Sensing, 1, 153-165

13) Curran P J (1982) Multispectral photographic remote sensing of green vegetation biomass and productivity. Photogrammetric Engineering and Remote Sensing, 48, 243-250

14) Curran P J (1983) Estimating green LAI from multispectral aerial photography. Photogrammetric Engineering and Remote Sensing, 49, 1709-1720

15) Curran P J (1983) Multispectral remote sensing for the estimation of green leaf area index. Philosophical Transactions of the Royal Society, London, Series A, 309, 257-270

16) Richardson A J and Weigand C L (1977) Distinguishing vegetation from soil background. Photogrammetric Engineering and Remote Sensing, 43, 1541-1552

Use of remote sensing to monitor Bracken encroachment in the North York Moors

R E Weaver

INTRODUCTION

Bracken dominates approximately 30,000 acres of moorland in the North York Moors National Park, and is spreading at the rate of 1% per annum[1]. Apart from adding colour to the landscape at different times of year, it is considered an undesirable element of the moorland scene because of its low economic and ecological value and its potential threat to the regeneration of heather after fire[2]. Bracken encroachment is seen as a serious problem by the North York Moors National Park Department and a system of grant-aided spraying exists within the Upland Management Scheme. This is responsive in that it relies on landowners contacting the National Park Department; clearly an 'active' or dynamic system would be preferable, but this requires detailed information on areas sprayed, regrowth, and the location of actively invading stands[1]. Given the areas involved, and the change from year to year, the latter is not realistic using conventional surveys. Remote sensing may be the only way in which this information can be provided regularly, efficiently, and with the accuracy needed for management.

This paper describes the capabilities of remote-sensing systems to: (i) map the location of bracken dominated areas, (ii) monitor success in primary and follow-up treatments, (iii) differentiate between active and established stands. The work forms part of a larger project to compare remote-sensing systems for the mapping and monitoring of moorland communities, with particular reference to the North York Moors[3].

REMOTE SENSING

Remote-sensing instruments measure the amount of radiation reflected or emitted from an object on the ground in different parts of the electro-magnetic spectrum. Different targets have different patterns of response across the spectrum, and thus give a relatively unique and characteristic 'spectral signature'.

The more spectral information (wavelengths) measured, the more easily one target will be separated or recognised from another. The number, positioning, and width of wavebands (spectral resolution) is one major characteristic of remote-sensing systems. The second is spatial resolution; typically and misleadingly, this is quoted as the instantaneous field of view (IFOV) of the sensor, the area on the ground corresponding to a single picture element or pixel. A more meaningful definition is the minimum distance between two objects that a sensor can record distinctly. This varies from scene to scene, and depends, amongst other things, on the spectral characteristics of the target[4]. A small target of high contrast with its background will alter the radiance of its picture element, so that it is visible while still below the IFOV. There is therefore some trade-off between spectral and spatial resolution. The third major characteristic of remote sensing is temporal resolution, referring to the time of day or year the data are acquired relative to any periodicity in the target. For vegetation surfaces, this generally refers to changes over the growing season. For example, the point of maximum difference between established and pioneer stands of bracken is in July, when the canopies are fully developed.

TABLE 1 Characteristics of different remote sensing systems

SYSTEM	IFOV	WAVEBANDS (limits in microns)		
Landsat Multispectral Scanner (MSS)	79m x 79m	MSS4	0.5 - 0.6	visible
		MSS5	0.6 - 0.7	"
		MSS6	0.7 - 0.8	near IR
27 May 1977		MSS7	0.8 - 1.1	"
Airborne simulation: SPOT	20m x 20m	XS1	0.52 - 0.6	visible
		XS2	0.605 - 0.69	"
		XS3	0.76 - 0.90	near IR
14 May 1984 7 July 1984				
	[satellite bands:	XS1	0.50 - 0.59	visible
		XS2	0.615 - 0.68	"
		XS3	0.79 - 0.89	near IR]
Airborne simulation Landsat Thematic Mapper (TM)	1.4 x 1.3m	TM1	0.45 - 0.52	visible
		TM2	0.52 - 0.60	"
	[Satellite:	TM3	0.63 - 0.69	"
	30m x 30m	TM4	0.76 - 0.90	near IR
9 September 1983		TM5	1.55 - 1.75	mid IR
	TM6 120m x	TM7	2.08 - 2.35	"
	120m]	TM6	8.50 - 13.00	thermal IR

Table 1 lists the sensor systems used in this work, and their spatial, spectral and temporal characteristics. The aim of data

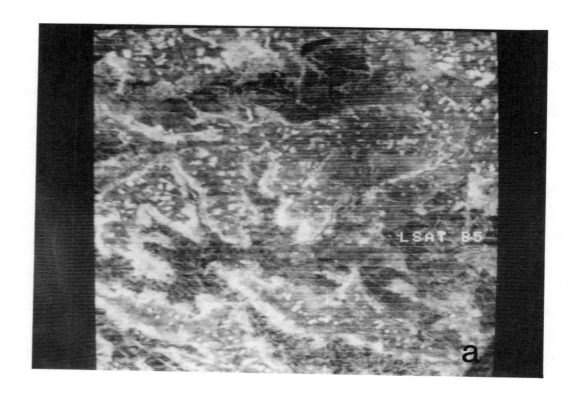

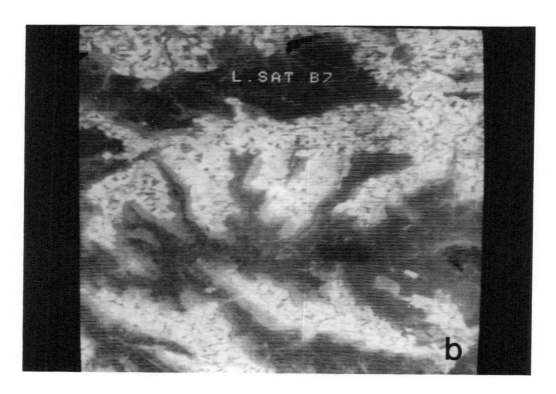

Figure 1 Landsat MSS images of the North York Moors (May). 1a - MSS5, 1b - MSS7. Images are approximately 15 x 12 miles. In both, the central dark area is heather moorland, surrounded by a fringe of bracken above the agricultural valleys.

analysis is to see how far these systems are relevant to the problem of monitoring bracken encroachment onto moorland, with the practical objective of assessing the possibility of changing from a passive to an active form of notification. The 'ground' information, on the location and nature of various test sites is from the Moorland Management Programme of the North York Moors National Park.

DATA ANALYSIS

Separation of bracken from moorland - Landsat MSS

As a first step it is important to establish the general location of bracken-dominated areas over the whole of the moorland. This scale of coverage is available from the Landsat MSS, recording radiance in four wavebands with an IFOV of 79m (Table 1). Figures 1a and 1b show the images formed from the radiance received in MSS5 (red) and MSS7 (reflected infrared). The bracken forms a more or less continuous belt on the slopes between the agricultural valleys and the moorland plateaux. These three communities are best delimited by the eye on the infrared (IR) image, and can be expressed more formally in graphical and numerical form, (Figure 2, Table 2). The different communities occupy more or less discrete parts of the grey-level distribution for the whole image (Fig.2). The matrices in Table 2 confirm the superior ability of MSS7 to separate these cover types.

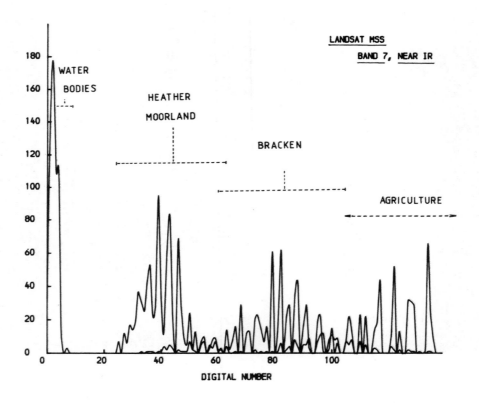

Figure 2 Distribution of response for major communities, Landsat MSS7. 'Digital Number' (DN) refers to grey-level recorded. Histograms represent samples of the cover types present.

TABLE 2 Normalised difference matrices: major communities, MSS5, MSS7
x_i = mean, class i; s_i = standard deviation, class i.

MSS5				Normalised Difference
	2	3	4	
1	.17	1.87	1.72	$x_i - x_j$
2		1.34	1.34	$\overline{\qquad}$
3			.28	$s_i - s_j$

MSS7

			2	3	4
1	Water bodies	1	4.29	4.52	5.68
2	Heather Moorland	2		1.73	3.16
3	Bracken	3			1.29
4	Agriculture				

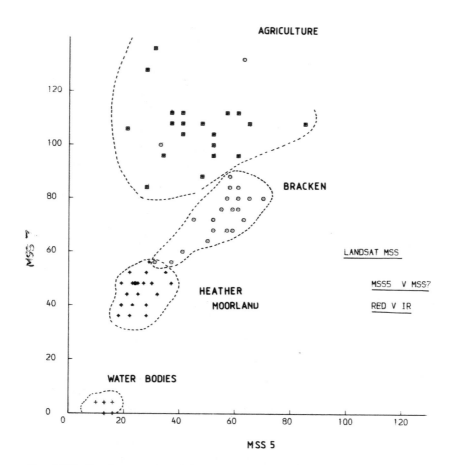

Figure 3 MSS 7 plotted against MSS 5, major communities, samples as Fig.2.

It was suggested in the introduction that a target vegetation community is more easily separated and delimited with increased independent spectral information. In Figure 3, where MSS7 is plotted aginst MSS5, the different cover types occupy different areas of the

69

feature space defined by these two wavebands. They are therefore more easily recognisable in terms of their spectral characteristics; this is important for automatic classification of remote-sensing data, as the success of the algorithms depends on the statistical separability of the groups to be differentiated.

An estimate of the probability of successful classification is given by the divergence value[5]. This measures the separation of pairs of classes with varying amounts of spectral information. Table 3 shows the change in divergence with the sequential addition of MSS wavebands, demonstrating that the bracken-dominated areas can be clearly differentiated from the heather moorland when at least one IR band is included in the analysis. The conclusion is that the bracken class can be isolated from heather moorland in Landsat MSS data. The location of the two can therefore be mapped and their relative proportions calculated.

Table 3   Divergence matrices for major communities in Landsat data. Transformed Divergence (TD) has maximum value of 2000, at which point classes are statistically separate. Note increase in TD with addition of IR bands

---

MSS4 + MSS5

	2	3	4
1	1895	*	*
2		1453	1708
3			1351

1 Water bodies
2 Heather moorland
3 Bracken
4 Agriculture
* TD = 2000

MSS4, MSS5 + MSS6

	2	3	4
1	*	*	*
2		1933	*
3			1669

MSS4, MSS5, MSS6 + MSS7

	2	3	4
1	*	*	*
2		1944	*
3			1742

Separation of growth states - SPOT

A 79m pixel size tends to gloss over variation in the bracken canopy so that the difference between an active, vigorous stand and one where regrowth is patchy can be subtle in spectral terms, and easily missed, particularly given the small size of areas sprayed relative to the sensor's resolution. This implies that a system with finer resolution is needed to monitor regrowth after treatment, and identify areas of active invasion. This is available in this instance from airborne simulation for the French SPOT satellite which is to be launched in October 1985. The system characteristics (of simulation and satellite) are listed in Table 1. The wavebands are broadly similar to the Landsat MSS, recording radiance in the green, red and IR wavelengths. Figure 4 shows imagery in band XS2. The aim here, is

to break down the general bracken signature into components corresponding to levels of cover or vigour of growth. This will identify areas of active invasion, and monitor the amount of regrowth after cutting or spraying. In an active system of management, this would allow the direction of resources to the most critical areas. Four sites were selected to cover a range of conditions:
1. Blakey Ridge (SE698974 to SE690988), sprayed in 1982, with 15% regrowth.
2. Crossley Sides (NZ708054 to NZ716066), actively invading stands.
3. Castleton Rigg (NZ683045, West Side), sprayed, irregular surface cover.
4. Castleton Rigg (NZ687045, East Side), more uniform cover, interspersed with Calluna.

The normalised difference and divergence measures were calculated for these units (Tables 4 and 5), and their distribution plotted relative to the general moorland signature. These data were collected in July, and therefore have the optimum temporal resolution to discriminate between full and partial cover.

Figure 4 SPOT simulation images of North York Moors (July). The image is a sub-section of scenes in Fig.1.

From Table 4, there is no clear 'best' band as in the Landsat data. The Crossley Sides site is clearly separated in XS1, but all the other sites are confused. In XS2 and XS3, Crossley Sides is rather less clearly defined, but there is new information on the separation of the two Castleton sites and Blakey Ridge. Intuitively, a lower separation between groups is expected as the distinction is now between relatively minor variations of a single species, rather

71

Table 4 Normalised difference values; bracken canopies, July SPOT simulation data

---

XS1

	2	3	4
1	1.20	.12	.19
2		1.81	1.50
3			.12

1 Blakey Ridge
2 Crossley Sides
3 Castleton E
4 Castleton W

XS2

	2	3	4
1	1.08	.36	.43
2		.48	1.54
3			.81

XS3

	2	3	4
1	.77	.76	.06
2		1.71	.96
3			.80

Table 5 Divergence matrices for bracken canopies, July SPOT simulation. Class identification as Table 4

XS1 + XS2

	2	3	4
1	1233	949	547
2		1971	1490
3			1706

XS2 + XS3

	2	3	4
1	1071	991	235
2		1946	1552
3			1192

XS1 + XS3

	2	3	4
1	1169	962	72
2		1957	1438
3			895

XS1, XS2 + XS3

	2	3	4
1	1337	1089	809
2		1989	1590
3			1795

---

than the differentiation of lifeform and communities seen in the Landsat data. The nature of the airborne data, moreover, allows considerable flexibility in matching the sensitivity of the sensor to the variability found on the ground. The SPOT data, therefore, span 0-250 of the 0-255 grey levels available. In effect, then, the differences between the bracken components in the scenes are very small in relation to the overall variation in the scene, and this is demonstrated by their small range on the x axis in Figure 5. The Crossley Sides and Castleton East sites have more or less discrete distributions of light and dark tones, respectively, in the visible imagery. The more variable tones of Castleton West and Blakey Ridge stretch across the full range of these two extremes. The divergence values for bracken are generally lower than those from Landsat for the major communities. The initial conclusion, then, is that there is some basis for delimiting cover types, though not a very strong one.

In addition, and in contrast to the Landsat MSS data, there is no clear separation of moor and bracken signatures, implying that

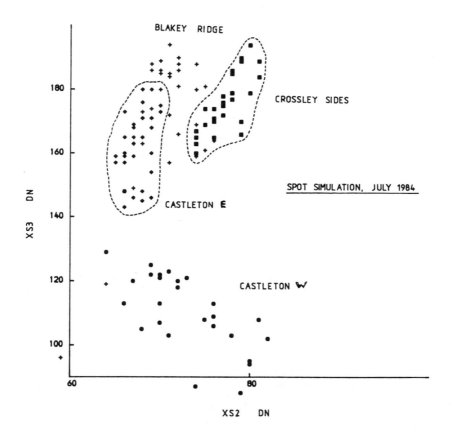

Figure 5   July SPOT simulation data: XS2 v XS3 (red v IR)

areas of bracken would be confused with areas of regenerating heather,
bare ground or Eriophorum species within the Calluna moorland. Data
for the same area were examined from a flight in late May, at which
time the sensor response is dominated by the bracken litter. In the
SPOT wavebands, this is more clearly separable from the moorland
signature than is the full canopy. This implies that the best results
would come from using these two dates sequentially or in combination,
the early date to delimit the bracken dominated areas, the later one,
to extract the detailed division into canopy types, thus demonstrating
the importance of temporal resolution to data interpretation.

The main conclusion from this analysis is that, given the
correct temporal information, bracken can be delimited and its overall
signature can be sub-divided, but the distinctions are subtle, and, in
remote sensing terms, insufficient to allow consistently accurate
identification. The Blakey Ridge and Castleton West sites have a wide
range of radiance values relative to the other groups (Fig.5). Their
recognition in imagery therefore depends as much on pattern or texture
as grey tone, and this is not considered by conventional
classification algorithms. However, the contrast stretched imagery
can be reasonably well interpreted by eye. This has the advantage of
considering texture and location in the image, needs little
specialised knowledge or equipment, and may give sufficient
information for management when combined with existing local
knowledge, such as exists within the National Park Department.

Thematic Mapper

The situation in the North York Moors is, nevertheless, relatively straightforward. Bracken-dominated areas are known to be largely confined to the slopes surrounding the central heather core, comparisons can be made between neighbouring stands, and field checking is relatively simple. In a landscape of greater topographic variety or of greater diversity in management the distribution of vegetation types would inevitably be more complex. To be of practical use here, remote sensing should provide reliable information with a minimum of user input and be amenable to machine classification. In other words, the different components of the bracken signature should be made more easily recognisable or spectrally separate. The clearest way to do this is to increase the amount of spectral information available. For this purpose, a feasible alternative to the SPOT system is the Landsat Thematic Mapper (Table 1), currently in orbit on Landsat 5. This extends wavelengths to the mid- and thermal IR, though with a concomitant increase in the data handling and processing involved. Simulated TM data are available for part of the North York Moors at a fine spatial scale (Table 1); for this reason only a small area is covered, but preliminary work has shown that the additional

Figure 6   TM Simulation, September 1983, Thermal IR Image subsampled to give 1km N-S, 500m E-W. Bracken occupies SW corner, and is easily discriminated from recolonising surface to the NE. The bracken can be divided into an established stand, with a northern fringe of more vigorous advancing growth.

spectral information available gives the system considerable potential in the machine-aided monitoring of moorland vegetation. Figure 6 demonstrates the clear separation of bracken from regenerating heather, and the differentiation of invading and established stands in the thermal IR waveband.

CONCLUSIONS

Remote sensing is a viable method of mapping and monitoring bracken stands surrounding heather moorland. Bracken can be differentiated from other major communities in Landsat MSS data, and sub-divided into components representing stage of regeneration or vigour of growth in a simulation of the forthcoming SPOT satellite. A second simulation, of the Landsat Thematic Mapper, demonstrates the further potential of this system. Taken together, these results imply the possibility of an active system of notification using remote sensing. The best results will come from using the detailed spectral and spatial information of summer SPOT or TM imagery, with scenes which isolate bracken from moorland. Examples of the latter are spring SPOT data or Landsat MSS.

The remaining problem is to transfer the analysis of these research data into everyday use in management decisions by the National Park Department and landowners. This is a large stumbling block, mainly because access to data, image processing, computing facilities, and advice, are more readily available in research establishments. However, given enthusiasm on both sides, it is possible for remote sensing to become a practical tool, initially as photographic products, leading on to specialised manipulation of digital imagery, should this be needed. A number of Universities now publicise their image-processing systems as providing an expert service for users unwilling or unable to invest in their own.

Given the ecological and economic pressures on moorlands in general and the North York Moors in particular, it appears that, if remote-sensing data can be introduced into normal management practice, bracken control can be predictive and effective, by identifying and concentrating resources on areas of active invasion, whilst monitoring the results of past and current clearance programmes.

ACKNOWLEDGEMENTS

This work was conducted under Research Studentship GT4/82/TLS/12 from the Natural Environment Research Council, which also provided simulated TM data under the MSS '83 and MSS '84 campaigns. The SPOT simulation data were acquired under a campaign funded by the National Remote Sensing Centre. Details of bracken distribution and general advice were supplied by Dr Roy Brown of the North York Moors National Park. The computer program used to calculate the divergence values was provided originally by Ashbindu Singh (Dept of Geography, Reading University), and adapted by the author.

REFERENCES

1) North York Moors National Park (1985) <u>Moorland Management Programme: Interim Report</u>

2) North York Moors National Park (1982) <u>Discussion Paper: The Future of the Moorland</u>

3) Weaver R E (1984) Integration of Remote Sensing data for Moorland Mapping in Northern England. Presented at the <u>Eighteenth International Symposium on Remote Sensing of Environment</u>, October, Paris

4) Simonett D S (1983) The development and principles of remote sensing, in R Colwell (ed) <u>Manual of Remote Sensing</u> 1, 1-35 USA, American Society of Photogrammetry

5) Swain P H and Davis S M (1978) <u>Remote Sensing: the Quantitative Approach</u>, New York, McGraw Hill

Bracken in the North York Moors:
Its ecological and amenity implications in national parks

R W Brown

INTRODUCTION

Although it is unlikely that bracken will ever be totally eradicated from the moorland scene, it is important that its spread is controlled in the long-term economic and ecological interests of the moorland as well as certain amenity considerations. The latter are of particular importance in National Parks as levels of public use and understanding continue to increase.

A survey carried out in 1981 established that some 511.5 km^2 (195.7 sq miles), approximately 36% of the National Park area, consisted of moorland and upland heath. No other part of England has such extensive tracts of heather moorland. The development and maintenance of this moorland has been dependent on a management regime involving sheep grazing and controlled heather burning. There are several reasons why the continued existence of moorland is important:-

(1) <u>Landscape</u>. One of the main reasons for the designation of the North York Moors National Park in 1952 was the presence of large sweeps of open heather moorland.

(2) <u>Recreation</u>. Closely allied to landscape is the fact that many visitors enjoy the open moorland from their cars while others may take a more active interest in walking. In both cases, the wilderness effect of large areas of moorland is an important factor.

(3) <u>Agriculture</u>. Some 50,000 sheep currently graze the moorland for part or all of the year. Over many years shepherds have contributed to the controlled burning of the moors in order to maintain the young heather growth which provides the nutritional resource required by the sheep. Many hill flocks have now been withdrawn for various social and economic reasons. Once continuous grazing is removed from an area it becomes a painstaking process to re-establish.

(4) <u>Game Conservation</u>. Many heather moors have been managed to encourage grouse. This process also involves controlled burning,

encouraging young heather growth and creating a multi-stage cover of heather to provide for the bird's needs. Well-managed grouse moors also encourage ground-nesting waders. Good grouse moors require fairly intensive management, but economic changes are again putting pressure on the system which has traditionally maintained such moors.
(5) Ecology. Large areas of the moors are of known ecological importance. Some of these are good examples of particular habitat while others contain unique features of local, county, regional or in two cases, national importance. Some moorland areas are known to be of national, if not international, ornithological significance.
(6) Archaeology. Much of the moorland is dotted with archaeological features and there are a number of prehistoric complexes which give the moorland particular archaeological value.
(7) Water Conservation. Although the moorland areas are comparatively low in altitude and experience only 1,000 mm of precipitation each year, the undisturbed moorland peat soils play a vital role in retaining and regulating the movement of water. Loss of these soils or change in land use could substantially alter the nature and efficiency of this process.

These reasons, taken together, make the continued existence of the open moorland in the North York Moors National Park a priority.

PRESSURES ON THE MOORLAND

Two main groups of processes threaten the continued existence of the moorland. These are:-
(1) Conversion to agriculture or forestry. Many of the soils on the upland parts of the North York Moors have been degraded by early and prolonged human activities. There is little doubt that they could be reclaimed for agriculture or afforested commercially. About one quarter of the open moorland was reclaimed for both of these purposes between 1950 and 1984 but the trend has recently slowed. It is unlikely that there will be any further major initiatives to convert moorland to other uses, unless its traditional economic activities decline to the point where landowners have little option but to consider large-scale afforestation.
(2) Direct loss or degradation through catastrophic events. Events such as catastrophic fires lead inevitably to substantial soil loss, and to insidious processes following changes in the intensity of management or type of land use.

Two main factors operate in this latter category. The first of these is direct erosion and soil degradation resulting principally from over-grazing, bad burning practices, uncontrolled summer fires and excessive visitor pressure. The second factor is the existence and encroachment of bracken to which the remainder of this paper is directed.

EXTENT OF BRACKEN IN THE NORTH YORK MOORS

Bracken is a normal constituent of the vegetation on the steeper, well-drained slopes of the North York Moors. It is a plant with a world-wide distribution and an ability to adapt to a wide range of conditions, except heavily waterlogged soils, although there is

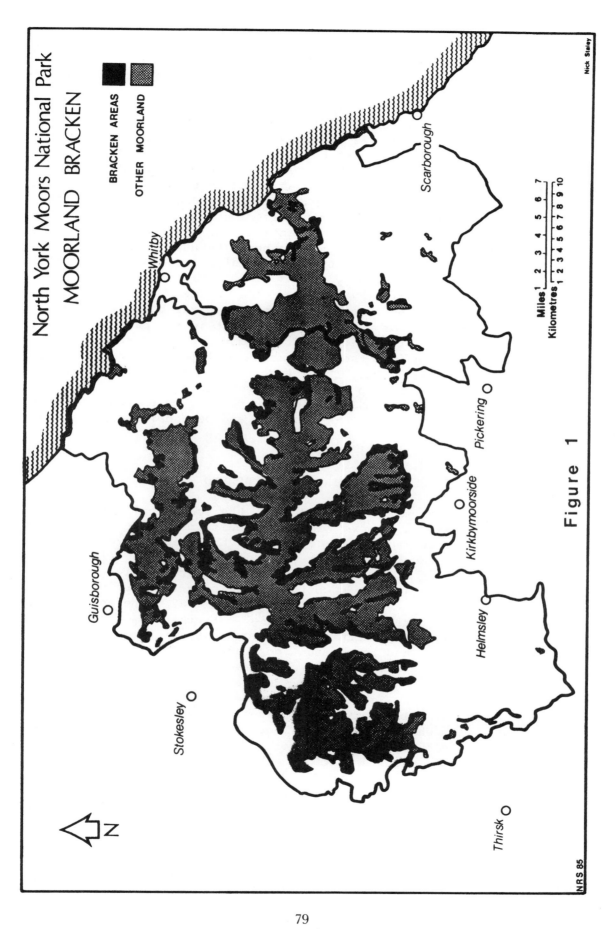

North York Moors National Park

MOORLAND BRACKEN

BRACKEN AREAS

OTHER MOORLAND

Whitby

Scarborough

Guisborough

Stokesley

Kirkbymoorside

Pickering

Helmsley

Thirsk

Miles 1 2 3 4 5 6 7

Kilometres 1 2 3 4 5 6 7 8 9 10

Figure 1

Nick Staley

NRS 85

79

some evidence in the North York Moors of bracken moving into wet, peaty habitats. Within the National Park, 101 km^2 (39 sq miles) of open heath or moor is dominated by bracken. This represents 20% of the total area. The term 'dominated' means at least a 70% ground cover by bracken fronds in July, and bracken litter of at least 5 cm depth. Outside the moorland on improved agricultural land, there is at least another 61 km^2 (23 sq miles) dominated by the fern. There is strong evidence that bracken is encroaching into the moorland at the rate of at least 120 hectares (300 acres) every year despite attempts at control. Figure 1 shows the distribution of bracken within the moorland area, and emphasises its predominantly marginal, steep-slope and moorland valley-side distribution. This distribution gives the species great visual prominence in the landscape.

Traditionally, bracken is thought to be associated with brown earth, steep-phase soils. Of the 101 km^2 of bracken-dominated soils in the North York Moors, only 28 km^2 are of this soil type while 72 km^2 are of the podzolic variety. The latter are generally on sloping, better drained areas or on land which has been improved for agricultural purposes or which carried forest in the past. There is evidence from some of the deep, fire-damaged peats that bracken is capable of spreading into the desiccated upper peat layers and, from there, tolerating much wetter conditions then it usually does. While the spread of bracken is generally restricted to the better-structured, well-drained soils, it does appear to be encroaching on a wide front in the North York Moors, and beyond its conventional range (see Smith, herein).

REASONS FOR BRACKEN SPREAD

Assuming the soil falls within the ecological tolerance of bracken, there are a number of factors which predispose an area of moor and heath to its spread. The first of these is inadvertent fire in areas where bracken and heather are in competition. Fires which are too intense or at the wrong time of the year may give bracken a competitive advantage. Many such fires have occurred over the years, with peaks in 1947, 1959, 1968, 1976 and 1982. The second is a reduction in the intensity of cutting. Bracken was formerly cut extensively for bedding within the Moors but, with changed socio-economic conditions and the present cost and availability of labour, this is no longer feasible. A third factor is the overgrazing of heather on dry, upland heath in the face of an advancing bracken front. Clear felling of woodland areas is a fourth factor, since bracken is a natural constituent of the undergrowth on well-drained acid soils, and, when trees are felled, it is able to spread from an established position as it becomes more vigorous with increased light availability. In such situations the other species of the ground flora may survive for years, and indeed may re-emerge if the bracken is removed at a later date. Fifthly and finally, there is the reduction in intensity of use of marginal, enclosed, well-drained hill land. If such fields are neglected they are invaded by bracken, and encroachment onto the moor quickly follows. Although much of the spread is vegetative, colonisation from spores takes place in a number of the bare, fire-damaged areas. The picture on the North York Moors, therefore, is one of rapid bracken encroachment with, as already stated, at least 20% of the existing moorland already dominated by the species.

TABLE 1 Positive and negative contributions of bracken to moorland amenity and ecology

Positive	Negative
AMENITY	
(1) Attractive in landscape/visual terms at certain times of the year.	(1) Loss of open heather moorland.
	(2) Reduces access. Unpleasant to walk through in summer and tends to concentrate people on moor outside bracken areas.
	(3) Of economic significance is the restriction, in terms of grazing, moorland plants and tree growth, imposed by well established bracken banks.
	(4) Toxic if consumed directly by vertebrates at certain times of year.
	(5) Spreading bracken is often a symptom of declining levels of management.
ECOLOGY	
(1) Provides cover for certain small mammals; cover too late for ground-nesting birds.	(1) Competition with other species from:- a) overshading by fronds; b) depletion of nutrients in the growing season; c) heavy litter production; and d) extensive rhizome systems.
(2) Frond system provides a micro-climate favouring certain groups of Diptera and other invertebrates.	(2) Exclusion of other moorland plant species, particularly Calluna vulgaris.
(3) Litter system is a valuable habitat for some groups of invertebrates.	(3) Simplification of fauna generally.
(4) Provided a very deep litter layer has not been established, areas of sprayed bracken can carry a varied moorland flora after treatment.	(4) Deep, unburnt litter encourages Sheep Tick Ixodes ricinus, with resultant debilitating and disease consequences for sheep, grouse and other vertebrates.
(5) Can act as a soil-improving and soil stabilising agent.	(5) Loss of breeding habitat for ground-nesting birds (eg. merlins and golden plovers).
	(6) Deep litter under sprayed bracken can render area sterile for plant recovery and may become physically unstable under sheep grazing or human activity.

THE QUALITIES OF BRACKEN

Table 1 summarises the amenity and ecological implications of bracken, and enumerates the positive and negative qualities of the plant. The negative factors greatly outweigh the positive ones. There is no doubt that, in landscape terms, bracken can be very attractive at certain times of the year, it can act as a soil-improving agent and can provide shelter for certain vertebrate and invertebrate groups. Its removal from a site can reveal a varied sward, which, under appropriate circumstances can soon be converted into good pasture. However, it is a species which is generally not welcomed in amenity, ecological or economic terms because of its aggressive nature. In National Parks, with their dual commitment to landscape conservation and recreational activity, its control is therefore of the greatest importance.

THE FAUNA IN BRACKEN

In the North York Moors, the Agricultural Development and Advisory Service (ADAS) has established an integrated, bracken-control programme in conjunction with the National Park Department's own Moorland Management Programme. One aspect of this is an investigation of the fauna associated with unsprayed and sprayed bracken and adjacent heather areas (Table 2). The data vary considerably but a number of common trends occur. In all cases, the densities are greatest on the heather areas. Coleoptera (beetle) numbers are high on open surfaces both on sprayed bracken and on recently burned heather. There is a positive correlation between the Opiliones (harvestmen) and heather in both sets of data, which were collected by two different workers. Finally, the Hymenoptera (ants) are also positively associated with increasing heather cover. At the time of sampling, July, a large number of Diptera (fly) larvae and adults were collected from the bare area of bracken which had been sprayed off. In terms of group representation, there is little difference between heather, unsprayed bracken and sprayed bracken areas. It can be seen, however, that densities are generally much greater on heather-dominated areas, although numbers do not increase consistently with the age of the heather plants. Since the bracken control experiment was initiated only in 1983, it is expected that differences between treated and untreated bracken areas will become more apparent as time goes by.

Another indicator of the ecological significance of bracken in the North York Moors is being obtained from small mammal trapping which is taking place on unsprayed, sprayed bracken and adjacent heather areas. Table 3 summarises data from the first year of trapping, 1983-84. There are intrinsic differences in the two sites included in the Table, and also the second site has so far only been monitored on a limited scale; but it is apparent that there are similarities. Perhaps the most surprising of these is that the woodmouse (_Apodemus sylvaticus_) is present on a number of the heather-dominated areas and also on both sprayed and unsprayed bracken areas where there is well-developed litter. Evidence from Spaunton Moor (Brown 1984, unpublished study) suggests a great deal of burrowing activity takes place in the litter layers by woodmice. On the

TABLE 2 Invertebrates collected in pitfall traps from bracken, sprayed bracken and heather control areas

A   Heather areas outside sprayed bracken (King, 1984 unpubl study)
B   Heather and bracken in bracken-spraying area (MAFF, 1984 unpubl study)

Invertebrate Group or Orders / Site or Transect	COLEOPTERA	OPILIONES	HYMENOPTERA	COLLEMBOLA	ACARINA	ARANEIDA	HEMIPTERA	DIPTERA	MYRIAPODA	ANALIDA	OTHERS	LARVAE	TOTAL
A													
1 Heather area burnt 2 years before	165	5	5	100	0	35	15	–	–	–	–	–	325
2 Heather area burnt 9 years before	52	15	10	65	35	20	10	–	–	–	–	–	197
3 Heather area burnt 25 years before	105	70	35	45	25	10	3	–	–	–	–	–	293
B													
1 Sprayed bracken	18	4	1	–	–	5	–	18	3	0	0	7	56
2 Heather within bracken-treatment area	13	14	0	–	–	2	–	10	2	0	0	10	51
3 Section from burned heather into sprayed bracken	38	2	1	–	–	14	–	16	0	0	0	10	81
4 Section from unburned heather into sprayed bracken	28	30	5	–	–	8	–	0	0	0	0	8	86
5 Unspryed bracken	17	3	6	–	–	3	–	4	0	0	2	0	35
6 Heather outside bracken-treatment area (9 year burn)	43	10	0	–	–	9	–	2	0	0	0	4	68

TABLE 3
SMALL MAMMAL TRAPPING RESULTS FROM BRACKEN SITES ON THE NORTH YORK MOORS.

A. SPAUNTON MOOR (BROWN, 1983-84)

SPECIES / LOCATION	WOOD MOUSE (Apodemus sylvaticus)				BANK VOLE (Clethrionomys glareolus)				COMMON SHREW (Sorex araneus)				PYGMY SHREW (Sorex minutus)				TOTAL				TOTAL
SEASON	S.	Su.	A.	W.	S.	Su.	A.	W.	S.	Su.	A.	W.	S.	Su.	A.	W.	S.	Su.	A.	W.	
1. Heather control (Litter present)	4	5	3	0	0	1	0	0	2	3	1	0	4	4	3	2	10	13	7	2	32
2. Unsprayed bracken (Deep litter)	7	2	5	3	0	0	0	0	0	1	0	0	1	2	0	2	8	5	5	5	23
3. Sprayed bracken (Deep litter)	5	4	7	4	1	1	0	0	0	0	0	0	0	0	1	1	6	5	8	5	24
4. Sprayed bracken (Shallow litter)	0	1	1	0	0	1	0	0	1	0	1	0	0	1	0	0	1	3	2	0	6
TOTALS	16	12	16	7	1	3	0	0	3	4	2	0	5	7	4	5	25	26	22	12	85

Numbers are total catch from 50 traps laid for 7 nights on each habitat in each season
S = Spring (March)   Su. = Summer (July)   A = Autumn (October)   W = Winter (January)

B. GLAISDALE RIGG (WRIGHT, 1983-84)

SPECIES / LOCATION	WOOD MOUSE		BANK VOLE		COMMON SHREW		PYGMY SHREW		TOTAL		TOTAL
	A.	Su.	A.	Su.	A.	Su.	A.	Su.	A.	Su.	
1. Sprayed bracken	-	0	-	0	-	0	-	0	-	0	0
2. Heather within bracken treatment area	-	0	-	0	-	1	-	1	-	2	2
3. From burned heather into sprayed bracken	5	0	0	0	5	0	0	0	10	0	10
4. From unburned heather into sprayed bracken	1	0	0	1	2	2	0	1	3	4	7
5. Unsprayed bracken	11	0	0	0	0	4	0	1	11	5	16
6. Heather outside treatment area	3	0	0	0	2	0	0	6	5	0	5
TOTALS	20	0	0	1	9	7	0	3	29	11	40

A. = 31st October to 4th November, 1983.   Su. = 30th July to 3rd August, 1984.

Glaisdale Rigg site (Wright 1984; pers comm) the woodmouse is present only in the autumn recordings whereas, on the Spaunton Moor site, there seems to be little seasonal variation. Pygmy shrew (Sorex minutus) and Common shrew (Sorex araneus) are present on the heather areas of both sites although these species also occur in limited numbers under bracken, whether sprayed or unsprayed. Small numbers of the bank vole (Cletherionomys glareolus) were trapped on both sites. There is no apparent explanation for this, but it serves as a further illustration of the lack of knowledge which currently exists about small mammal activity on moorland areas in general, and in association with bracken in particular.

BRACKEN CONTROL IN THE INTERESTS OF AMENITY AND ECOLOGY

It has been established that the heather moorland of the North York Moors is of vital significance in economic, ecological and amenity terms, and it is one of the National Park Department's statutory duties to conserve the landscape. The moorland areas play a major role in this strategy and any changes, including bracken encroachment, which reduce the area involved, are negative. It is extremely important that those areas of bracken which are suitable for treatment are distinguished. There are some areas where bracken will always have a competitive advantage, and eradication or control can never be fully effective. At present these include some areas with deep bracken litter and also some of the steeper slopes. It is estimated that 50% of the bracken area on the open moorland within the North York Moors could be effectively eradicated. This is dependent on the correct application of sprays, on the subsequent follow-up treatment both in terms of preventing further growth and removal of bracken, and finally, on effective range management. In some cases, this involves the temporary exclosure of sheep from the moors while vegetation regeneration takes place.

SIGNIFICANCE OF BRACKEN CONTROL FOR FUTURE LAND MANAGEMENT

Nearly all (96%) of the remaining open moorland within the North York Moors National Park could be, or is being, modified in some way. A total of 88% is suitable for agricultural conversion and/or afforestation and, of the remaining 12%, a further 7.5% is susceptible to erosion or degradation. Some 12% of the moors which is susceptible to erosion and degradation could, providing the soil conditions do not deteriorate further, be used for agriculture or afforestation. If such areas continue to erode and degrade, then not only will the moorland be lost but also the option of using the land for any other purpose will disappear and it will become derelict. Although 88% of the moorland could theoretically be converted, about 19% is actually in danger of being lost through degradation or erosion at the present time. Bracken encroachment is one of the major factors involved. The situation is made worse because, of the 60% of the moorland which is dominated by heather, very nearly half of the area consists of vegetation which is outside normal, controlled-burning management. There is a risk of uncontrolled summer fires on this old heather and, even if such fires do not result in complete soil loss, they frequently give bracken a competitive advantage and hence accelerate its expansion into the moorland area. It is vital, in the long-term interests of the heather moorland, that bracken, with its generally negative role in relation to both landscape and wildlife conservation, is effectively controlled in, if not eradicated from, as many areas as possible.

Further investigations into the impact of bracken in the North York Moors are being actively encouraged by the National Park Department. This work will continue to form a central part of the Moorland Management Programme[2] which is designed to improve the economic, ecological and amenity status of the most important and extensive habitat and landscape component in the National Park[3,4].

ACKNOWLEDGEMENTS

A number of people have helped by providing background information and data for this report. In particular I would like to thank Dr M Auld (Moorland Project Officer, North York Moors), Mr C King (Open University), Dr C Margules (CSIRO) and Mr B Wright (MAFF).

REFERENCES

1) North York Moors National Park (1981) The Future of the Moorland. (North York Moors National Park Department)

2) North York Moors National Park (1984) North York Moors National Park Plan First Review (North York Moors National Park Department)

3) North York Moors National Park (1980) Moorland Research 1977-79 (North York Moors National Park)

4) North York Moors National Park (1985) Moorland Management 1980-84 (North York Moors National Park)

Bracken on the North York Moors:
The agricultural problem

D D Barber

INTRODUCTION

Physically, the North York Moors cannot be classed as a hill area although most of the central core and the surrounding valleys are within the EEC-designated 'Less Favoured Areas'. The maximum altitude is less than 500m.O.D. and much of the area has an average rainfall of less than 1000 mm per annum. From a climatic standpoint, the most outstanding feature is the exposure to north and east winds. The pattern of farming, however, is similar to that in a hill area with the moors being utilized for hill sheep production whilst the valleys have a range from upland beef and sheep farming to intensive dairying. For the hill sheep farmer the moor is an extension of the in-bye, thus allowing additional stock to be kept.

The area of bracken associated with the North York Moors has been estimated at 11,600 hectares. Of this, approximately one-third infests enclosed land, the balance being on the open moor. The distribution of the plant is typical in that it infests the drier, better soils which in the North York Moors are found on the slopes between the plateau heather moorland and the lower valley land. Bracken is increasing here at the rate of approximately one per cent per annum, but this is mostly associated with the open moor.

The problem of bracken, can, therefore, be considered in two distinct parts, that associated with the in-bye land and that associated with the open moor.

IN-BYE LAND

The benefits of bracken control on this area of the farm are easy to calculate as it is often a matter of turning derelict land into land with productive potential. Not only is bracken-infested land unproductive in itself but it has, in fact, a depressant effect on the productivity of adjacent land, bearing in mind the associated livestock disorders it is known to cause.

TABLE 1 MOORLAND DECLINE

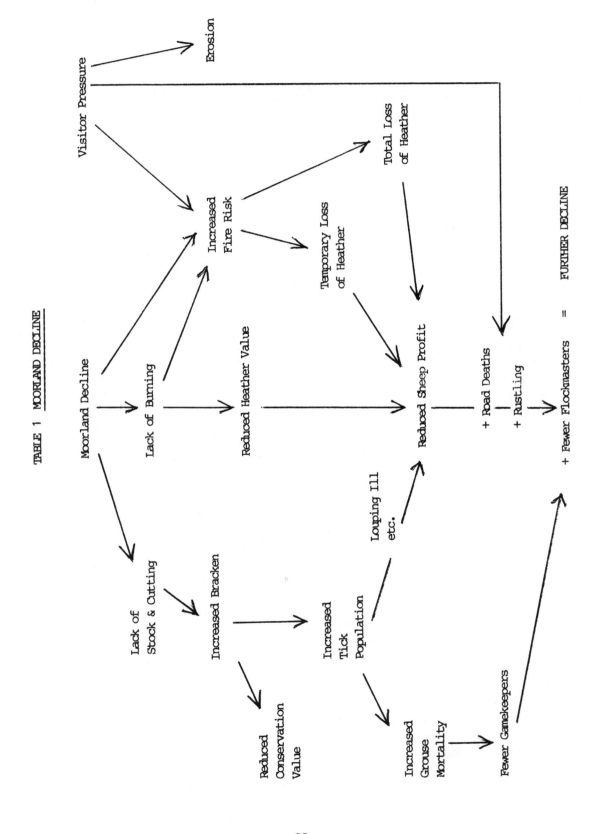

The combined costs of spraying, lime and phosphate, net of the 30% grant, are likely to be in the order of £125 per hectare (at 1985 prices). In many upland situations, if a sward is present under the bracken canopy, it is likely to be Agrostis/Festuca which, with 75 kg per hectare of nitrogen, is likely to give a dry matter yield of over 2.5 tonnes per hectare. If this is utilized by the grazing animal it is likely to be worth about £200 per hectare. If the bracken had no under-sward, then reseeding would be necessary with an additional net cost of about £100 per hectare. A ryegrass/clover sward would then respond to a greater amount of nitrogen, yielding perhaps 5 tonnes per hectare of dry matter with a value on our original basis of £400 per hectare. It can be seen in both cases that the costs of improvement are covered in the first year, assuming that the capital is available, although the margins would have to cover financing charges. These margins would be achieved only if there were additional stock to utilize the extra output, and this brings in other farm management considerations.

MOORLAND

It is generally accepted that the quality of moorland within the North York Moors is declining, due to a number of contributory factors (Table 1), one of which is the spread of bracken (see Brown R, herein). The moors are used not only for hill sheep rearing, but also for grouse production, and have immense conservation and recreation value. The heather moors are declining because of a reduction of the human resources that are necessary for their optimal management.

Hill sheep rearing is a hard way of life with low profitability. It is not surprising, therefore, that the numbers of flocks have declined in recent years. Grouse production reveals the same trend; whereas before 1940 there were over 50 gamekeepers in the moorland area, there are now only 14. This reduction in labour means that the heather is not burnt in a satisfactorily close rotation, with the consequence that there are large areas of over-aged heather. With increased visitor-pressure on the moors, there is also an increased risk of fire, particularly in dry summers like 1976. Such fires lead to destruction of the peat and to the total loss of moorland vegetation. Moorland decline leads to lack of profit and, with the high cost of existing bracken control measures, eradication is now being undertaken only by the National Park Authority for improvement of visual amenity, and, on a more limited scale, by the landowners, to improve grouse production. There is a lack of data on the economic benefits of large-scale bracken control in the moorland situation where stock control is not possible.

BRACKEN CONTROL USING ASULAM

Asulam is an extremely effective herbicide for the control of bracken. Complete control has been achieved both on enclosed land and on open moorland. Where less than adequate control has been obtained, incorrect timing in relation to the stage of growth of the plant and/ or poor application have been the cause.

Work carried out in the northern region of ADAS shows that,

where good control is achieved with an undergrowth of surviving vegetation, this can quickly colonize to give full sward cover and prevent further bracken growth. Where deep bracken litter occurs and good control has been achieved, this land tends to remain derelict because of surface erosion and the inhospitable nature of the surface for seedling establishment. On land where good control is not achieved, then re-colonization by the weed can occur extremely quickly and full bracken cover can be re-established within 4-5 years.

TABLE 2   Bracken control - frond counts from 10 m x 10 m areas in September

Site		Sprayed	1975	1976	1977	1978
1	A	1974	2	7	37	46
	B	1974	226	976	2171	4414
2	A	1974	42	51	40	109
	B	1974	0	0	0	0
3	A	1973	510	712	1265	2134
	B	1973	32	80	91	244

The figures in Table 2 demonstrate the rate of recovery in terms of number of bracken fronds, on sites where varying degrees of control have been achieved by aerial application of asulam. On site 2B, where there was an initial understorey of Vaccinium myrtillus and Agrostis-Festuca sward, heavy sheep grazing occurred and the bracken did not produce new fronds.

There is, therefore, a strong case for choosing for eradication those areas that are likely to be eligible for grant, areas with a ground cover of sheep meat (pasture sward) but bearing in mind that percentage control on such land tends to be less than in deep litter bracken areas. It is also essential that follow-up treatment is planned well ahead, allowing for one man with ground equipment to cope with about 25 acres (10 ha) per year. It is also becoming clear that follow-up treatment should be delayed until the second year after initial spraying, to overcome the problem of dormant rhizome buds (see Kirkwood and Archibald, herein).

On moorland there is no possibility of adequate stock control because of the lack of enclosure. This results in less effective or more costly follow-up treatment. The economic benefit of bracken control on moorlands is, therefore, much less certain, firstly because of the uncertainty of the grant being paid, and secondly because of the lack of proof of economic benefit. The view has been expressed that the development of a cheaper chemical would put a different complexion on moorland bracken control. There is certainly a will on the part of grouse moor owners and tenant sheep farmers to rid the moors of this noxious weed.

AN ADAS COLLABORATIVE PROJECT

ADAS in conjunction with the North York Moors National Park Authority has, for the above reasons, initiated and is undertaking a project on the effects of large-scale bracken control on (1) sheep production; (2) grouse production; (3) conservation; and (4) visual amenity. This project has the full support of the tenant sheep farmers, the moorland owners and the North of England Grouse Research Project.

Is it expected that valuable technical information will be obtained, but more important, it will be an example of how those concerned with different aspects of land use can work together in harmony for its improvement.

Bracken and the Common Lands of Wales

E J Hughes and J W Aitchison

INTRODUCTION

No discussion of the distribution of bracken in England and Wales, or of associated land management problems, would be complete without reference to the issue of common land. In 1958 the Royal Commission on Common Land[1] estimated that approximately 4% of the total land area of England and Wales was "common"; in Wales, with over 182,000 hectares, the commons accounted for a notable 9% of the surface area. The recent process of common land registration[2], following the Commons Registration Act 1965, will necessitate a modification of these figures - when outstanding legal arguments concerning disputed areas have been resolved - but, whatever the final outcome, it is evident that these unique and ancient systems of tenure continue to claim a substantial hold on the landscape. Of particular relevance to the present discussion is the fact that commons throughout England and Wales are covered by extensive tracts of bracken. This is especially true of the great upland commons of the north and west. The widespread association of the bracken fern with common land arises partly from the nature of the terrain concerned, partly from changes in the structure and intensity of pastoral farming systems (eg. the increased prevalence of sheep as opposed to cattle in many upland regions) and the role played by common grazings, and partly from the legal constraints with which such areas are encumbered. These constraints, such as the controls on fencing imposed by the Law of Property Act, Section 194, 1925, place limitations on management practices and can create difficulties for those keen to engage in pasture improvement projects. In the discussion that follows, these and other issues will be alluded to, with reference being made to a series of studies of common land in Wales. Figure 1 shows the distribution of final and provisional areas of common land in the Principality and is based on an analysis of the recently compiled registers of common land.

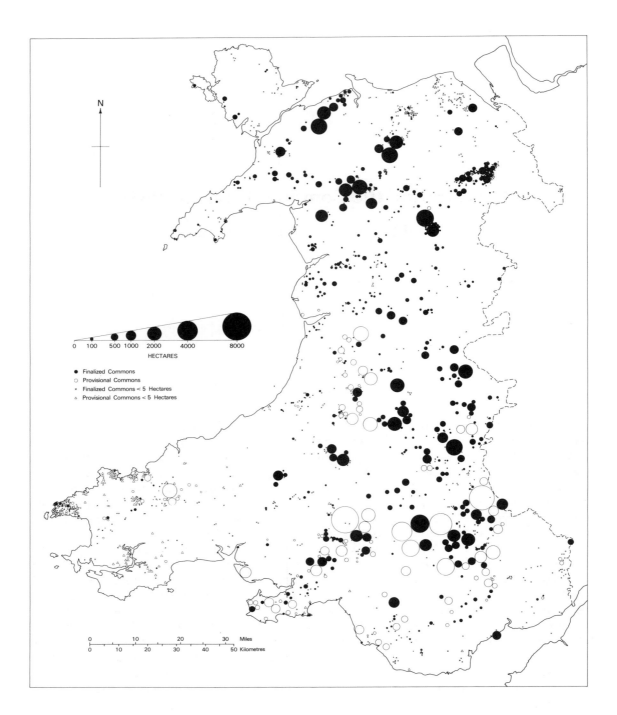

Fig.1. Wales: finalised and provisional commons, 1984

BRACKEN AND RIGHTS OF ESTOVERS

Given that it is currently regarded by many as a problem
species - creating day-to-day management difficulties for farmers,
reducing the grazing potential of hill pastures, contributing little
to the scenic qualities of some of our most cherished landscapes, and,
in places, denying access and mobility to ramblers and other active

94

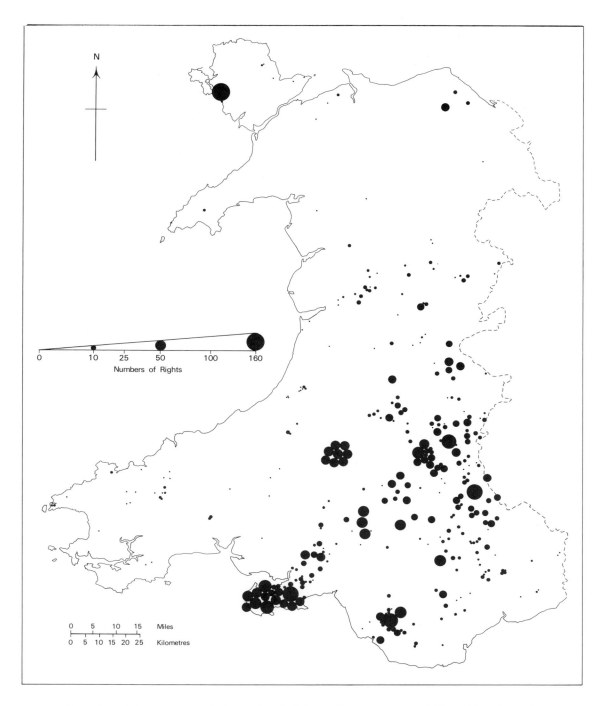

Fig.2. Wales: registered rights of estovers (finalised and provisional)

users of the countryside – it is perhaps a little ironic that for many commoners the right to cut bracken is regarded as an important facility. The practice of harvesting bracken for the winter bedding of livestock is less prevalent than it used to be, reflecting in part the decline in cattle numbers in the hills and uplands, but the common land registers (compiled between 1967 and 1972 in accordance with the directives of the Commons Registration Act 1965) still contain large numbers of entries relating to rights of "estovers" (ie. rights to take bracken, rushes or underwood from a specified area of common land). In the common land registers for Wales, rights of this type are pre-eminently for "the cutting of bracken". Traditionally, commoners have the right to take as much bracken as is needed to cater for the bedding requirements of livestock on the dominant tenement (ie. the holding to which the rights are actually attached). However, some entries in the registers detail the amounts of bracken that may be cut (eg. 300 bales per year or 1/2 ton per year). Interestingly, a few entries specify a right "to control bracken". Strictly speaking, this is not a registrable right of common. Figure 2 shows the distribution and number of rights of estovers listed in the common land registers of Wales, whilst Table 1 records the numbers of commons (final and provisional) with rights of estovers and their associated areas. Entries in the registers sometimes fail to state the type of material to which the right relates, but it can be assumed that the vast majority refer to bracken. Rights to take rushes and underwood, where specified, have been excluded from the aggregate statistics used in compiling Figure 2 and Table 1. The distribution in Figure 2 makes intersting comparison with Taylor's bracken map of Wales, herein.

TABLE 1   The common lands of Wales and rights of estovers

Rights of Estovers (number of entries)	Number of Commons	Area of Common Land (Hectares)
1	97	12,677
2 - 5	110	17,339
6 - 10	48	8,713
11 - 20	32	22,101
21 - 50	50	28,682
51 - 100	14	17,672
> 100	3	7,163
Totals	354	114,347

The common land registers for Wales contain 4,278 entries relating to rights of estovers. Rights of this type are recorded for 354 commons - 21% of the final and provisional units in the registers. Whilst bracken clearly does not cover the full expanse of these units, it is noteworthy that commons with rights of estovers cover 60% of the total area of common land in Wales. The distribution displayed in Figure 2 cannot be analysed in any detail here, but it underlines the strong concentration of rights of estovers in the uplands of South Wales - especially the districts of Brecknock and Radnor - where cattle constitute a strong, if not dominant, element in farming systems. In the uplands of North Wales, by contrast, grazing systems exhibit a more specialized focus on the rearing and fattening of sheep[3]. The rights of pasture enumerated in the registers confirm this regional difference. Rights of estovers are much more frequently listed for commons with rights to graze cattle. In the past, when more cattle grazed the hills of North Wales, rights to cut bracken could well have been much more prevalent. Whilst the registers should ostensibly record historic rights of this type it is evident that, in registering rights between 1967 and 1970, many rightholders simply referenced those of contemporary significance. In commenting upon the distribution of estovers in Wales, it should be noted that in certain areas (eg. the Gower Peninsula) large numbers of rights have been registered on behalf of whole communities and by individuals who have no grazing rights at all.

The fact that rights of estovers have been registered does not necessarily mean that they are used; this can be ascertained only through field inquiries. Various studies have shown that the situation varies from region to region. In Powys, for example, Terry[4] has indicated that, despite the ready availability of straw for bedding, commoners on Mynydd Eppynt and on the Llandeilo, Llanbedr and Glascwm Hills of north-east Radnor, still cut extensive areas of bracken. On Mynydd Illtyd near Brecon, most of the 31 commoners regularly cut and round-bale bracken. Surveys by Hughes[5] have shown, however, that in the neighbouring Brecon Beacons area, rights to cut bracken are not currently exercised.

COMMONS, BRACKEN AND SECOND-STAGE LEGISLATION

Whilst a consideration of rights of estovers yields interesting insights into an ancient customary use of the bracken fern, it clearly does not reflect the actual incidence of bracken on common land. A simple comparison of the two distributions (Figure 1 and the map of brackenprepared from the Vegetation Survey of Wales by Taylor[6] and reproduced herein) confirms that this is so. As to the extent of bracken on common land, a sample study of the 291 commons in Powys has shown that 56% have significant areas of bracken, especially around their outer margins, just above the in-bye lands of farms located in surrounding valleys. In a survey of 491 rightholders[7,8] in the counties of Powys, Clwyd and Gwynedd, 64% of respondents stated that more than a quarter of their commons were under bracken. A notable 19% claimed that the bracken fern had succeeded in colonizing over three-quarters of the area of common land on which they had rights. Interestingly, however, only 27% of the rightholders were of the opinion that the cover of bracken had increased over the last ten years. The majority (65%) felt that there had been little, if any, change. While this may be so, it is evident that over the years a large number of commons have been overwhelmed by bracken. The rightholders of Tir Stent common on the slopes of Cader Idris (Meirionydd), for example, recognize that the steady reduction in the number of grazing cattle on their common is responsible for the rapid encroachment of bracken and the loss of valuable areas of hill pasture. In the survey of 491 rightholders, 65% of respondents felt there was a need to improve the quality of grazings on their commons.

When asked what types of improvement were desirable, 23% called specifically for programmes of bracken eradication while 33% cited improvements involving 'surface treatment'. In all, 29% mentioned the need for more fencing on commons, both internal, and around external perimeters.

On a number of commons such improvements have been carried out. In the Clwydian Range of north-east Wales, for instance, bracken has been eradicated from extensive areas of common, initially through crushing operations and, more recently, by spraying, leading to a dramatic increase in grazing potential. This, and many other similar ventures, have had to be launched in the face of a highly constraining set of statutes relating to the use and management of common land. It is not possible here to enter into a detailed discussion of the relevant legal complexities of the situation. Suffice it to say that rightholders are not in a position to carry out certain developments on common land, such as fencing or building, without seeking approval from the Secretary of State for the Environment or, in the Welsh case, the Secretary of State for Wales. Given the conditions that need to be satisfied and the objections which are likely to be lodged by other interested parties (eg. recreationalists and conservationists), seeking approval can be a time-consuming and not always successful process.

Since the common land of England and Wales is such avaluable asset, and one that is not always being gainfully utilized (both from an agricultural point of view and from the point of view of countryside management in general), it is evident that new legislation is urgently required. Only through a radical change in the law, will it be possible to ensure a balanced and integrated development of what is clearly a major, but currently much wasted, national resource. As long ago as 1958 the Royal Commission on Common Land made recommendations concerning a new approach to the management of common land; only now are these recommendations being seriously considered. It is to be hoped that the deliberations of the recently constituted Common Land Forum will reach a successful conclusion, and that the long-awaited second-stage legislation will soon find its way into the Statute Books. Only when it does, can an effective assault be launched on this insidious species within common lands.

ACKNOWLEDGEMENTS

Much of the data presented in this paper were derived from studies funded both by the Social Science Research Council and the Countryside Commission.

REFERENCES

1) Royal Commission on Common Land 1955-58 (1958) Cmnd. 462. HMSO

2) Aitchison J W and Hughes E J (1982) The common land registers of England and Wales, Area, 151-156

3) Aitchison J W (1982) Livestock Distributions, National Atlas of Wales, Sheet 5.4, University of Wales Press

4)   Terry A K (1980)   The Utilization and Management of Common Land in Powys, unpublished PhD thesis, University of Wales

5)   These surveys are included in a PhD dissertation to be submitted by one of us (EJH) in July 1985.   The thesis is entitled "Agriculture and recreation in the Brecon Beacons National Park"

6)   Taylor J A (1978)   The British upland environment and its management. Geography, 63, 338-353

7)   Aitchison J W (1983)   The common lands of Wales : problems and opportunities. Countryside Commission, Office for Wales

8)   Aitchison J W and Hughes E J (1983)   The common lands of Wales : a cartographic and statistical summary. Report prepared for the Social Science Research Council

Soil and Slope conditions under Bracken in Wales

T R E Thompson, C C Rudeforth, R Hartnup, J W Lea and P S Wright

INTRODUCTION

The habitat for bracken has been described as 'woods, heaths etc, mainly on light acid soils'[1]. Bracken is said to be 'rare on limestone and on wet peat but dominant in the field layers of woods on acid soils and in areas of former acid grassland and heather'. This catholic taste results in a widespread distribution, and it is absent from only 3, 10 x 10 km squares in the whole of Wales[2]. Taylor[3] gives more detailed information on its actual distribution based on field and air photographic data. Bracken ranges from mature dunes and peaty banks on raised lowland mosses to slopes high in the Welsh mountains but is most extensive on well aerated, acid, loamy soils excluded from tillage by rockiness or steepness. Such land is widespread in Wales.

Bracken's sensitivity to soil oxygen deprivation is documented by Poel[4], and Anderson[5] further concludes that diffusion rates within the surface soil are actually increased by bracken invasion. While the species is found mainly on acid, nutrient-poor soil its absence from more fertile land is more the result of historical and economic factors than of an inability to grow on such soils[6]. Smith (herein) suggests that soil available water capacity is also important, possibly more so than aeration, and this is reinforced by the findings of Pitman and Pitman (also herein).

This paper, a byproduct of the Soil Survey of England and Wales's National Soil Inventory, reports on soil and site conditions under bracken in Wales.

METHODS

In 1979, the Soil Survey of England and Wales began work on a set of National Soil Maps at a scale of 1:250,000. Most of the field work involved free survey in which the surveyor locates sampling sites subjectively to help draw soil boundaries. At the same time, however, sites at 5km spacing, based on the Ordnance Survey national grid, were visited. Soil and site characteristics were recorded and samples taken for analysis. At sites where semi-natural vegetation occurred, this was also recorded by cover-abundance. The data were collected by five surveyors using standardised techniques and conventions.

Recording is now complete and the data have been verified. There are some 830 records for Wales and bracken formed some part of the vegetation in 64 of these. (This is 7.7%, which is compatible with estimates provided by Taylor, herein, for the bracken of Wales which was 5.8% some 20 years or so ago - Ed.). The species was recorded as dominant where it had the greatest cover-abundance value of any species recorded. At many sites, where dominant, it had shaded out all other species to form a pure stand. Where only sparsely present along with other plants, it was simply recorded as present. The composition of the bracken subset has been characterised by the ranges of soil type, soil association, and slope.

RESULTS

Of the 64 bracken records (7.7 per cent), the species was dominant at 14 sites (1.7 per cent) and recorded as present at the remainder. The sites are spread across Wales with a bias towards mid-Wales. The average land gradient is 19° (± 11°) and aspect appears biased towards south and east. Figure 1 illustrates the range of soil

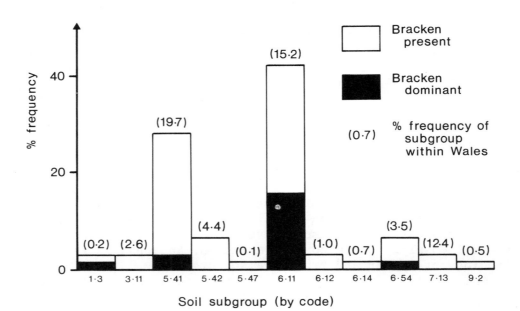

Figure 1   The distribution of bracken within soil subgroups expressed as a percentage of the total number of bracken records. Explanation of codes - 1.3 Raw skeletal soils, 3.11 Humic rankers, 5.41 Typical brown earths, 5.42 Stagnogleyic brown earths, 5.47 Colluvial brown earths, 6.11 Typical brown podzolic soils, 6.12 Humic brown podzolic soils, 6.14 Stagnogleyic brown podzolic soils, 6.54 Ferric stagnopodzols, 7.13 Cambic stagnogley soils, 9.2 Disturbed soils.

types on which bracken was recorded. Soil subgroup codes are used for
convenience. The digit before the point refers to the major soil
group 1 - undeveloped <u>Terrestrial raw soils</u>, 3 - shallow <u>Lithomorphic
soils</u>, 5 - deeper, mostly permeable <u>Brown soils</u>, 6 - acid <u>Podzolic
soils</u>, 7 - impermeable <u>Surface-water gley soils</u>, 8 - permeable but
periodically waterlogged <u>Ground-water gley soils</u>, 9 - <u>Man-made soils</u>.
Figures in brackets give the approximate percentage of Wales in each
subgroup. Seventy per cent of sites where bracken was recorded
(either as a dominant or non-dominant species) have typical brown
podzolic soils or typical brown earths, many of which are on steep
slopes. In Wales, these permeable, moderately stony soils are mostly
fine loamy or fine silty and overlie bedrock within 1m. They are
seldom waterlogged but have a range of water-holding capacities.
Some, particularly where shallow, are droughty in summer. Ferric
stagnopodzols (6.54) have a peaty topsoil and occupy upper valley
sides and plateau edges in the Welsh uplands. The average gradient for
all ferric stagnopodzols is 12° but for those under bracken it is 27°.
Bracken-covered typical brown earths are also concentrated on steeper
than average slopes.

Spatial soil variation is shown on soilmaps by aggregating
closely related soils into soil map units, identified usually by the
dominant soil type, in most cases, a soil series. On small scale maps
such as the National Soil Map[7] the units are called soil
associations. Figure 2 shows the distribution of bracken sites across

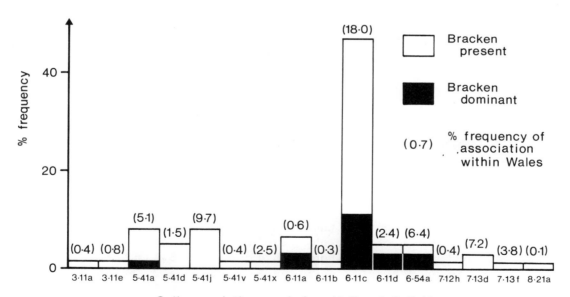

Figure 2   The distribution of bracken within soil associations
expressed as a percentage of the total number of bracken records.
Explanation of association symbols - 3.11a Revidge, 3.11e Bangor,
5.41a Milford, 5.41d Eardiston 2, 5.41j Denbigh 1, 5.41v Rheidol,
5.41x East Keswick 1, 6.11a Malvern, 6.11b Moretonhamstead, 6.11c
Manod, 6.11d Withnell 1, 6.54a Hafren, 7.12h Foggathorpe 1, 7.13d
Cegin, 7.13f Brickfield 2, 8.21a Everingham.

103

the soil associations of Wales. One association, the Manod (6.11c), contains nearly half the bracken records, both total and dominant. This, the most extensive association in Wales, is dominated by typical brown podzolic soils of the Manod and Banc series. Although the Milford (5.41a) and Denbigh (5.41j) associations also contain appreciable numbers of bracken sites, many of the typical brown earths recorded in Figure 1 are on land within the Manod association. The Malvern (6.11a) and Withnell 1 (6.11d) associations contain soils similar to the Manod but are on different parent materials. The bracken sites within the Hafren association (6.54a) have an average gradient of 20°, whereas, for those within brown earth dominant associations, it is 14°. Both figures are atypically steep. Combining these data with the actual extent of the more widespread soil associations (Fig.3) gives a clear impression of the importance of the Manod association to the distribution of bracken in Wales.

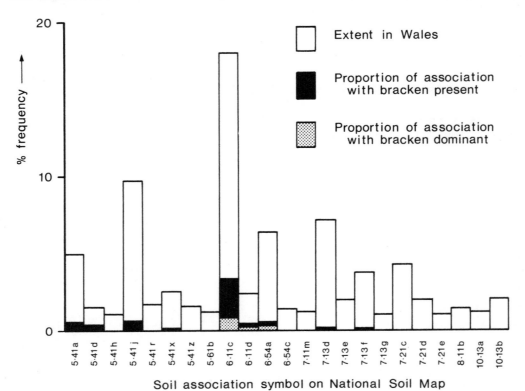

Figure 3   The extent of the largest soil associations within Wales and the distribution of bracken. Explanation of association symbols – 5.41a Milford, 5.41d Eardiston 2, 5.41h Neath, 5.41j Denbigh 1, 5.41r Wick 1, 5.41x East Keswick 1, 5.41z East Keswick 3, 5.61b Teme, 6.11c Manod, 6.11d Withnell 1, 6.54a Hafren, 6.54c Gelligaer, 7.11m Salop, 7.13d Cegin, 7.13e Brickfield 1, 7.13f Brickfield 2, 7.13g Brickfield 3, 7.21c Wilcocks 1, 7.21d Wilcocks 2, 7.21e Wenallt, 8.11b Conway, 10.13a Crowdy 1, 10.13b Crowdy 2.

The Manod association is very extensive on steeper ground not easily cultivated or fertilised. It is here, on the 'ffridd' land, where there is sufficient depth of well aerated soil, that bracken thrives. Figure 4 shows the distribution of slopes within Wales for

(1) all land, (2) the Manod association, and (3) land under bracken. Slopes of less than 5° under bracken were so few as to be unsampled by the 5km grid, and there are proportionally more very steep slopes. The distribution of slopes within the Manod association is intermediate between (1) and (3) with 14 per cent of records having less than 5° slopes.

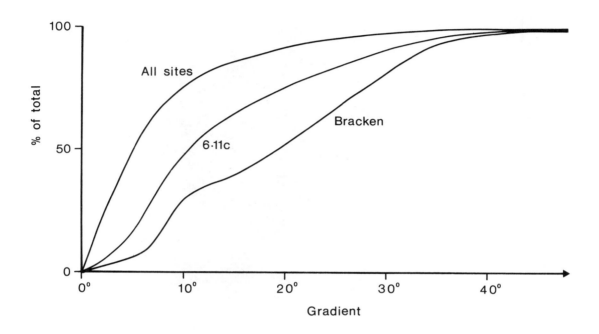

Figure 4   Accumulated frequency curves of gradient for (i) all records, (ii) those in the Manod association, and (iii) those with bracken.

CONCLUSIONS

These results demonstrate the strong relationship between bracken and the nature of the underlying soil. They indicate that, at present, bracken occupies, with a few exceptions, a relatively narrow range of soil and site conditions. In Wales, at least, it has not spread out onto the open moorland hilltops, nor is it extensive in the lowlands.

Given the Welsh soil/slope province that bracken partly occupies, namely the Manod series and related soils on slopes in excess of 5°, it is possible to identify the full extent of that province and estimate the fern's potential distribution. At 4500km^2, it is some 20 per cent of Wales. Some of this, however, is afforested (22 per cent), slopes steeper than 5° can be, and are, ploughed and fertilised, and some ground will have an unfavourable aspect. Even with allowances for these factors, it remains clear that bracken occupies but a small part of its potential soil/slope province.

The distribution of the four most extensive soil associations with more than 15 per cent bracken cover is shown in Figure 5, which is derived from the National Soil Map. These four are the Manod,

Withnell 1, Eardiston 2, and Malvern associations. Provided its ecological adaptability does not change, any future spread of bracken will most likely be on these closely related soils. This is where any retrenchment in agriculture, in the form of less frequent liming or reseeding, will first take place, and it is also where conditions seem most to suit the growth of bracken.

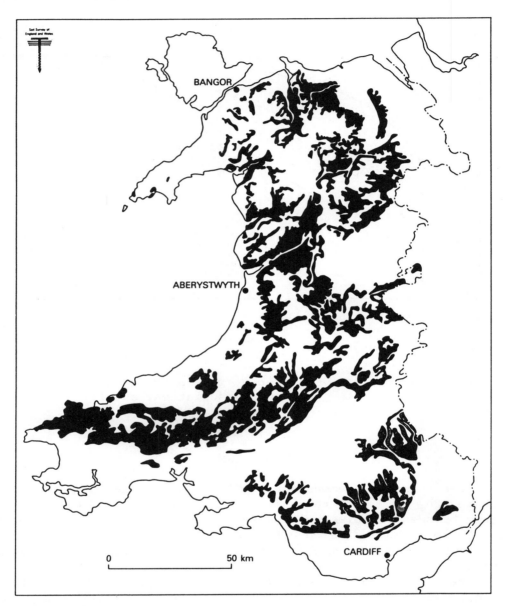

Figure 5   The Welsh bracken province.

ACKNOWLEDGEMENTS

The authors wish to acknowledge helpful comments and advice from Dr P Bullock and other colleagues within the Soil Survey. Figures 1 to 4 where drawn by Bowler Graphics of Aberystwyth while Figure 5 was produced by E M Thomson and his staff.

106

REFERENCES

1) Clapham A R, Tutin T G and Warburg E F (1962) Flora of the British Isles. 2nd Ed. Cambridge University Press

2) Perring F H and Walters S M (eds.) (1962) Atlas of the British Flora. London: Nelson

3) Taylor J A (1985) Bracken encroachment rates in Britain. Soil Use and Management, 1, 53-56

4) Poel L W (1961) Soil aeration as a limiting factor in the growth of Pteridium aquilinum (L.) Kuhn. J. Ecol., 49, 107-111

5) Anderson D J (1961) The structure of some upland plant communities in Caernarvonshire. 1. The pattern shown by Pteridium aquilinum. J. Ecol., 49, 369-376

6) Watt A S (1976) The ecological status of bracken. Bot. J. Linn. Soc., 73, 217-239

7) Rudeforth C C, Hartnup R, Lea J W, Thompson T R E and Wright P S (1983) Soils of Wales. Harpenden: Soil Survey of England and Wales

Factors affecting the distribution, abundance and economic status of bracken (Pteridium esculentum) in New South Wales

J A Thomson, C Willoughby and C M Shearer

INTRODUCTION

Bracken fern, _Pteridium esculentum_ (Forst.f.) Cockayne is a widespread species indigenous to southern and eastern Australia woodland understorey and forest margins. Bracken is becoming increasingly important in these parts of the continent as an aggressive coloniser of cleared land, as well as forest and heathland communities subjected to frequent fire[1,3]. Bracken occurs as a locally significant species on the eastern slopes of the Dividing Range from northern Queensland through New South Wales to central Victoria, the south-eastern region of South Australia, Tasmania and the south-western corner of West Australia roughly delimited by a line from Perth to Albany. No attempt appears to have been made to quantify the broad scale status and economic significance of bracken in any Australian region prior to the present study[4] in New South Wales (NSW).

STATUS AND ECONOMIC SIGNIFICANCE OF BRACKEN IN NSW

Distribution and Abundance

Detailed first-hand information on the distribution, abundance and apparent significance of bracken was provided in questionnaires returned by resident officers of 63 agronomy-districts and by 46 returns, covering 64 national parks and reserves east of the 147° meridian of longitude, received from officers of the National Parks and Wildlife Service. In addition, returns were received from officers of the Forestry Commission covering 120 state forests totalling 19,015 km^2, about 55% of the total area of state forest in NSW. Questions were designed to provide a detailed, standardised framework, demanding quantitative replies within 10-25% intervals, depending on the kind of estimate required.

Surveys were made by the authors at 60 selected sites within

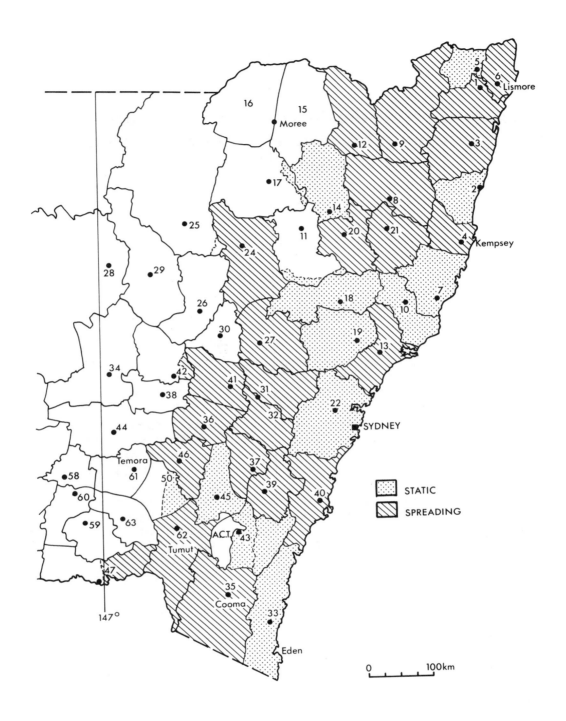

Figure 1   The agronomic districts of NSW showing the distribution
of bracken and its reported status in cleared agricultural
land.

the present area of distribution of bracken in NSW. For these sites, detailed analyses of aerial photographs going back 25-40 years were used to follow change in bracken distribution and for measurement of rates of spread of bracken under different land-use patterns.

Indices of abundance (IA) of bracken in cleared agricultural land were defined with reference to the district areas shown in Fig.1 as follows: (1) bracken absent; (2) bracken in small, localised stands without agricultural significance; (3) significant infestations of bracken on a few properties in part of the district (taken conservatively as 1%); (4) bracken, a widespread and aggressive coloniser constituting a signficant problem in 10-25% of the district; (5) bracken, a dominant and aggressive invader over large areas, constituting the predominant problem in pasture management over 25% or more of the district. Bracken was considered to be a problem on a particular holding if 10% or more of the pasture was infested.

TABLE 1   Bracken in cleared agricultural land, NSW

	Index of abundance				
	2	3	4	5	Totals
Districts affected (Fig.1)	11,17,42	1,3,8,9 12,14,18, 20,21,22, 24,27,32, 35,36,37, 41,43,45, 46,50	13,19,31, 39,43,47	2,4,5,6, 7,10,33, 40,62	
Total area (km^2 x 10^3)	28.0	172.6	37.7	55.1	293.4
Agriculture, 1982 (ha x 10^3)	2122	12189	2052	2217	18580
Bracken affected area (%)	<.01	1	10	25	
area (ha x 10^3)	negligible	120	178	554	852
Bracken cover area (%)	negligible	0.1	1.0	2.5	
area (ha x 10^3)	negligible	12.0	17.8	55.4	85.2

The extent of bracken infestation of agricultural land in NSW is summarised in Table 1. An estimated 850,000 ha of cleared land is significantly affected by bracken while the area actually covered by bracken is about 85,000 ha. It should be noted that these figures for agricultural land are underestimates because the lower limits of bracken abundance for each category were used for purposes of calculation. Allowance was made for the limited distribution of bracken in districts 47 and 50 (Fig.1) in compiling Table 1. Further, it is important to recognise that the agricultural significance of bracken infestation is not related to area of infestation alone. Bracken is a disproportionately greater problem in the potentially more productive beef- and dairy-cattle country in NSW than in less valuable, drier grazing districts.

The index of abundance of bracken in woodland communities was estimated on the following basis: (1) bracken absent; (2) small localised stands of bracken restricted to special micro-habitats; (3) bracken locally significant and not dominant in typical understorey associations; (4) bracken, a common element of woodland associations, locally dominant over part of the district; (5) bracken, a very common species and dominant in woodland understorey and forest clearings throughout the district.

Overall, bracken is most abundant along the coastal strip and on the eastern slopes of the Dividing Range which parallels the east coast of NSW. Agronomists in 8 (numbers 2, 4, 5, 6, 7, 10, 33, 40; see Fig.1) of 12 districts to the east of that range report bracken as an aggressive invader over large areas and a predominant problem in 25% or more of their districts. The abundance of bracken declines dramatically inland from the Dividing Range. More than 300 km from the coast, bracken occurs only in small localised stands in special situations and is of no economic significance. Bracken is very abundant and a widespread agricultural problem in inland districts covering the south-western slopes of the Dividing Range (district 62) and those of the New England plateau forming its north-western flank (especially districts 8, 9, 21).

The index of abundance of bracken as reported for woodland, rangeland and heathland correlates closely with that reported for cleared land in the same district (Spearman rank-order correlation coefficient, $r_s = 0.83$, $t_{37} = 9.13$, $p < 0.01$).

Correlates of Abundance

The relative importance of a number of geographic, climatic, vegetational and land-use variables in determining the abundance of bracken was assessed for both cleared agricultural land and woodland using multivariate analysis. A grid of unit size 30' latitude x 30' longitude, approximately 2,500 km^2, was used to divide the area of NSW east of the 147° meridian into 163 sections (Figures 2-3). Variables examined were: indices of bracken abundance in cleared lands and in woodland, latitude, longitude, altitude, January (summer) maximum, and July (winter) minimum temperatures; summer, winter and combined annual rainfalls, farm type, soil type, natural vegetation before settlement, and present-day vegetational associations[4]. Initially, the intensity of association between these environmental parameters and the abundance of bracken in cleared and woodland communities was examined using Spearman's rank-order correlation, since the relative abundance of bracken is expressed as ranked scores 1-5 (see above). Environmental parameters showing significant correlation ($p < 0.05$) were included in the multiple regression analysis.

Bracken is most abundant in cleared agricultural land at high altitudes, in high rainfall areas, and where January maximum and July minimum temperatures are low, natural vegetation was dry-sclerophyll woodland, and the soils are deep, well-structured and initially of high fertility. In woodland communities the correlates of bracken abundance are similar, but include association with mixed eucalypt forests, and with deep coarse-textured soil types showing good drainage. The pattern of relative abundance of bracken in agricultural land and in woodland communities based on the survey data reported here is shown in Figures 2A and 3A. Annual rainfall is the single most important factor correlated with bracken abundance in cleared land and in woodland communities, with the highest correlation coefficients in each case ($r_s = 0.8472$, $p \ll 0.001$; $r_s = 0.8599$, $p \ll 0.001$ respectively).

Inclusion of four climatic variables and two farm types permits formulation of a predictive multiple regression equation accounting for 76% of the variance of the index of abundance (IA) of bracken in cleared land as follows:

$$IA = -1.7092 + 3.557 \log_{10} \text{(annual rainfall, cm)} - 0.1336$$
(January maximum temperature, °C) − 0.0997 (July minimum temperature, °C) + 0.6197 $\log_{10}$ (altitude, m) + 0.3816 (farm type F1, beef cattle) + 0.4822 (farm type F2, dairy cattle).....................(1).

The corresponding equation including variables accounting for 75% of the variance of IA of bracken in woodland communities is:

$$IA = -1.8401 + 2.8025 \log_{10} \text{(annual rainfall, cm)} - 0.1158$$
(January maximum temperature, °C) + 0.7322 (vegetation type V9, mixed eucalypt communities) + 2.0192 $\log_{10}$ (summer rainfall, cm).....(2).

Exclusion of other variables from these two equations reflects high standard errors and low F values.

Patterns of bracken abundance predicted using Equations (1) and (2) are shown in Figures 2B and 3B. For both cleared land and woodland communities the constructs simulate observed bracken abundance quite closely. Bracken is most abundant in coastal areas of NSW near Lismore, Kempsey and Eden, and on the western slopes of the Dividing Range near Tumut; less abundant further inland in the north and on the Monaro Tablelands surrounding Cooma to the south; rare or absent east of Moree and north of Temora. The smoother appearance of the predictive diagrams compared with the observed is due to the inclusion of real values between 1 and 5 for the IA of bracken determined by the predictive equations, whereas integer values of 1 through 5 were used for observational values.

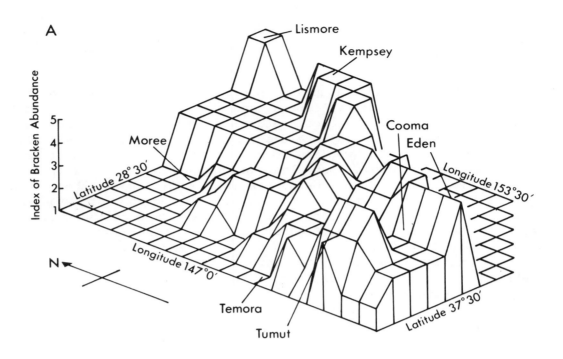

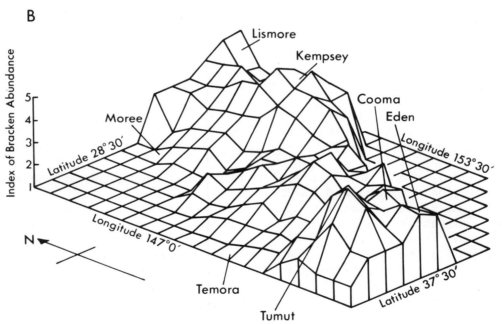

Figure 2

Topographical representations of the abundance of bracken in
cleared agricultural land, NSW. A, reported; B, modelled
using predictive equation (1) described in the text.

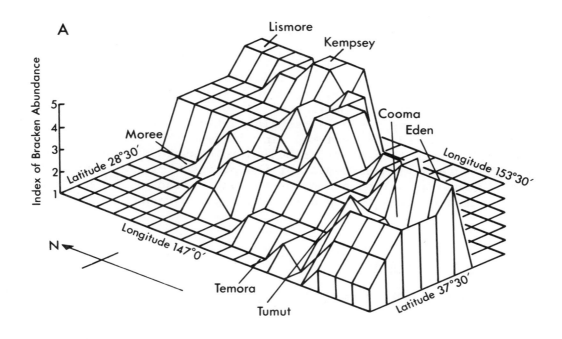

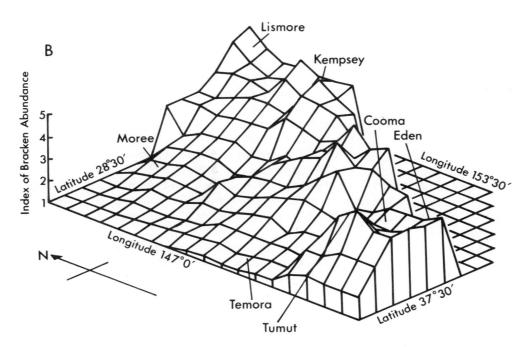

Figure 3

Topographical representations of the abundance of bracken
in woodland ecosystems, NSW. A, reported; B, modelled using
predictive equation (2) described in the text.

Age and Rate of Spread of Stands

Agronomists in 63% (24/38) of districts reporting bracken consider the areas of infestions to be increasing (Fig.1). Factors mentioned as likely to contribute to bracken spread included recent clearing, fertility decline in older pastures, low stocking rates, seasonal influences such as drought, and the increasing cost of labour and fuel for control measures.

Semi-quantitive, and in certain instances precise measurement, of rates of spread of bracken in different climatic and edaphic regions within its area of distribution in eastern NSW were made from aerial photographs. Measurement of the position of the bracken front encroaching into grassland showed an average spread of 2-3 m per annum over 15 ungrazed sites followed in aerial photographs for 15 years or more.

Genetic Structure of Stands

The spread of P.esculentum is considered to be predominantly vegetative in cleared land[2]. Relict stands at forest edges, fencelines, roadways, railway lines and broken ground, including gully heads and rocky outcrops, serve as foci for re-invasion. Over centuries - a realistic time scale for Pteridium[5] - no assessment has yet been made of the role of sporeling establishment, nor of genetic divergence amongst the vegetative offspring of individual sporophytes of P.esculentum.

Bracken stands exemplifying three distinctive situations have so far been examined using isozyme patterns revealed by starch-gel electrophoresis[4]. The first category comprises aggressively spreading stands already covering areas of 1-20 ha of formerly cleared land, and spreading behind a continuous invading front. In two such cases of rapid colonisation of highly favourable areas, at Pearl Beach and Mt. Tomah, fronds separated by 50 m or more clearly belonged to distinct genets as shown by multiple isozyme[4] and morphological[5] differences. At the scale of this analysis, no spatial and genetic hierarchy was detected which related the genotypes in these stands to a spatial or temporal sequence. Thus no indication was obtained of differentiation of ancestral genets by somatic mutation[6]. Colonisation at these localities appears to have involved multiple sporeling establishment on an unknown time-scale; present short-term spread at these sites appears to occur vegetatively from persistent marginal relicts.[5]

The second category of bracken stand comprises isolated, circumscribed areas of up to about 0.5 ha. In an example of this kind at Oxford Falls, a single dominant genotype was present, spreading out into adjacent grassland from a creek bank. Within the area covered by this genet, only one other genotype was found. The latter extended over no more than 2-5 m^2, and was surrounded by, and interspersed with vigorous fronds of the dominant genotype with which it is presumably unable to compete successfully. Again, the two distinct genets appear likely to have originated from separate sporophytes at some time in the past, as isozyme analysis reveals multiple genetic differences between them.

The third category of stand to be examined is illustrated by

116

the situation along the west escarpment bordering Lake George. Here, isolated bracken patches occur in a eucalypt-dominated woodland and edging grassland in broken ground at gully heads in the hillsides. No significant expansion of these stands has occurred over the last 40 years. In the present climate, the steep, dry slopes at this locality appear unfavourable for bracken spread. Isozyme analysis of seven stands on a 9 km transect along the escarpment showed fronds from within stands to be qualitatively uniform, whereas samples from separate stands showed multiple enzymic differences. Thus, even the closer stands, separated by as little as 300 m, appear not to be relicts of a more extensive ancestral stand dating back to a period of wetter climate, but rather to have originated from separate sporelings.

Significance in Agriculture

Agronomists from 79% of districts in which bracken occurs (Fig.1) reported, on subjective grounds, that competition between bracken and pasture (or occasionally, crop) species decreased productivity on more than 5% of properties to a degree causing economic concern in the absence of control measures. In 11 of the 15 most heavily infested districts, productivity on 10-75% of properties was considered to be affected.

To establish a preliminary quantitive basis for considering loss of productivity due to competition with pasture/forage species, estimates were made of the dry mass of such material inside and outside bracken stands with 75-90% frond canopy. Representative sites were selected on cleared agricultural land in enclosures or paddocks from which stock had been excluded for a minimum of 18 months. The study sites were at Termeil (south coast), Mt Tomah (central) and Lismore (north coast) respectively. Plots were harvested at the end of the spring-summer growing season. In the three areas, the dry mass of the standing crop of pasture/forage species inside the bracken averaged 35, 29 and 42% respectively of that outside the perimeter of the stands. The depression of productivity over the three sites was highly significant (analysis of variance, $F_{1,29} = 33.66$, $p \ll 0.01$) and consistent in pattern, although different in magnitude[4].

Bracken was reported as contributing significantly to the fire hazard on more than 5% of properties in 10 of 38 agronomic districts in which it occurs. Remnant stands along fencelines both increase losses of fencing during bushfires and serve as corridors for spread of fire.

Agronomists in 18 districts in which bracken is found were aware of stock losses attributable to bracken poisoning, particularly amongst cattle but also occasionally in sheep and horses. However, such losses appear to be of little economic significance except in periods of food shortage due to overstocking, drought, or fire.

Significance in Forestry

In 23% (19/82) of state forests in which bracken occurs and for which information is available, foresters considered bracken to be a significant competitor of naturally-regenerating or planted trees in their early stages. When bracken infestation of softwood plantings is heavy, it was noted that survival may not be affected directly, but that early growth of Pinus radiata appears to be reduced by as much as 20-30%. State foresters report that bracken is a significant fire hazard due to high standing levels in more than 5% of the overall area covered by 43 of 82 forests. Within compartments of these 82 forests, bracken was considered to be a fire hazard in 30% of softwood plantings and 48% of hardwood plantings. An additional problem associated with bracken infestation of forests was reported to be provision of cover for vermin, especially rabbits (29% of forests) and feral pigs (10% of forests).

At present, attempts to control bracken are practised in only 5 of 83 state forests (6%). Foresters report that for 13% of forests some systematic control measures covering 5-25% of the forest areas would be beneficial.

Significance in Parkland Management

Staff of the National Parks and Wildlife Service reported bracken cover of 10% or more in 53 of 64 National Parks situated east of longitude 147°. One third (12/40) of the reporting officers consider that bracken causes community changes by replacing other native species. This ability is seen as related to rapid regeneration of bracken after fire and its competitive advantage over species dependent on seed-based replacement, and to possible allelopathic inhibition of other species[7].

Bracken is considered to represent a significant fire hazard in 47% (27/58) of parklands in which it occurs. Control is mostly limited to burning for fuel reduction. More effective systematic control measures were considered particularly necessary in 6 of the reserves covered by the survey.

Bracken in Relation to Fire

A particular problem arises in forest and parkland management in relation to the frequency of wildfires fuelled by bracken growth, and to the necessary frequency of prescribed burning for fuel reduction in fire control programmes. Raison and his colleagues[8] showed that nutrient losses due to a single burn of understorey and litter in sclerophyll forests may reach 54-75% for nitrogen and 37-50% for phosphorus. Replacement times, estimated at 11 years for nitrogen and 20 years for phosphorus, highlight the problem posed by the present burn cycles of 3-8 years. Even worse, bracken spread in sclerophyll forests and heathlands is increasing the frequency of wildfire and/or prescribed burning towards a 3-4 year periodicity, which may be incompatible with maintenance of soil nutrient levels and soil structure. A further consequence of increasing bracken density is a change in the species composition of plant communities. This is a serious consideration in the establishment of under-storey legumes needed to contribute to recovery of nitrogen levels. These aspects of the spread of bracken in eastern Australia have not received detailed, and certainly not quantitative consideration to date.

ACKNOWLEDGEMENTS

We are greatly indebted to those officers of the NSW Department of Agriculture, Forestry Commission and National Parks and Wildlife Service who generously contributed information for the survey aspects of this work, and to Robyne Byatt for collaboration in electrophoretic analysis. Financial support for several aspects of the work reported here was received through the Australian Research Grants Scheme (D1/8115351) and the Rural Credits Development Fund of the Reserve Bank of Australia.

REFERENCES

1) Watson R (1981) Bracken Fern. In Agfact. p 7.6.2; 1-6 Sydney: NSW Department of Agriculture

2) O'Brien T P (1963) The morphology and growth of Pteridium aquilinum var. esculentum (Forst.) Kuhn. Ann. Bot., NS, 27; 253-267

3) Willis J H (1962) A Handbook to Plants in Victoria. 1. Ferns, Conifers, and Monocotyledons. 2nd Ed. Melbourne: Melbourne University Press

4) Thomson J A and Willoughby C (1985) The Status and Economic Significance of Bracken Fern (Pteridium) in NSW. Sydney: University of Sydney, School of Biological Sciences

5) Oinonen E (1967) Sporal regeneration of bracken (Pteridium aquilinum (L.) Kuhn) in Finland in the light of the dimensions and the age of its clones. Acta For. Fenn. 83, 1-96

6) Whitham T G and Slobodchikoff C N (1981) Evolution by individuals, plants-herbivore interactions, and mosaics of genetic variability: the adaptive significance of somatic mutations in plants. Oecologia, 49, 287-292

7) Gliessman S R (1976) Allelopathy in a broad spectrum of environments as illustrated by bracken. Bot. J. Linn. Soc., 73, 95-104

8) Considine M L (1984) Prescribed burning and forest nutrition. Ecos, 42, 9-12

The acute diseases caused by Bracken in animals

W C Evans

There are two distinct acute diseases which can be produced when bracken fern, either as green frond or rhizome, is incorporated into the feed of animals; avitaminosis and acute bracken poisoning.

AVITAMINOSIS B_1

When simple-stomached animals like the rat, pig or horse are fed a diet containing about 30% of low-temperature dried, milled, green bracken frond or rhizome, they develop incoordination symptoms within a month and rapidly lose condition. This polyneuritic syndrome shows all the characteristics of a thiamine deficiency; vitamin B_1 therapy is effective in curing the animal, provided it is administered at the onset of clinical symptoms. The causative agent is an enzyme, Thiaminase I (EC 2.5.1.2)[1] which catalyses the decomposition of thiamine by a base-exchange reaction involving a nucleophilic displacement on the methylene group of the pyrimidine moiety by a base BH. The products formed are the 'pyrimidine-base' compound and the thiazole moiety, as shown on the page following. Effectively, the thiamine in the diet is destroyed and the products formed are incapable of replacing the vitamin as a coenzyme in obligatory biochemical reactions, which are its functions in animal nutrition. The enzyme is inactivated when the bracken is subjected to live-steam or autoclaving, the product being incapable of causing the disease. The base or co-substrate can be a variety of naturally occurring compounds like hypotaurine, proline, cysteine, nicotinic acid or Δ' - pyrroline ie. although thiamine and/or thiamine pyrophosphate (co-carboxylase) are rather specific substrates for thiaminase, the co-substrates are of low specificity.

Ruminating animals, like sheep and cattle, are normally independent of exogenous sources of thiamine in the diet because some of the rumen micro-flora synthesize enough of this vitamin to fulfil

121

H_3C ... NH_2 ... S ... $CH_2 \cdot CH_2 \cdot OH$ ... CH_3

$+ BH \rightleftharpoons$ ... H_3C ... N ... NH_2 ... CH_2-B ... S ... $CH_2 \cdot CH_2 \cdot OH$ ... CH_3 ... $+ H^+$

Thiaminase I occurs in certain fish, shellfish, ferns and bacteria; BH, the co-substrate can be a wide range of bases or sulphydryl compounds.

the needs of the host animal. It had therefore been thought impossible to produce a thiamine deficiency in these species by manipulating the diet. However, it was found that the concentration of thiaminase in bracken rhizomes is sufficiently high, that feeding a diet containing 15-30% rhizome mixed with green, dried grass to mature ruminating sheep, produced acute thiamine deficiency within a month[2]. The lesions produced in the brain were identical with those shown in Cerebrocortical necrosis (CCN)[10], a naturally-occurring disease of ruminants. The latter is due to the proliferation of microbes in the gastro-intestinal tract which make a bacterial thiaminase, giving rise to a thiamine deficiency with terminal lesions of CCN. This condition responds to thiamine therapy if promptly administered (See Table 1).

TABLE 1 Occurrence and effects of thiaminase in animals

Source of thiaminase	Animal species (avitaminosis B_1)
Cyprinidae	
Carp viscera	Silver fox (Chastek paralysis)[3]
Pteridophytes	
Bracken (fronds)	Rat[4]
Bracken (fronds)	Horse (staggers)[5]
Bracken (rhizomes)	Pig[6]
Bracken (rhizomes)	Sheep[2]
Horsetail	Horse (staggers)[7]
Micro-organisms	
Bacillus thiaminolyticus	Human (a form of beri-beri)[8]
Clostridium thiaminolyticum	(also cats, guinea pigs, rats,
Bacillus aneurinolyticus	hens, and rabbits)[9]
Unidentified	Sheep and cattle (CCN)[10]
Clostridium sporogenes?	Sheep and cattle (CCN)[11,12]

122

Under field conditions of bracken infestation, an induced thiamine deficiency, bracken staggers, used to occur commonly in the horse when this animal was the major source of power in agricultural operations. It is doubtful, however, whether the concentration of thiaminase in green bracken fronds (as distinct from rhizomes) is high enough to precipitate acute avitaminosis B_1 in adult ruminants. These polygastric animals are nevertheless susceptible to other toxic principles.

ACUTE CATTLE BRACKEN POISONING

Acute bracken poisoning[13] is cumulative, so that the animal has to eat some green fronds or rhizomes (about 1 kg dry matter/day or less, depending on the toxicity of the bracken) for a period of two to four weeks. The clinical symptoms at the crisis include dullness, petechial haemorrhages in the mucus membrane of the nose, conjunctiva and vulva, while haematuria and clots of blood in the faeces sometimes occurs. An increased mucus discharge from the nostrils and a high temperature (41.7 - 42.8°C) are also invariably observed during the acute stage of the disease, death ensuing within a few days. At post mortem, severe and extensive haemorrhages are seen in the cadaver, often with ulceration of the intestinal mucosa. There is no gross thiamine deficiency; the disease, with its predominantly haemorrhagic character, does not respond to any vitamin or nutritional therapy and is the result of an intoxication.

Haematology reveals a severe leucopenia, with almost complete disappearance of the white blood cells, except a few lymphocytes and a thrombocytopenia in the circulating blood. The animal shows an increased capillary fragility, a prolonged bleeding time and defective clot retraction. Sternal marrow biopsy reveals aplasia of the granulocytic and thrombocytic series, with hypoplasia of the erythrocytic series. The fundamental lesion in acute bovine bracken poisoning is, therefore, a severe depression in bone-marrow activity, leading to blood dyscrasia.

Studies by I Antice Evans[14] on the cellular and humoral changes which occur in acute cattle bracken poisoning revealed (1) damage to the crypt cells lining the gastro-intestinal tract, (2) an increase, and violent perturbations in, the number of mast cells, (3) discontinuous increase in blood heparin and histamine levels, and (4) abnormal fibrinogen and seromucoid blood levels. These latter observations are responsible for the well-known streaking of blood smears at the acute stage of the disease. Such changes are characteristic of an acute systemic inflammatory condition; the pyrexia is likely to be caused by injured cells producing endogenous pyrogens affecting the thermoregulatory centre in the hypothalamus, since there is no septicaemia.

In view of this state of affairs in acute bracken poisoning, mortality is high; blood transfusion has not been particularly successful in treatment, neither has nutritional therapy; bone-marrow stimulants like butyl alcohol have been tried but corticosteroid therapy (Prednisolone), together with magnesium trisilicate by drench and wide-span antibiotic treatment, offers the best hope for recovery. The outcome is dependent on the extent of bone-marrow damage which is a function of the toxicity of the bracken and the amount consumed. Animals with a leucocyte count below 2,000 per cmm and platelets below 50,000 per cmm are likely to succumb; the hazards of internal haemorrhages and ulceration leading to perforation of the intestinal mucosa are factors difficult to control; nevertheless some animals do recover (B Widdop and I A Evans, 1967; unpublished work).

The picture presented of acute bovine bracken poisoning has also been described in sheep on the North York Moors. Sheep are, however, more resistant to the effects of the toxic principle(s) present in the bracken plant than cattle, and simple-stomached animals even more so.

THE SEARCH FOR THE BONE-MARROW POISON

In spite of the fact that field cases of bracken poisoning of livestock had been clearly described towards the end of the last century and Sir Stewart Stockman[15] in 1922 had correctly come to the conclusion that the cattle condition was an intoxication, subsequent attempts to extract the toxic principle(s) from the plant were unsuccessful for many years[16]. In retrospect, the main reason for these failures was a lack of knowledge of the cumulative nature of the disease. Bracken or extracts must be administered daily for 2-3 weeks to precipitate the acute fatal syndrome during the fourth week. The progress of the bone-marrow aplasia can be followed from the leucocyte and thrombocyte counts.

In 1958, Evans and his collaborators[17] reproduced acute cattle bracken poisoning with a fraction extracted from the fern with boiling ethanol. This result eliminated thiaminase from involvement in the disease and incriminated another toxic principle. Calves (castrated males, 3-4 months old) were used, and a pronounced depression in circulating leucocytes and thrombocytes after 20-30 days administration of a known quantity of specified fraction is regarded as proof of the presence of the bone-marrow poison. During the purification of the principle(s) (Table 2), dosing of certain fractions was terminated before cell counts became too depressed (ie. below 3,000 leucocytes per cmm and 100,000 platelets per cmm) since there is a risk of killing the animal unnecessarily. However, the calf experiments, shown in Figures 1 and 2, were continued to the stage when the animals were showing the classical clinical symptoms of acute cattle bracken poisoning and diagnosable as such. In the case of the calf used in Figure 1 the condition progressed too far, and the animal succumbed.

Table 2 gives details of the procedures evolved for the extraction and purification of the cattle bracken poisoning principle(s) from fresh young bracken fronds (5 Kg = 1 Kg dry matter). This is a daily dose amply sufficient to kill a bovine animal within one month. Mincing into hot ethanol gives a soluble fraction (150 g dry matter) which, when given daily by drench to a calf for 25 days proved lethal (Fig.1). Methanol precipitation of this extract removed about half the dry weight as inactive material (mainly flavonoids). The most effective purification step was achieved by pouring the methanol-soluble concentrate into a large volume of ethyl acetate; the whitish-grey hygroscopic precipitate (mainly carbohydrates) was allowed to settle. It was inactive. The ethyl acetate soluble

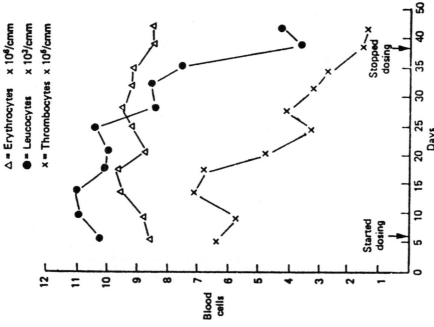

Figure 1 Calf (105 kg) receiving the primary hot ethanol extract (i) 150 g per day from 5 kg fresh young bracken fronds (see Table 2)

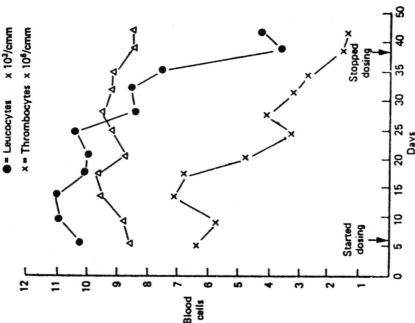

Figure 2 Calf (69 kg) receiving 5 g per day aqueous phase of fraction (iv) (see Table 2)

TABLE 2 Flow sheet for purification of the cattle bracken toxins[13]

Fresh green fronds (May and June. 5 kg = 1 kg dry matter = 1 daily dose)

Plant residue (discard) *Calf − ve*	Mince into boiling ETHANOL (16 l) i. Ethanol extract (60–80% ethanol) filtered and cyclosed at 30°C (vacuum). Concentrate = 500 ml. 150 g dry matter. *Calf + ve*. (Fig.1 using 150 g/day).
Yellow ppt. 62 g dry matter (flavonoids, etc.) *Calf − ve*	Pour into cold METHANOL (8 l). Filter ppt. ii. Methanol extract cyclosed at 30°C (vacuum). Concentrate = 200 ml. Remove water and suspend in methanol.
Whitish-grey ppt. 78 g dry matter (sugars, etc.) *Calf − ve*	Pour into cold ETHYL ACETATE (8 l). Filter ppt. + gum. iii. Ethyl acetate extract cyclosed at 30°C (vacuum) 10 g dry matter.
Ether extract 2 g dry matter *Calf − ve*	Add WATER and extract with DIETHYL-ETHER to remove pigment etc. (pH of aqueous phase = 3) iv. Aqueous phase. 8 g dry matter. *Calf + ve*. (Fig.2 using 5 g daily dose). LEAD ACETATE. Fractionation Aqueous phase (5 g) treated with excess saturated lead acetate soln. pH adjusted to 6 with NH_3. Yellow Pb ppt. filtered, suspended in 50% methanol/water and decomposed with H_2S: Supernatant gased with H_2S separately. PbS ppts. washed with boiling methanol/H_2O, and added to the appropriate extracts.
Pb ppt. (1 g) vi *Calf − ve* using 3·3 g/day i.e. 3 × appropriate dose	v. Pb supernatant fraction (4 g). *Calf + ve* CHLOROFORM EXTRACTION Aqueous Pb supernatant (v) extracted 10 times with equal volume of solvent each time.
Chloroform sol. fraction. viii. *Calf − ve* 0·5 g/day	vii. Aqueous residue (most of the dry matter stayed here). *Calf + ve* 4 g/day

fraction was cycloned at low temperature and the residue transferred into water; the aqueous suspension (pH 3) was extracted with diethyl ether to remove green pigment, lipids and other acid-ether soluble components. This extracted aqueous phase (fraction iv) proved active on a calf at a dose level of 5 g per day for 30 days (Fig 2). The amount of organic material in this fraction was between 2 and 3 g which represents about a 400-fold purification.

An alternative method of extracting the active principle(s) from the fresh plant is to mince into hot water, cool and adjust to pH 3 with glacial acetic acid, to coagulate the leaf proteins, filter through muslin and concentrate the aqueous extract at 30°C under reduced pressure in a climbing-film evaporator. This method economizes on solvents and appears to be just as efficient for the initial solubilization of the cattle poison(s) prior to further purification.

In order to identify chemically the active principle(s) the next step was to find out the components which make up fraction (iv), ie. the 2-3 g organic matter, the daily dose sufficient to reproduce the disease. Further investigation of this fraction showed that it was soluble in polar solvents and was unlikely to be a polyphenol (behaviour with lead acetate). Application of thin-layer chromatography showed the presence of pterosin, pteroside B, isoquercitrin, astragalin, tiliroside, ponasterone A and pterosterone, together with some unidentified components.

126

It is tempting to suspect the involvement of unusual components of the plant, eg. the pterosins and pterosides, the protoilludane type of sesquiterpenoids, as being responsible for cattle bracken poisoning. Over thirty of this group have been isolated from bracken and their structures determined by the Japanese workers[18], the most plentiful being pterosin B (I). It had also been suspected[14] that the cattle bracken poisoning principle(s) and the carcinogen(s) in bracken are the same; boiling 70% methanol extracts prepared in Japan, using metallic containers and possibly excessively long boiling (8h), proved to have lost their carcinogenicity although they contained appreciable quantities of pterosins and pterosides. These extracts, from both bracken fronds and rhizomes, were also inactive when tested on calves[19]. The most common pterosins, B, A and C do not, therefore, seem to be involved in the causation of the cattle disease or as carcinogens; the experiment does not exclude unstable members of this group. Recently, a norsesquiterpene glucoside, ptaquiloside (II) was isolated from bracken by Niwa and coworkers[20] and independently by van der Hoeven and colleagues[21] who called it aquilide A. It was rather unstable under both acidic and basic conditions, being rapidly converted to pterosin B (I). The latter workers found aquilide A to be mutagenic in the Ames Salmonella liver microsome test, and genotoxic to mammalian cells in vitro, whilst Hirono and his colleagues[22] have used ptaquiloside to induce mammary cancers in female CD rats; they also claim that it induced acute bracken poisoning in a calf[23]. It is instructive to evaluate the results of this experiment as reported by the authors.

In spite of administering ptaquiloside to a six-month old female calf (Wt. 137 Kg) at the rate of 400 mg/day for 24 days, followed by 800 mg/day for 14 days and then 1,600 mg/day for 4 days - giving a total of 27.2 g ptaquiloside - at no time did the animal show the classical clinical symptoms of acute cattle bracken poisoning. Figure 3 reproduces their results for comparison with Fig.1. They show that, after an initial leucocytosis, the total count fell but still remained within normal limits. However, the neutrophils were severely depressed by the 50th day. Thrombocytes showed a relatively slow decline but still remained between 100,000 and 200,000 per cmm whilst erythrocytes were unaffected. The calf was autopsied 86 days after the start of ptaquiloside administration, (39 days after cessation of dosing) and the body weight was 165 Kg. Haemorrhages were not observed and the sternal bone-marrow appeared almost normal; histology showed a dilation of the small blood vessels in the villi, and bone-marrow smears appeared to be deficient in granulopoietic cells, although not grossly aplasic.

The most that can be claimed from this toxicity trial on ptaquiloside is that it simulated, in a mild form, an effect on the bone-marrow reminiscent of the early stage of the disease; either the dosage was too low or the activity of ptaquiloside was too weak to reproduce acute cattle bracken poisoning.

The Japanese workers[23] used 130 Kg of dried bracken to extract the 27.2 g of ptaquiloside used in their calf experiment - giving a yield of 0.02%; van der Hoeven and colleagues[21] quote a yield of 0.25% of the same compound from freeze-dried bracken. Evans and co-workers[13] consistently produced acute cattle bracken poisoning with 0.5 - 1 Kg low-temperature, dried, June bracken-frond, fed daily for 20 days; the clinical symptoms appeared between days 25

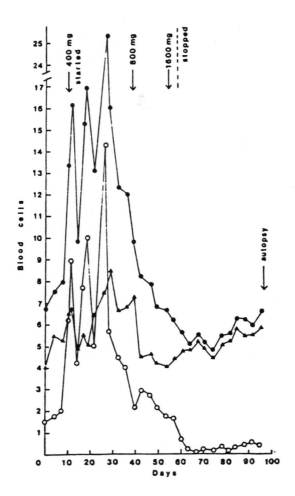

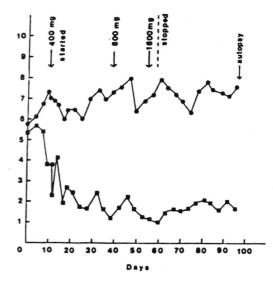

Figure 3 (a) Leucocyte and
differential leucocyte counts
(x 10^9 litre) of a calf
receiving a drench of ptaquiloside. ● Leucocytes, ▲
lymphocytes, O neutrophils.

Figure 3(b) Erythrocyte and
thrombocyte counts of a calf
receiving a drench of
ptaquiloside. ● Erythrocytes
(x10^{12} / litre), ■ thrombocytes (x 10^{11} / litre)

and 30 with a fatal outcome. If the concentration of ptaquiloside
found by van der Hoeven is taken as correct (as seems likely because
of their milder isolation procedures), between 1.25 and 2.5 g per day
for 20 days would be required ie. a total of 25-50 g ptaquiloside,
assuming this is the sole active principle in bracken causing the
acute disease. Hirono and his collaborators used 27.2 g, which falls
within this range, although the dosage per day was spread over 42
days. However, the acute disease was not produced; therefore, the
search for the most active toxic principle in bracken, capable of
reproducing the acute disease in a convincing manner, has still to be
accomplished.

Ptaquiloside (II) possesses an illudane-type structure similar
to the poisons present in Jack o'Lantern mushroom <u>Clitocybe illudens</u>

128

since renamed <u>Omphalotus olearius</u>[24] ie. illudin S[25] and M[26] (III) shown below:

Ptaquiloside
(II)

Pterosin B
(I)

Illudin S (R = OH)

Illudin M (R = H)

(III)

The acute toxicity of these to rats is about 150 times that of ptaquiloside; one dose of illudin S (200 mg), given by drench, proved fatal to a three-month old calf (Wt. 75 Kg) overnight. (W Charles Evans, Trevor C McMorris and Kam-Mui Eva Ng, 1985, to be published). This illustrates the profound effect that substituent groups on the illudane structure have on the toxicity of the molecule.

The illudins possess two sites for nucleophilic attack, in the cyclopropane ring and in the five-membered ring. Ptaquiloside is a monofunctional alkylating agent which may account for the greater toxicity of the illudins. The plethora of pterosins and pterosides which occur in bracken are unique; some work on their biosynthesis has been reported[27]. Although illudin S and M have not been shown to occur in bracken, their biosynthesis[28] is closely analogous. Ptaquiloside is probably the precursor of pterosin B, to which it is easily converted. It is reasonable to expect that a family of illudane precursors are synthesized by bracken, differing slightly in structure and toxicity to animals. The fact that ptaquiloside did severely depress neutrophilic granulocytes in the calf experiment of Hirono and his collaborators[23] without producing the acute clinical symptoms of the disease, indicates that it is one of the active principles in bracken contributing to the syndrome. Whether it is capable of reproducing acute cattle bracken poisoning, if administered at a higher dosage, remains to be demonstrated. Alternatively, other illudanes, more active than ptaquiloside, are present in the plant which are necessary to reproduce the complete symptoms. It is conceded that isolating enough of these rather unstable natural products in a pure state for a calf toxicity test is a formidable task; further painstaking work will be required to clarify the problem.

ACKNOWLEDGEMENTS

I am grateful to the Royal Society for a grant towards defraying laboratory expenses and to the University College of North Wales, Bangor, for providing research facilities.

REFERENCES

1) Evans W C (1975) Thiaminases and their effects on animals. Vitamins and Hormones, 33, 467-504

2) Evans W C, Evans I A, Humphreys D J, Lewin B, Davies W J and Axford R F E (1975) Induction of thiamine deficiency in sheep with lesions similar to cerebrocortical necrosis. J. Comp. Path., 85, 253-267

3) Evans C A, Carlson W E and Green R G (1942) The pathology of Chastek paralysis in foxes. A counterpart of Wernicke's haemorrhagic polioencephalitis in man. Am. J. Path., 18, 79-90

4) Weswig P H, Freed A M and Haag J R (1946) Antithiamine activity of plant materials. J. Biol. Chem., 165, 737-738

5) Roberts H E, Evans E T R and Evans W C (1949) The production of bracken staggers in the horse and its treatment with vitamin B_1 therapy. Vet. Rec., 61, 549-550

6) Evans I A, Humphreys D J, Goulden L, Thomas A J and Evans W C (1963) Effects of bracken rhizomes on the pig. J. Comp. Path., 73, 229-243

7) Forenbacher S (1950) Equisetum poisoning of horses and the vitamin B complex. Vet. Arh., 20, 405-471

8) Matsukawa T, Misawa H, Fujimaya M, Kobayashi H, Horikama Y and Takato T (1954) Studies on thiamine deficiency due to bacterial thiaminase. Investigations on intestinal contents. J. Vitaminol., 1, 43-60

9) Kimura R (1965) Thiamine decomposing bacteria. Review of Japanese literature on Beri-beri and thiamine. Proceedings of the vitamin B Research Committee of Japan (ed) Shimazono N and Katsura E. 255-271. Tokyo: Igaku-Shoin

10) Pill A H (1967) Evidence of thiamine deficiency in calves affected with cerebrocortical necrosis. Vet. Rec., 81, 178-181

11) Edwin E E, Jackman R, Machin A F and Quick M P (1976) The importance of Δ' -pyrroline in the aetiology of cerebrocortical necrosis. Biochem. Biophys. Res. Commun., 70, 1190-1197

12) Morgan K T and Lawson G H K (1974) Thiaminase type-I producing bacilli and ovine polioencephalomalacia. Vet. Rec., 95, 361-363

13) Evans W C, Patel M C and Koohy Y (1982) Acute bracken poisoning in homogastric and ruminant animals. Proc. Roy. Soc. Edin., 81B, 29-64

14) Evans I A (1968) The radiomimetic nature of bracken toxin. Cancer Res., 28, 2252-2261

15) Stockman S (1922) Bracken poisoning of cattle in Great Britain. J. Comp. Path., 35, 273-275

16) Shearer G D (1945) Some observations on the poisonous properties of bracken (Pteridium aquilinum). J. Comp. Path., 55, 301-307

17) Evans W C, Evans I A, Thomas A J, Watkin J E and Chamberlain A T (1958) Studies on bracken poisoning in cattle. Brit. Vet. J., 114, 180-267

18) Fukuoka M, Kuroyanagi M, Yoshihira K and Natori S (1978) Chemical and toxicological studies on bracken fern (Pteridium aquilinum var. latiusculum) II. Structures of pterosins, sesquiterpenes having 1-indanone skeleton. Chem. Pharm. Bull., Tokyo, 26, 2365-2385

19) Evans W C, Korn T, Natori S, Yoshihira K and Fukuoka M (1983) Chemical and toxicological studies on bracken fern (Pteridium aquilinum var. latiusculum). VIII. The inability of bracken extracts containing pterosins to cause cattle bracken poisoning. J. Pharm. Dyn., 6, 938-940

20) Niwa H, Ojika M, Wakamatsu K, Yamada K, Hirono I and Matsushita K (1983) Ptaquiloside, a novel norsesquiterpene glucoside from bracken (Pteridium aquilinum var. latiusculum). Tetrahedron Letters, 24, 4117-4120

21) van der Hoeven J C M, Lagerweij W J, Posthumus M A, Veldhuizen A van and Holterman H A J (1983) Aquilide A, a new mutagenic compound isolated from bracken fern (Pteridium aquilinum (L) Kuhn) Carcinogenesis, 4, 1587-1590

22) Hirono I, Aiso S, Yamaji T, Mori H, Yamada K, Niwa H, Ojika M, Wakamatsu K, Kigoshi H, Niiyama K and Uosaki Y (1984) Carcinogenicity in rats of ptaquiloside isolated from bracken. Gann, 75, 833-836

23) Hirono I, Kono Y, Takahashi K, Yamada K, Niwa H, Ojika M, Kigoshi H, Niiyama K and Uosaki Y (1984) Reproduction of acute bracken poisoning in a calf with ptaquiloside, a bracken constituent. Vet. Rec., 115, 375-378

24) Miller O K Jr (1972) Mushrooms of North America (p.84) (ed)

Dutton E P, New York

25) McMorris T C and Anchel M (1963) The structures of the Basidiomycete metabolites Illudin S and Illudin M. J. Am. Chem. Soc., 85, 831-832

26) McMorris T C and Anchel M (1965) Fungal Metabolites. The structures of the novel sesquiterpenoids Illudin S and M. J. Am. Chem. Soc., 87, 1594-1600

27) Hikino H, Miyasi T and Takemoto T (1976) Biosynthesis of pteroside B in Pteridium aquilinum var. latiusculum. Proof of the sesquiterpenoid origin of the pterosides. Phytochemistry, 15, 121-123

28) Bradshaw A P W, Hanson J R and Sadler I H (1982) Studies in terpenoid biosynthesis. Part 26. Application of ^{2}H and ^{13}C NMR spectroscopy to the biosynthesis of the Illudin sesquiterpenoids. J. Chem. Soc. Perkin Trans., I, 2445-2448

Bracken poisoning in farm animals
with special reference to the North York Moors

D A R Hannam

THE AETIOLOGY OF PLANT POISONING IN ANIMALS

It is impossible to be sure exactly why an animal should decide to eat a poisonous plant. Various reasons have been suggested[1], including hunger, depraved appetite and craving, curiosity and indiscretion. Hunger may cause animals to sample poisonous plants in certain weather conditions, for instance snow cover may leave only evergreens available, such as Rhododendron or Cherry Laurel[2]. Drought conditions may also reduce available grazing so that animals are obliged to eat poisonous plants. However, examination of records at Thirsk Veterinary Investigation Centre and National VIDA Records[3] gives no convincing association of bracken poisoning with prevailing weather conditions, although these records are influenced by a large number of variable factors, making interpretation uncertain (Table 1). The effect of the drought of 1976 on the health of cattle, sheep, and other farm livestock in England and Wales has been reviewed[4]. The possibility of drought predisposing animals to plant poisoning was considered, but problems more specifically related to the drought included nitrate/nitrite poisoning, salt poisoning and syndromes resembling Migram and Ryegrass staggers. Hunger may also play a part where bracken is the predominant plant species; however, it is much more likely that animals would move to an area of moor where there is less bracken.

The importance of craving or depraved appetites is difficult to assess with respect to plant poisonings, although there are reports of convalescent animals eating the poisonous plants again[1,5]. It is also perhaps significant that craving is described in sheep on bracken-feeding experiments[6]. Curiosity and indiscretion seem much more likely reasons for plant poisoning. Cases have been brought to our notice where animals have grazed fields containing poisonous plants without ill effect until the plant has been cut down, withered, or appeared unusual. Such cases include yew, laurel, and laburnum poisoning in bullocks. Cases of acute bracken poisoning in sheep and cattle have usually occurred in young animals recently moved from a

TABLE 1   Diagnoses of plant poisonings in sheep and cattle: 1975-1982
VIDA II

CATTLE	1975	1976	1977	1978	1979	1980	1981	1982
Bracken	44	29	26	24	14	6	13	14
Ragwort	12	14	31	14	12	19	9	14
Plant not specified	28	39	24	20	14	15	15	16
SHEEP								
Bracken	1	3	0	3	0	7	3	2
Brassica sp.	10	7	11	13	17	8	19	22
Plant not specified	6	14	9	7	19	13	14	22
TOTALS	101	106	101	81	76	68	73	90

non-bracken to a bracken area. These cases normally occur in late summer and autumn, and they may be a result of store sales or stock management causing exposure to bracken, rather than for any other reason. Chronic bracken poisoning probably occurs through indiscretion or indifference. Cases of cumulative bracken poisoning invariably occur in aged sheep. These sheep have been grazing moorland and intakes which support a considerable bracken population, and it seems likely that sheep are unable to avoid occasional ingestion of bracken sufficient to cause them eventual harm. (Particular exposure may occur early in bracken growth when fresh uncurling croziers are presented and before access to these areas becomes restricted. Ed.).

THE TOXIC EFFECTS OF BRACKEN POISONING

This paper will not deal with aspects of poisoning in horses, cattle or pigs as these species are the subject of the paper by W C Evans (herein). However, there is anecdotal evidence that bracken poisoning in cattle used to be well recognised by farmers on the North York Moors. When cattle were housed for the winter and dried bracken was used as bedding, boys kept the cattle moving in the yards until the bracken was crushed and unpalatable to prevent consumption.

Bracken poisoning in sheep may occur in one of three ways; by (1) Acute bracken poisoning, (2) Bright Blindness, or (3) Tumour formation.

Acute bracken poisoning in sheep in the British Isles was first described by Parker and McCrea[7] in 1965, although single suspected cases had previously been reported by Fletcher[8] and Foggie[9]. Parker and McCrea described a Haemorrhagic Syndrome. A short illness of increasing weakness, with the passage of dark, loose faeces, usually occurred. Post-mortem examination revealed anaemia; bleeding into the intestine, and haemorrhage in the submucosa of the abomasum; haemorrhage on the peritoneal surface of the omasum and large intestine, and haemorrhage in the epicardium and the pleura and parenchyma of the lung. Parker and McCrea instituted a survey of sheep mortality, and of the 43 carcasses submitted, 16 deaths were attributed to bracken poisoning. In these cases, haemorrhages were present in 3 or more sites, most frequently in the stomach and lungs, heart, spleen and small intestine; less frequently, in the serous membranes, large intestine, subcutis and kidneys. In some cases, blood samples were taken before death: erythrocyte and total leucocyte counts were reduced, as were platelet numbers. Half of the carcasses showed bacterial invasion, the commonest isolates being Pasteurella species.

Bright blindness was first recognised in 1965[10]. It was reported as a progressive degeneration of the neuro-epithelium of the retina of hill sheep. A connection between this form of blindness and bracken-grazing was suggested. Shearlings were rarely affected, cases being most frequent in 2, 3 and 4 year-old sheep. Field cases have never been confirmed in rams, although the condition has been reproduced experimentally in rams and wethers[6,11]. The general bodily condition of bright-blind sheep is below average. They appear more alert than normal sheep and adopt an erect attitude. The pupils of affected animals are dilated and have poor to absent light reflex. The cornea, lens and aqueous and vitreous humours are clear, giving the typical glassy-eyed appearance. There are no signs of inflammatory lesions in the eyes, such as keratitis or conjunctivitis. Examination using an opthalmoscope shows that, in affected sheep, the optic disc becomes pale and the Tapetum lucidum shows increased reflection, often with a yellow to orange sheen. The retinal blood vessels are noticeably narrower than those of normal sheep. Histological examination of the retina reveals progressive destruction of the rods and cones, and nuclear layers. In advanced cases, rods, cones and the outer nuclear layer are destroyed, with some destruction of the inner nuclear layer. This destruction leaves the pigment epithelium exposed to reflect more light. Watson had confirmed the condition in 253 flocks of hill sheep by 1972[12] although it had been recognised by farmers for fifty years prior to this. No breed, sexual or genetic susceptibilities have been demonstrated other than by their association with bracken areas and consequent risks of prolonged exposure to bracken[6,13].

Tumour formation was noted in sheep by Parker and McCrea in 1964, but not reported. The condition was investigated more thoroughly by McCrea and Head[14] in a survey lasting from 1964 to 1977, during which time 86 tumours were found in 62 sheep from 7 farms on the North York Moors. The majority of the tumours were fibrosarcomas and most of these were in the jaws. Papilloma of the rumen were next most frequent, together with adenocarcinomas of the intestine. Other tumours included squamous cell carcinomas of the upper intestine, carcinoma of the liver, localised lymphosarcomas, and one epithelial thymoma. McCrea and Head carried out a bracken-feeding experiment[11], and reproduced both fibrosarcoma of the maxilla and mandible and bright blindness in single sheep. The remaining sheep (except one which died from acute bracken poisoning) developed carcinoma of the bladder.

The differences in tumour formation between experimental and field cases may have been caused by several factors. The experimental sheep were wethers; lack of circulating sex hormones may have played a part; the bracken was fed continually and was dried and pelleted, unlike sporadic ingestion of fresh bracken; moor water has a pH of 3.2 to 5.0, whereas the mains water had a pH of 7.3; the diet of the experimental sheep was of good quality compared with that of moorland sheep, which are on a deficient diet, suffer buccal damage from rough forage and are normally hypocupraemic.

Intestinal adenocarcinomas are considered to be the commonest form of neoplasm in sheep, but are thought not to be associated with bracken consumption[15,16,17].

CURRENT INVESTIGATIONS

Cases of bracken poisoning are still presented to the Veterinary Investigation Centre for diagnosis, but infrequently. Since the work by Parker, McCrea and Head, many of the farmers on the North York Moors are well able to recognise both Jaw Tumours and Bright Blindness. Indeed, most cases of jaw tumours are presented to us out of interest by the farmer concerned, rather than as a request by him for a diagnosis. Because of this selection, any figures of incidence must be interpreted with extreme caution.

Several cases of acute bracken poisoning have been investigated in depth. In one, 650 store lambs had been bought from a non-bracken area and put on to moorland which, although reclaimed, still had some bracken growth. Two weeks after the move, lambs started to die and 26 died in the next 2 months, after which time the Veterinary Investigation Centre was requested to carry out a post-mortem examination. Haemorrhages were present subcutaneously, in the lungs, in the abomasum and along the length of the small intestine and in the liver and kidneys. No blood was present in the urine. $\underline{Pasteurella}$ $\underline{haemolytica}$ type T was isolated in septicaemic distribution. Two more lambs were examined with similar symptoms and one of these had haematuria. A number of sheep were blood sampled on the farm and low platelet counts were demonstrated. Ten samples showed a range from 0.091×10^6 per ml to 0.32×10^6 per ml with a mean of 0.18×10^6 and SD 0.07. The erythrocyte counts were only slightly depressed, whereas the leucocyte counts were low (0.6×10^3 per ml to 2.7×10^3 per ml. Mean 1.61×10^3 per ml. SD 0.57). In a second case, 80 lambs aged 5 months died, out of a total of 120 over a 3 week period. Classical signs of acute bracken poisoning were seen at post-mortem, and some depressed leucocyte and platelet counts were demonstrated. However, other causes of death were also demonstrated, such as Intestinal Haemorrhage Syndrome and Louping Ill. The following year, 20 more lambs died out of 180 and acute bracken poisoning was again diagnosed. Secondary Staphylococcal Septicaemia was also present in these cases.

CONCLUSION

Bracken undoubtedly continues to cause significant sheep losses on the North York Moors, although the pattern of loss is probably changing. Fewer sheep are now grazed on the moor, and lambs are usually taken off the moor sooner than formerly. These changes are due in part to market forces. Acute bracken poisoning is now rarely diagnosed, although there are sporadic reports of both Jaw Tumours and Bright Blindness. However, mortality in sheep on the moor is still high and still linked directly to bracken. Tickborne diseases (Louping ill, Staphylococcal pyaemia, and Tickborne fever) are major causes of loss, and the habitat of the sheep tick, Ixodes ricinus, is predominantly the heather/bracken interface.

REFERENCES

1) Spratling R (1980) Is it plant poisoning? In Practice, 22, 22-31

2) Higgins R J, Hannam D A R, Humphreys D J and Stodulski J B J (1985) Rhododendron poisoning in sheep. Veterinary Record, 116, 294-295

3) Veterinary Investigation Diagnosis, Analysis II (1975-82) Ministry of Agriculture, Fisheries and Food, Welsh Office Agriculture Department, Department of Agriculture and Fisheries for Scotland.

4) The State Veterinary Service (1982) Effect of the drought of 1976 on the health of cattle, sheep and other farm livestock in England and Wales. Veterinary Record, 111, 407-411

5) Hannam D A R (1985) Hemlock (Conium maculatum) poisoning in the pig. Veterinary Record, 116, 12, 322

6) Barnett K C and Watson W A (1970) Bright Blindness in sheep. A primary retinopathy due to feeding bracken (Pteris aquilina). Research in Veterinary Science, 11, 289-290

7) Parker W H and McCrea C T (1965) Bracken (Pteris aquilina) poisoning of sheep in the North York Moors. Veterinary Record, 77, 30, 861-866

8) Fletcher J M (1944) Bracken poisoning in cattle. Veterinary Record 56, 478

9) Foggie A (1951) Suspected bracken poisoning in sheep. Veterinary Record, 13, 63, 242

10) Watson W A, Barlow R M and Barnett K C (1965) Bright blindness - a condition prevalent in Yorkshire hill sheep. Veterinary Record, 77, 37, 1060-1069

11) McCrea C T and Head K W (1981) Sheep tumours in North-East Yorkshire: II. Experimental production of tumours. British Veterinary Journal, 137, 1, 21-30

12) Watson W A, Barnett K C and Terlecki S (1972) Progressive Retinal Degeneration (Bright Blindness) in sheep: a review.

Veterinary Record, 91, 655-670

13) Terlecki S, Young G B and Buntain D (1973) Absence of simple genetic factors in Progressive Retinal Degeneration (Bright Blindness) in sheep. British Veterinary Journal, 129, 4, 45-47

14) McCrea C T and Head K W (1978) Sheep tumours in North East Yorkshire: I. Prevalence on seven moorland farms. British Veterinary Journal, 134, 454-461

15) Ross A D and Williams P A (1983) Neoplasms of sheep in Great Britain. Veterinary Record, 113, 598-599

16) Georgsson G and Vigfusson H (1973) Carcinoma of the small intestine of sheep in Iceland. A pathological and zoological study. Acta. Vet. Scand., 14, 392-409

17) Ross A D (1980) Small intestinal carcinoma in sheep. Australian Veterinary Journal, 56, 25-28

The Carcinogenic, Mutagenic and Teratogenic Toxicity of Bracken

I A Evans

INTRODUCTION

A comprehensive toxicological survey of the field of bracken carcinogenicity can be found in the revised edition of an American Chemical Society Monograph[1]. This material has now been updated in a review article, with emphasis on recent chemical developments[2]. Rather than attempting to precis the massive amount of material now available, this paper will focus attention on three distinct areas which were pioneered and studied almost exclusively by the author and her co-workers in Bangor, and therefore may not be so familiar to those interested in the wide range of biological effects elicited by ferns of the Pteridium group. Firstly, the acute inflammatory condition arising from bracken consumption will be discussed together with its immunological response in bovines. The teratogenic effects in developing mammalian and avian embryos will then be discussed followed by the carcenogenicity of bracken spores in two strains of mice. A concluding section will attempt to evaluate the human hazard and suggest practicable precautions.

THE ACUTE INFLAMMATORY CRISIS AND IMMUNOLOGICAL RESPONSE IN BOVINES

The co-workers involved in this work were Dr R M Howell and Dr J Mason, and, although the research[3] was done as long ago as 1962 to 1965, it is of much significance in the current context where the inflammatory and haemorrhagic nature of acute bracken poisoning in cattle is under question[4]. In the intervening years our understanding of the complexities of the immunological system has expanded enormously, and it is therefore of added interest to look again at our findings and the possibility of their relationship to cancer induction.

Everyone is now conversant with the idea of monitoring the cellular changes in the circulation and bone marrow concerned with the body's defence system, and they are also aware of the harmful effects of radiation. A calf dying from acute bracken poisoning shows many of the changes induced by radiation, and they are all characteristic of an acute systemic inflammatory condition. In the experiment to be described, we attempted not only to monitor changes in the circulation but also concurrently in the extravascular subcutaneous connective tissue; this is not often done and, as we suspected, the two parameters frequently ran counter to each other. Marathons are now all the rage but this one took place in 1965 and lasted for over one hundred days, sponsored by an enlightened DSIR and Ministry of Agriculture. It confirmed the results of our previous experiments which had indicated that changes can happen in such rapid succession that daily sampling in critical periods is advisable. The results of experiments on a calf are shown in Fig.1.

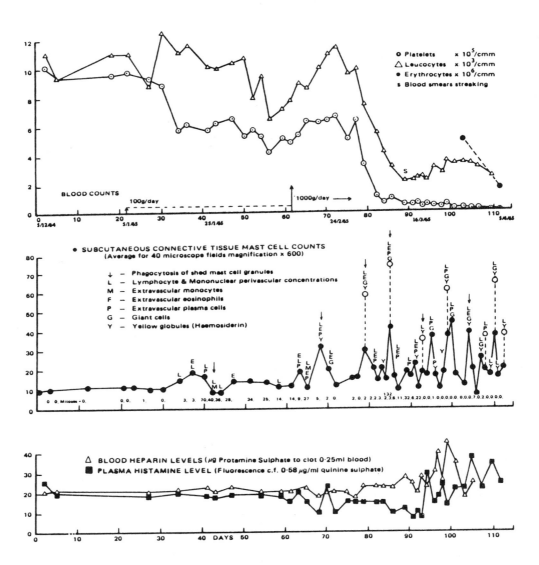

Fig.1. Calf fed 100 gm dried bracken/day for 40 days followed by 1000 gm/day till death. Blood counts; tissue mast cells, inflammatory cells, and mitotic counts; circulating heparin and histamine.

The calf was given a low sensitising dose of 100 gms of dried bracken per day for about 40 days and then the customary daily kilogram, resulting in the usual terminal haemorrhagic syndrome with high pyrexia and bone marrow aplasia reflected in loss of circulating blood cells, which is always complete in the case of platelets (Top Graph). One of the most striking features found from examination of the tissue spreads was the very large, discontinuous increases in mast cell numbers which occur terminally or at times of low numbers of circulating leucocytes and platelets. Increases can be as much as fourfold and, in some localised areas, as much as sevenfold (Middle Graph, dotted lines). The number can drop just as rapidly to reach normal levels, so it appears that, at least in the tissues studied, there is a most dynamic mast cell population. This results in marked fluctuations in the level of circulating heparin and histamine (Bottom Graph), both substances with extensive and well documented physiological properties including effects on blood clotting and tissue permeability. The mast cells are factories producing not only heparin and histamine but also a variety of pharmacologically active compounds including proteolytic enzymes, and they are found throughout the animal kingdom. Recent work[5] suggests that heparin, together with endothelial mitogens, is involved in the stimulation of endothelial blood tube formation, a hitherto unsuspected function.

Japanese workers have confirmed our findings concerning the circulation of a heparin-like substance in bracken-poisoned bovines[6,7], and Ishii et al[8] have reported the release of histamine from rat peritoneal mast cells in response to a bracken extract.

Accompanying the mast cell increases are extravascular invasions of varying intensities including lymphocytes, plasma cells, monocytic types, eosinophils, and giant cells containing large numbers of peripheral nuclei characteristic of a delayed hypersensitivity reaction (Fig.1, Middle Graph). The periodic appearance of cells at all stages of mitosis was particularly unusual since these are not normally seen in the tissue samples. Day 85 was remarkable both for the high number of mitoses and the spectrum of cell types involved, which would indicate a systemic stimulant. It was also interesting that mitotic stimulation occurred after only a few days on bracken and long before the major pathological events; thus it may well play a part in the initiation of carcinogenesis. The multifactorial nature of the aetiology of cancer is becoming generally accepted and, as this experiment demonstrates, bracken induces a situation involving not only chemical excitation but also rapid and marked fluctuations in the DNA replication. The presence of large numbers of immunologically active cells in the tissues, including ones with phagocytic activity thought to involve release of free radicles, might also be of significance with respect to the radiomimetic aspect.

Successful therapeutic treatment[9] of bracken-poisoned calves by parental administration of a synthetic hydrocorticosteroid (Betsolan, Glaxo Ltd) adds confirmation to the inflammatory nature of the syndrome, since these drugs are used extensively in a wide variety of such disorders, including autoimmune conditions. Acute cattle bracken poisoning has been produced experimentally in many parts of the world, including Japan, with the consistent findings of bone marrow aplasia, inflammation, widespread haemorrhage and terminal high temperature. China is no exception, as Xu Leren and colleagues have reported the production of bracken poisoning in heifers, with all the classic features[10].

TERATOGENICITY

The thalidomide disaster drew public attention to the tragedy of malformations of the foetus resulting from the administration of a teratogenic agent to the mother. It also demonstrated that the response to such an agent may be positive in one species or strain of animal and have no effect on another; nor should the results of animal experiments be extrapolated to man. Not all agents are toxic, for abnormal development of the embryo can result from such factors as dietary deficiencies and viral infections during pregnancy. However, many chemicals of a toxic nature can affect embryogenesis in one way or another from sterility and mutagenic defects to straightforward teratological malformations. These can include deformities in various organs, especially the central nervous system, eg anencephaly and spina bifida, reduction or loss of eyes, and abnormalities in the limbs and skeletal system. A number of different deformities can occur in the same embryo.

Evidence had already been gathered from work conducted with Dr G D Barber and Dr M A Osman that bracken extracts containing shikimic acid and commercial shikimic acid were mutagenic at optimal low doses in fruit flies and mice[11]. It therefore seemed worthwhile to look for possible teratogenic effects. The Japanese quail (_Cotornix cotornix Japonicus_) was chosen as the test animal since it had many advantages both with regard to maintenance, rapidity of life cycle, ease of marking and dosing, either parental or by egg injection, and detection of deformities both of a gross nature and as revealed after clearing and staining the skeleton. Most important is the fact that the number of spontaneous abnormalities in the quail embryo is minimal. Dr J H Prorok[12] followed the regime of parental dosing with shikimic acid and obtained evidence of a teratogenic influence, again only in response to a low dose level. Beak deformities, absence of eyes and skeletal malformations were encountered. Dr M H A Al-Salmani[13] obtained similar results using a larger number of birds and extended the experiment to include direct injection into the yolk sac of quail eggs. He also tested commercial and bracken-derived indanones (pterosins and pterosides) and obtained a wide variety of malformations. In this case, the eye deformities appeared to be characteristic, which would suggest that the indanones exert their effect predominantly in the early stages of embryogenesis just prior to the development of eye buds.

With regard to mammalian embryos, it has been recorded that bracken extracts, bracken-derived shikimic acid and commercial shikimic acid delayed the ossification of the embryonic sternebrae or ribs in mice and rats[13,14], but in these animals and in guinea pigs, gross deformities were not obtained.

CARCINOGENICITY OF BRACKEN SPORES

Although both aerial fronds and underground rhizomes of bracken had given positive results when submitted to long-term cancer studies, the carcinogenicity of spores had not been tested. The electron micrograph scan (Fig.2) shows the sporangium or spore case which explodes like a catapult to release the spores, one of which is adhering to the case. At a higher magnification, the spores can be seen to have a rough surface covered by scutes and, since these air-borne cells are small (31-32 μm diameter), it is obvious that they can be inhaled in the same way as pollen grains and mould spores. They would become entrapped on the respiratory tract mucous stream and eventually reach the stomach. Unlike the rest of the plant, the spores have a low water content which would effectively concentrate any toxic metabolites if they were present.

The author and Robert Smith collected spores which were sieved to remove the sporangia and then given orally, suspended in water, to two strains of mice. The dose was deliberately kept at a low level, given in about 10 fairly closely spaced administrations and generally did not exceed a total of 200 mgs. Control mice were given water only. The larger group of experimental animals were dosed with spores which had been stored at room temperature for at least 5 months after they had been shed and collected, but a smaller group had fresh spores only a day or so old at the commencement of dosing. The results are given in Table 1.

TABLE 1 Experimental oral dosing of mice with bracken spores for long-term tumour production

	Mice receiving bracken spores	Control mice water only
Total numbers	98	49
Mice with tumours	53 (54.1%)	2 (4.1%)
Mice with leukemias	28 (28.6%)	- (0%)
Mice receiving freshly-shed spores	17 (17.3%)	- (0%)
Mice with gastric tumours	6 (6.1%)	- (0%)

Out of 49 control mice, only two had developed cancers, both mammary. Of the 98 experimental animals given bracken spores, 53 mice had cancers, with leukemias accounting for 28 of these. Gastric tumours were found in 6 mice, 5 of which were in the group of 17 receiving freshly shed spores. This unequal distribution suggests the presence of at least two carcinogens which is in agreement with our previous findings with bracken. Fig.3 shows a section of a glandular stomach tumour produced in a mouse by bracken spores. One of the findings from this experiment which merits emphasis is that a single frond of bracken could generate enough spores to induce cancer in five mice (5 x 200 mgs = 1.0 gm). Full details of the work will be published elsewhere.

Fig.2 Bracken sporangium or spore case (EMS) from the underside of a sporulating frond. Spores can be seen around it, and one on the outside of the case. (x 330)

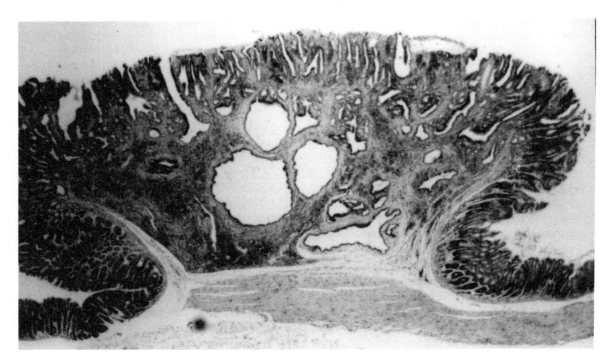

Fig.3 Section of a carcinoma _in situ_ in the glandular area of a mouse stomach produced by bracken spores. (x 35)

The regional distribution of human gastric cancer in England and Wales shows that there is a high incidence in North Wales, which occurs particularly among farmers. North Wales also has a high incidence, again in both sexes, of some cancers which are leukemic in nature, including Hodgkin's disease and chronic lymphatic leukemia.

SAFETY MEASURES

For people working in dense bracken areas the use of face masks is to be advocated in the same way as they are already worn for harvesting and for protection in hazardous industrial operations. Many people, especially in Japan, are still partial to eating bracken. The marketing of a safe product is quite possible, providing the croziers are submitted to boiling under alkaline conditions, and this step should be included in any method of preparation or preservation. It should also be mandatory that milking cows do not have access to bracken-infested pastures, especially if milk is retailed locally and not bulked.

Having said that, the fact must be faced that there may be some environmental carcinogens which although in low amounts, are so widespread as to be unavoidable. Small particles of biological origin, such as bracken and mould spores, and chemicals with a wide distribution in edible plant material, for example shikimic acid and quercetin, would come in this category.

ACKNOWLEDGEMENTS

The author is most grateful to the North West Cancer Research Fund for its sustained financial help.

REFERENCES

1) Evans I A (1984) Bracken Carcinogenicity. In C E Searle (ed) Chemical Carcinogens. American Chemical Society, Monograph 182. 2nd Ed, Vol 2, 1171-1204 Washington D C

2) Evans I A (1985) Bracken Carcinogenicity. In G V James (ed) International Quarterly Scientific Reviews, "Reviews on Environmental Health" Freund Publishing House Ltd, Tel-Aviv, Israel (In press)

3) Evans I A (1968) The radiomimetic nature of bracken toxin. Cancer Res, 28, 2252-2261

4) Hirono I, Kono Y, Takahashi K, Yamada K, Niwa H, Ojiika M, Kigoshi H, Niijama K and Uosaki Y (1984). Reproduction of acute bracken poisoning in a calf with ptaquiloside, a bracken constituent. Vet. Rec., 115, 375-378

5) Geison M J (1985) Report on the BSCB/COB Symposium on growth factors and their receptors - Glasgow 1985. British Society for Cell Biology Newsletter, No 10, 8-9

6) Yamane O, Hayashi T, Sako S, Kihara T and Koyama M (1975) Studies on haemorrhagic diathesis of experimental bovine bracken poisoning. I. Detection of circulating anticoagulants. Jap. J. Vet. Sci., 37, 335-340

7) Yamane O, Hayashi T, Sako S, Tatematsu S, Takeda K and Fukushima H (1975) Studies on haemorrhagic diathesis of experimental bovine bracken poisoning. II. Heparin-like substance level in blood. Jap. J. Vet. Sci. 37, 341-347

8) Ishii K, Saito T and Sakatani M (1974) Histamine releasing action of acetone dried powder of bracken fern on the rat peritoneal mast cells. Journal of the Faculty of Agriculture, Tottori University, 9, 27-33

9) Widdop B (1967) Separation and characterisation of various toxicological components of bracken. PhD Thesis, University of Wales

10) Yongda W, Leren X, Lunji W, Wanlun M, Shizhong Y, Kuirong H and Kaixiong Y (1984) Studies on experimental bovine bracken poisoning. Acta Veterinaria et Zootechnica Sinica. 15, 235-239

11) Evans I A and Osman M A (1974) Carcinogenicity of bracken and shikimic acid. Nature (Lond), 250, 348-349

12) Prorok J H (1978) Bracken-derived morphogenic dyscrasias. PhD Thesis, University of Wales

13) Al-Salmani M H (1980) Studies on plant-derived teratogenicity and infertility. PhD Thesis, University of Wales

14) Yasuda Y, Kihara T and Nishimura H (1974) Embryotoxic effects of feeding bracken (Pteridium aquilinum) to pregnant mice. Toxicol. Appl. Pharmacol. 28, 264-268

Bracken, stomach cancer and water supplies:
Is there a link?

O P Galpin and R M M Smith

INTRODUCTION

Cancer is one of the major causes of mortality throughout the developed world. It is generally more common in later life and the proportion and number of tumour deaths have increased this century, as non-cancer deaths have declined.

In North Wales, an unusually high mortality from gastric cancer has been observed for many years. Stocks[1] observed that, during the period 1921-30, the northern counties of Wales showed a marked excess for mortality from gastric cancer[2], with female mortality being greater than the corresponding male mortality in each age group. During the 5-year period 1979-83, 3,473 out of a total of 15,989 deaths in Gwynedd (21.7%) were certified as being due to malignant tumours[3]. North-west Wales has seen, over the past 30 or so years, in common with the United Kingdom as a whole, a gradual decline in mortality from gastric cancer (Figure 1), which itself mirrors a trend that may be seen throughout the developed world (Table 1) even though the case-fatality rate is still about 90%[4]. Perhaps the most encouraging feature of these trends is that they are continuing downward in each age-group throughout middle age, suggesting that the decreases seen today in old age will continue throughout this century and, optimistically, beyond.

This investigation sets out to examine the current pattern of mortality from gastric cancer in Gwynedd, and the influence of certain environmental factors upon its incidence. There have been many reviews[5] of the epidemiological evidence relating to gastric cancer, but it remains evident that while the causes of stomach cancer in man remain unknown, a number of risk-associated factors, in both environment and diet, are emerging from epidemiological and laboratory-based studies. The almost certain multifactorial aetiology of gastric cancer may involve a wide range of carcinogenic precursors and tumour accelerators, in addition to factors which produce localised damage to the gastric mucosa, such as high salt intake which can facilitate carcinogen absorption.

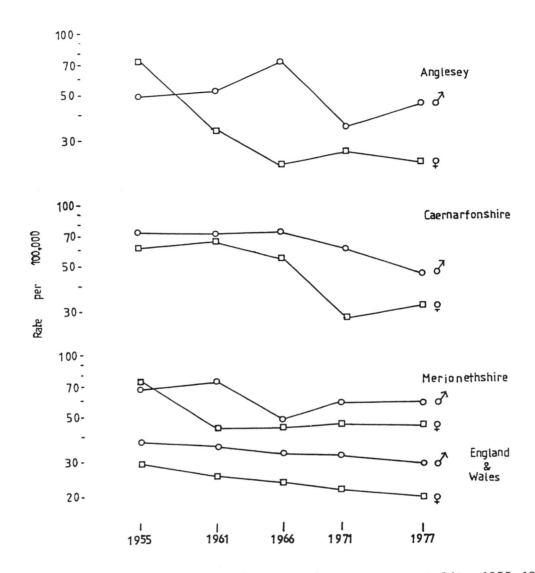

Figure 1   Gwynedd: Changes in gastric cancer mortality 1955-1977, compared with England and Wales.

Interest in bracken as a human hazard is emphasised by the fact that in one of the countries with the highest risk of development of human gastric cancer, Japan, the recent demand for bracken fronds was so high, that bracken has had to be imported from Siberia since 1969. Over 300,000 kg of young fronds are consumed every year in Tokyo alone[6]. The London Japanese are known to obtain their supplies from Richmond Park[7].   Although bracken is not known to be consumed in England and Wales, recipes for cooking bracken fronds appeared in British newspapers during the 1914-18 war[8], and there has even been correspondence in 'The Times' a few years ago, advocating the consumption of bracken as a "health food".

The acute effects of bracken on both cattle and sheep have been

148

TABLE 1   International changes since 1950 in death certification rates
for cancer of the stomach (adapted from Doll and Peto[4])

Country	Period	Percentage change in mortality from cancer of the stomach*
Australia	1950-51 to 1975	-53
Austria	1952-53 to 1976	-53
Chile	1950-51 to 1975	-56
Denmark	1952-53 to 1976	-62
England & Wales	1950-51 to 1975	-49
West Germany	1952-53 to 1975	-50
Ireland	1950-51 to 1975	-54
Israel	1950-51 to 1975	-49
Japan	1950-51 to 1976	-37
The Netherlands	1950-51 to 1976	-60
New Zealand	1950-51 to 1975	-54
Norway	1952-53 to 1975	-59
Scotland	1950-51 to 1975	-46
Switzerland	1952-53 to 1976	-64
United States	1950-51 to 1975	-61

*   Average of male and female rates at ages 35-64 yr, standardised for
age as in IARC (1976)

well-documented[9-14], but it was not until experiments[15] with rats
had been completed, that bracken was shown to be unequivocally
carcinogenic.   The radiomimetic effects of bracken were described by
Evans[16], who used a wide range of species in her studies on the
biological effects of bracken and its extracts, work which has been
confirmed and extended by other groups of workers[17,18].

The chemical components of bracken produce a number of species-
specific effects, including gastric cancer, in both the glandular and
squamous regions of mouse stomach.

The milk pathway

The passage into milk of the group of toxins responsible for
chronic enzootic haematuria and carcinogenicity has also been
studied[19].   A calf, given milk from a cow receiving a sub-lethal
dietary bracken supplement, showed evidence of a haematological
response which would be typical of a calf consuming bracken directly
at a low rate.   Therefore, when considering the possibility of
indirect human consumption, milk and dairy products should be

examined. For this reason milk supplies initially appeared to be the most promising vector in the aetiology of local gastric cancer. In the 1930s, North Wales, and Gwynedd in particular, had the greatest density of small producer-retailers of milk in England and Wales (J P Jones, pers comm). It appeared, therefore, that the distribution of milk to communities throughout the area would be readily traceable. Surplus milk production was converted into butter for local sales and the residual buttermilk was often consumed on the farm.

Following the inception of the Milk Marketing Board in 1932, producers were steadily encouraged to sell their milk through dairies run by the Board; this is one of the factors which has led to the steady decline in the number of producer-retailers throughout the area, with only the larger dairy units remaining in production. Following this decline, local milk supplies have become increasingly difficult to trace with the degree of accuracy required for an investigation of this nature. Records, which include locations of producers, are destroyed some 5 years after cessation of production.

Potable water sources

Water supplies from bracken-infested catchments constitute the second most obvious potential route of contamination. The fractionation procedures used in attempts to isolate water-soluble carcinogenic agents from bracken have been described[20,21]. Our attention turned, therefore, to the possibility of the presence in the water supply of an, as yet, unidentified toxin derived from bracken.

Leachates from the seasonal fronds are known to have allelopathic effects[22], but bracken also has a very extensive perennial underground system of rhizomes which are toxic and carcinogenic[23] (on average, 17 tons/ha), which are also leached by drainage water. Throughout Gwynedd, water supplies are essentially localised, and those serving urban administrative districts have, in most cases, been established since before the turn of the century. Due to topograpical constraints, the urban communities are often restricted to relatively well-defined geographical areas, usually with a single water source supplying the entire population. The inhabitants of rural districts, on the other hand, live in small villages, hamlets and farmsteads each of which may have had its own unique water supply, such as a spring or a well.

MATERIALS AND METHODS

Standardisation

The Standardised Mortality Ratio (SMR) is used as an index of relative mortality, adjusted for age. The SMR was calculated for each administrative district by the indirect method, for ages 35 to 74 years. The expected deaths were calculated using the England and Wales age-specific rates based on 1961, for the period 1954 to 1965, and 1971, for the years 1966 to 1977. Standard death rates, per million of the population by age and sex, were obtained from the Registrar General's Statistical Reviews of England and Wales. The limitation of low numbers of observed deaths that occur when considering small administrative districts (resulting in large standard errors) has been partly overcome by the aggregation of deaths into two periods, 1954-65 and 1966-77.

Assessment of bracken coverage

Initially, it was intended that bracken cover should be mapped from aerial photograph cover obtained from the Welsh Office, taken between 1945 and 1964. However, the coverage was found to be random, not uniform in scale or age, and to suffer from cloud cover and the use of different camera angles. Except at a limited number of points, it was not possible to exploit this material. The final assessment of bracken cover was made from maps of the Vegetation Survey of Wales[24] at a scale of 1:25,000, which was kindly loaned to the authors by its director, J A Taylor.

For each of the 21 urban areas, the gathering grounds of the water catchments were extracted from Ordnance Survey data at a scale of 1:25,000, and these were confirmed by the Gwynedd Division of the Welsh Water Authority. Permanent streams were marked and overlays prepared, giving the surface distribution of Pteridium aquilinum. Field visits were made to each of the catchment areas to provide up-to-date visual confirmation. It was not possible to determine the full extent of the rhizome biomass but it was assumed to correlate with the observed aerial distribution of the plant. An example of a water catchment with mapped bracken is shown in Figure 2.

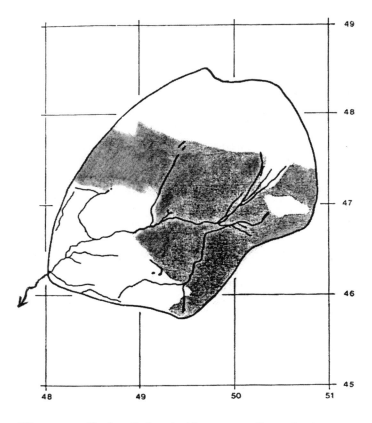

Figure 2 Ffynnonn Haf, Criccieth: example of the mapped distribution of bracken on a water catchment (Original scale 1:25,000)

151

<u>Water supply data</u>

All the necessary information was kindly provided by the Gwynedd Division of the Welsh Water Authority. This included details of catchments and distribution of supplies, runoff, treatment and abstraction data for each source of supply. Historical records relating to each catchment were obtained from Water Authority and Gwynedd County Archives.

It is possible to obtain an index of potential concentration of a bracken-derived toxin present in the water supply, by taking into account a broad spectrum of scientific parameters and ending up with a very complicated model. However, it was felt that in the circumstances a simplistic approach was more realistic. This required certain assumptions to be made. The small, high-altitude catchments of Snowdonia have sparse vegetation, shallow soil and areas of bare rock, all of which tend to reduce losses by evapotranspiration[25]. The high rainfall characteristic of the area would thus lead to high levels of runoff, theoretically capable of removing all the available toxin by leaching, from both frond and rhizome. The bulk of this leachate is therefore destined to reach the abstraction point of the water supply. The concentration of toxin entering the water supply thus depends on the dilution afforded by the runoff in the catchment. It must also be assumed that the toxin remains stable in water, although it may be chemically bound to a filterable organic carrier material. An estimate of potential annual average contamination can be calculated as follows:

$$\frac{\text{Area occupied by bracken}}{\text{Runoff}} = \text{Mean toxin index}$$

Measurements of the area occupied by bracken have been regarded as proportional to the total biomass of frond and perennial rhizome. Runoff was calculated by use of the equation shown in Figure 3.

RESULTS

The mortality data for the two periods under consideration are given in Table 2 and bracken coverage taken at the mid-point, in Table 3.

As will be seen from Figures 4 and 5, there is no positive correlation between deaths from gastric cancer and the percentage of bracken in water catchments in the areas studied, since the points are randomly scattered. The Spearman-Rank Correlation was used in the statistical analysis of these results and gave negative values of 0.24 and 0.15. Similarly, examination of the relationship between the theoretical mean toxin index and the SMR for the whole period also failed to show any positive correlation (Figure 6). (Spearman-Rank, -0.33).

DISCUSSION

Mortality from gastric cancer in Gwynedd, although now declining at a similar rate to that of England and Wales, lags behind the remainder of the country, perhaps by as much as a decade. The

152

Isohyets mm (r)									TOTALS
Area km^2 (a)									(A)
(r) x (a)									(B)
Average Rainfall ('41-'70)	B/A = ... / .... =								mm
Catchment losses							START		- 500
Elevation Adjustment	$\dfrac{(2 \times \text{lowest} + \text{Highest}) \text{ (ft)}}{15 \times (3.281)}$ = $\dfrac{2 \times \quad . + .}{15 \times (3.281)}$ =								
Exposure Adjustment	N +20	NE +10	NW +10	E 0	W 0	SE -10	SW -10	S -20 =	
Afforestation Adjustment	Percentage Forestry = F %				2 x F	=			-
Estimated Avg. Annual Runoff							TOTAL =		mm(P)
Estimated Avg. Flow	0.00003171 A x P = 0.00003171 x .... x ...... =								m^3/s

Figure 3 Form for estimation of annual catchment losses (from Jack[25])

epidemiological data so far obtainable, biological chemical and social, tends to support environmental involvement in the aetiology but does not indicate any precise agent. The results of the present investigation have failed to implicate waterborne contamination derived from bracken.

It should be remembered that there are certain disadvantages which limit the value of epidemiological observations. In particular, records that can be made on humans are limited to the conditions which have actually occurred. Long latent periods are common for cancers. In the case of gastric cancer the induction period is thought to be a minimum of 18-20 years, and in many cases is probably considerably longer than this. Thus, when attempting to examine possible environmental effects, those thought to have been in existence some 20 or more years ago, especially conditions prevailing during childhood and adolescence, are thought to be of overriding importance in the aetiology of this disease.

Until about a century ago, most of the population had to depend on wells and springs located fairly close to their homes. In the towns, water was also obtained from wells and rivers. The water was often polluted, thus giving rise to epidemics of typhoid and cholera. Eventually the towns constructed their own water supplies, Bangor being the first to construct its own reservoir, in 1854. The dilution factor, inherent in the modern reservoir, is obviously much greater than that obtaining in a well or spring, and the fact that the latter have largely been replaced as direct water supplies may play a part in the overall reduction of gastric cancer. For example, reports[26] have suggested a correlation between elevated nitrate levels in water

TABLE 2 Gastric cancer mortality (male and female) in North Wales

District		1954 - 1965			1966 - 1977		
		Observed Mortality	SMR	Signif-icance	Observed Mortality	SMR	Signif-icance
Amlwch	UD	15	90	NS	12	102	NS
Beaumaris	MB	7	76	NS	7	89	NS
Holyhead	UD	61	152	++	41	127	NS
Llangefni	UD	11	108	NS	23	229	++
Menai Bridge	UD	11	124	NS	50	135	NS
Aethwy	RD	62	135	NS	50	144	+
Valley	RD	97	229	++	43	109	NS
Twrcelyn	RD	55	145	+	50	144	+
Bangor	MB	84	175	++	35	121	NS
Bethesda	UD	38	224	++	25	241	++
Betws-Y-Coed	UD	7	204	NS	2	106	NS
Caernarfon	MB	66	167	++	43	194	++
Conwy	MB	60	100	NS	32	80	NS
Criccieth	UD	5	57	NS	9	172	NS
Llandudno	UD	116	109	NS	67	97	NS
Llanfairfechan	UD	25	167	+	15	149	NS
Penmaenmawr	UD	41	192	++	22	173	NS
Porthmadog	UD	28	152	+	22	223	++
Pwllheli	MB	40	217	++	15	144	NS
Gwyrfai	RD	195	206	++	95	178	++
Lleyn	RD	157	190	++	83	179	++
Ogwen	RD	54	216	++	20	139	NS
Nant Conwy	RD	48	203	++	23	172	++
Bala	UD	17	219	++	12	198	NS
Barmouth	UD	16	136	NS	15	167	NS
Dolgellau	UD	13	138	NS	19	236	++
Ffestiniog	UD	50	195	++	32	165	+
Tywyn	UD	30	167	+	15	84	NS
Deudraeth	RD	51	163	++	29	120	NS
Dolgellau	RD	38	109	NS	38	133	NS
Edeyrnion	RD	24	143	NS	30	222	++
Penllyn	RD	17	154	NS	7	88	NS

+ = P < 0.02   ++ = P < 0.001   NS = Not Significant

and stomach cancer, with those taking their supplies from wells and boreholes being at greatest risk.

Studies[27,28] in this country and in the Netherlands[29,30] have revealed cases where higher gastric cancer mortalities were positively associated with poorly drained, acid peaty soils of the type likely to produce water with a solvent action in piped supplies. Water which has been in contact with peat and the roots of peat-forming plants, becomes acidic. Such a situation is prevalent in Gwynedd where the water is generally very soft and lacking in calcium. The negative results obtained from these bracken studies do not preclude the possibility that this more general aspect of the quality

TABLE 3 Bracken areas on urban water catchments in Gwynedd, 1961-66

Administrative District	Nature of supply	Area of bracken on catchment (km^2)
Amlwch	Borehole	Nil
Beaumaris	Impounding reservoir	0.06
Holyhead	Upland lake	0.22
Llangefni	Spring	Nil
Menai Bridge	Spring	Nil
Bangor	Mountain stream	Nil
Bethesda	Mountain stream	0.5
Betws-Y-Coed	Mountain lake	0.29
Caernarfon	Mountain lake	5.4
Conwy	Mountain lake	0.27
Criccieth	Spring	2.56
Llandudno	Mountain lakes	Nil
Llanfairfechan	Mountain stream	Nil
Penmaenmawr	Mountain stream	Nil
Porthmadog	Mountain lake	0.17
Pwllheli	Spring	0.03
Bala	Mountain lake	0.2
Barmouth	Mountain lake	0.68
Dolgellau	Mountain lake	0.22
Ffestiniog	Mountain lake	Nil
Tywyn	Mountain stream	6.10

of the North Wales domestic water supply, in both urban and rural communities, may still be a causal factor in the above-average incidence of stomach cancer in this area.

Final comment added later by O P Galpin

When the idea for this study grew, it was intended to look at other possibilities alongside bracken contamination. Although this was the foremost aim, we also considered nitrate levels, pH and trace elements but with similar negative results.

The method of study really depends upon the demonstration of reasonably consistent, within-region differences in SMR in order to link with observed differences in water supply. The relatively small populations studied showed chance fluctuations but by amalgamation of the data into two 10-year periods and by using urban areas only, one could be reasonably sure that the top and bottom of the SMR scale in particular were secure. Dr Peter Oldham (MRC-Cardiff) calculated the true correlation between the two periods of study as +0.73, and therefore there was strong evidence of persistent high or low mortality in the different urban areas.

At the onset of the study, there was no proof that carcinogenic substances could be extracted from bracken by leaching with water, but this has now been confirmed by Dr Antice Evans and her team, although

155

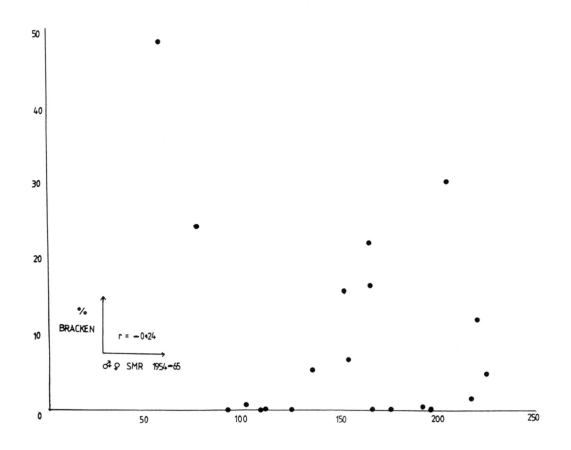

Figure 4   Relationship between bracken and SMR (1954-65)

there is still uncertainty about the precise structure of the potent carcinogen. There is also uncertainty about its behaviour when passing through soil, when stored in large reservoirs or when subjected to various treatment methods. This work used isolated fronds or rhizome rather than the whole plant in its normal environment. Although there has been much evidence from animal experiments (eg W C and A Evans, herein), there had been nothing definite to indicate a risk to human beings until the work of Hirayama[31] showed a three-times greater risk of oesophageal cancer in those Japanese who eat bracken daily compared with those who never touch it. Contamination of water by small doses of carcinogenic substances can, in theory, be a risk to human health because of the long periods and continuous nature of the exposure, and there is some evidence that chlorination of water by halogenation or organic material could be a factor in causing bladder cancer[32], these compounds having been found carcinogenic in laboratory animals and also in man. At the present time, however, we can be reasonably certain that bracken contamination of large water sources is not a prime cause of stomach cancer in North Wales.

156

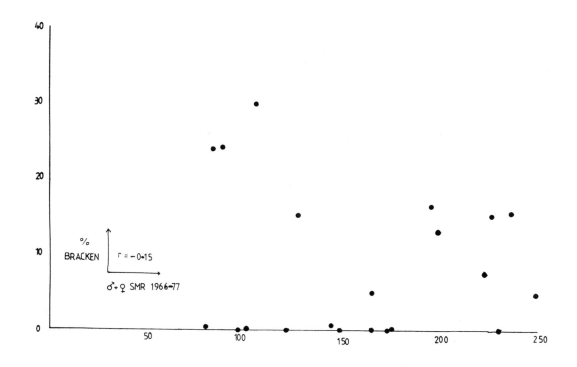

Figure 5   Relationship between bracken and SMR (1966-77)

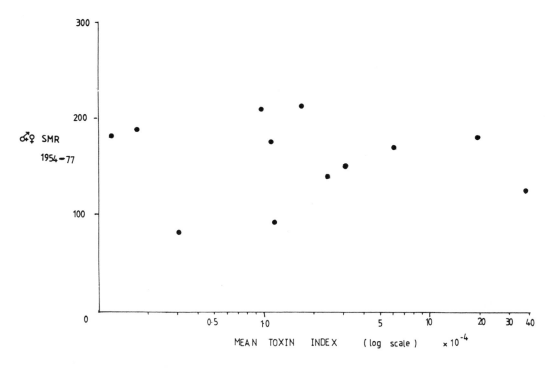

Figure 6   Relationship between SMR (1954-77) and log Mean Toxin Index

REFERENCES

1) Stocks P (1936)   British Empire Cancer Campaign, Annual Report,

157

239-280

2) Griffith G W (1968) The sex ratio in gastric cancer and hypothetical considerations relative to aetiology. Brit. J. Cancer, 22, 163-172

3) Chief Area Medical Officer's Statistical Review, (1983) Gwynedd Health Authority

4) Doll R and Peto R (1981) The causes of cancer, Oxford and New York; Oxford University Press

5) International Union Against Cancer (1970) Cancer Incidence in five continents Vol II. In: Doll R, Muir C S, Waterhouse J A (eds), Geneva, IUAC

6) Rymer L (1976) The history and ethnobotany of bracken. Bot. J. Linn. Soc., 73, 151-176

7) Moyes A (1970) Bracken on the menu. What?, 26-7

8) Braid R W (1934) Bracken as a colonist. Scot. J. Agric., 17, 59-70

9) Storrarr D M (1893) J. Comp. Path. 6, 275-279

10) Stockman S (1916) J. Comp. Path., 29, 95

11) Stockman S (1917) J. Comp. Path., 30, 311-316

12) Stockman S (1922) J. Comp. Path., 35, 273-275

13) Boddie G F (1947) Vet. Rec., 59, 471-478

14) Parker W H and McCrea C T (1965) Bracken (Pteris aquilina) poisoning of sheep in the North York Moors. Vet. Rec., 77, 861-866

15) Evans I A and Mason J (1965) Carcinogenic activity of bracken. Nature, 208, 913-914

16) Evans I A (1968) The radiomimetic nature of bracken toxin. Cancer Res., 28, 2252-2261

17) Evans I A (1984) Bracken Carcinogenicity, In C E Searle (ed) Chemical carcinogens, Volume 2. Monograph 182, 1177-1204, American Chemical Society, Washington DC (2nd Edn)

18) Evans I A (1985) In press

19) Evans I A, Jones R S and Mainwaring-Burton R (1972) Passage of bracken fern toxicity into milk. Nature, 237, 107-108

20) Evans I A, Al-Salmani A M H, Smith R M M (1984) Bracken toxicology: identification of some water soluble compounds from crozier and rhizome. Res. Vet. Sci., 37, 261-265

21) Evans I A (1984)   In, C E Searle (ed) <u>Chemical Carcinogens</u>, Second Edition, Volume 2.   Monograph 182, 1177-1204, American Chemical Society, Washington DC

22) Gliessman S R (1976)   Allelopathy in a broad spectrum of environments as illustrated by bracken. <u>Bot. J. Linn. Soc.</u>, 73, 95-104

23) Hirono I, Shibuya C, Shimiku M and Fushimi M (1972) Carcinogenic activity of processed bracken. <u>J. Natl. Cancer Inst.</u>, 48, 1245-1250

24) Taylor J A (1961-66)   Vegetation survey of Wales. Aberystwyth (see Taylor, herein)

25) Jack W L (1977)   <u>Institution of Water Engineers</u>; 280-284

26) Hill M J, Hawksworth G and Tattersall G (1973)   Bacteria, nitrosamines and cancer of the stomach. <u>Brit. J. Cancer</u>, 28, 562

27) Davies R I and Wynne Griffith G (1954)   Cancer and soils in the County of Anglesey. <u>Brit. J. Cancer</u> 8, 56

28) Stocks P and Davies R I (1960)   Investigation of a localised high incidence of gastric cancer. <u>Public Health</u>, 74 (11), 408-412

29) Tromp S W (1956)   The geographical distribution of cancer of the stomach in the Netherlands. (1946-1952). <u>Brit. J. Cancer</u>, 10, 265-281

30) Tromp S W and Diehl J C (1959)   A statistical study of the possible relationship between cancer of the stomach and soil. <u>Brit. J. Cancer</u>, 9, 349-357

31) Hirayama T (1979) Diet and cancer. <u>Nutr. Cancer</u>, 1, 67-81

32) Cantor, <u>et al</u> (1978)   Associations of cancer mortality with halomethanes in drinking water. <u>J. Nat. Cancer Inst.</u>, 61, 979-985

Bracken and ticks on grouse moors in the North of England

P J Hudson

INTRODUCTION

Bracken encroachment onto heather-dominant moorland has resulted in a significant reduction in the amount of heather available to stock and game. In the North Yorkshire Moors, it has been estimated[1] that nearly a fifth of the moorland is dominated by bracken and the weed is currently spreading at the rate of 1.0% per annum. The direct replacement of heather by bracken results in the loss of winter food for sheep[2] and a reduction in grouse-producing ground[3]. Other disadvantages of bracken include its toxic[4] and carcinogenic[5] properties as well as harbouring parasites harmful to grouse and sheep[6].

The sheep tick, Ixodes ricinus, is an ectoparasite of both sheep and grouse and transmits a number of harmful diseases including louping-ill, tick-borne fever and tick pyaemia. Ticks and their associated diseases result in financial loss for both the hill farmer[7] and grouse-shooting interests[8]. Control of the tick usually involves the treatment of sheep with an ixodicide to reduce the incidence of tick infestation and, when necessary, the administration of drugs to combat disease. The owner or tenant of a grouse moor is unable to control directly the tick infestation on the grouse but may implement effective control through the removal of habitat beneficial to the over-winter survival of ticks. In studies on ticks, Milne[9] has found an association between rough grazing and ticks, with a positive correlation between mat thickness and tick population density. The ticks require a humid habitat in which to survive, and this is provided by the thick mat layer associated with rough moorland grasses and bracken.

This paper examines the association between bracken and ticks and reports some findings from a pilot experiment to test the idea that the removal of bracken could result in a decrease in mat thickness and consequently a decrease in tick abundance.

Bracken and ticks - comparisons between grouse moors

Grouse moor owners in the North of England were sent a questionnaire in 1979 which asked for details about management practices used in the production of grouse. Within this questionnaire, they were asked if they had made active attempts to control the bracken. The object was to discover whether the problem of bracken encroachment on the moor was large enough to warrant control measures. The questionnaire also asked if ticks were known to be present on the moor.

Bracken and ticks - comparisons within a grouse moor

Ticks were sampled, using two methods, on Egton High Moor, North Yorkshire. Standardised blanket drags of 50 metres were conducted in early June 1983 when ticks were known to be active. The principle of blanket dragging is to simulate a sheep walking through the vegetation, so that questing ticks become attached to the blanket and the population can be sampled. The technique has certain limitations and needs testing further but, within the present study, the drags were conducted at times when the height of all types of vegetation was similar and adequately suited the needs of the present study. Drags were made on either bracken or heather-dominant vegetation, and some sampling was done in bracken beds that had previously been sprayed with asulam herbicide.

Since there are a number of limitations with blanket dragging as a method for sampling questing ticks, trained dogs (pointers and setters) were used to locate grouse chicks in the summer of 1983 and the number of ticks infesting each chick were counted. The dogs were trained to quarter the ground, locate a brood and point individual chicks which were then caught by hand and examined. The number of nymphal and larval ticks were counted on each chick and the dominant vegetation in which the chick was found, noted.

Bracken treatment, mat thickness and ticks

As part of a programme of bracken control on Ramsgill Moor, Nidderdale, North Yorkshire, a series of blocks of bracken ground were sprayed with asulam between 1978 and 1980. The ground was known to be infested with ticks, after a series of blanket drags conducted by Miss J Currer-Briggs in 1979. In May 1980 four study plots were established, one in an area of unsprayed bracken and the remaining three in areas sprayed in 1978, 1979 and one to be sprayed in July of 1980, respectively. Follow-up treatment on each sprayed plot included spot-spraying individual fronds with asulam and the pulling-up of any recently emerged fronds. Each study plot, was 50m by 50m in area and within each plot were placed 9 evenly spaced pegs. In late May at each peg, a metre-square quadrat was placed and the percentage cover of the vegetation recorded. Within each plot, 10 core samples were taken and the thickness of the bracken mat layer measured. In 1981 and 1982, 5 blanket drags were conducted on each plot and the number of ticks recorded.

RESULTS

Bracken and ticks - comparisons between grouse moors

Of the 91 questionnaires returned from moor owners, all had answered the questions on the control of bracken and the presence of ticks; of these, 37 (41%) had undertaken measures to control bracken (Figure 1a) and 32 (35%) recorded the presence of ticks (Figure 1b) on the moor. Of the 37 with a bracken problem, 22 had also recorded the presence of ticks. The proportion of moors which recorded both a bracken and tick problem was greater then could be expected by chance (2 x 2 chi-squared with Yates's correction = 15.3; $p < 0.001$) demonstrating a positive association between bracken and ticks in a comparison between grouse moors in the north of England.

Bracken and ticks - comparisons within a grouse moor

A total of 82 blanket drags were conducted, 24 on heather-dominant vegetation, 45 on unsprayed bracken and 13 on sprayed bracken. The frequency distribution of ticks per drag (Figure 2) had a variance greater than the mean, indicating that the questing ticks were contagiously distributed within each vegetation type and conformed to the negative binomial probability distribution. The drags in the unsprayed bracken ground recorded the presence of ticks significantly more often (2 x 2 chi-squared with Yates's correction = 26.9; $p < 0.001$) than on heather-dominant vegetation. These results demonstrate an association between bracken and ticks within a grouse moor. Too few drags were conducted on sprayed bracken to make a statistical comparison between sprayed and unsprayed bracken.

A total of 120 chicks were caught in 1984, 70 from heather-dominant vegetation, 24 from bracken-dominant vegetation and 26 from bracken previously treated with asulam. As with the sampling of questing ticks, the frequency distribution of ticks on grouse chicks was aggregated and conformed to the negative binomial (Figure 3). Significantly more of the chicks found in bracken carried ticks, than those found in heather (2 x 2 chi-squared with Yates's correction = 8.1; $p < 0.005$). Grouse chicks found in sprayed bracken ground were also less likely to be infested than chicks from untreated bracken (2 x 2 chi-squared with Yates's correction = 16.8; $p < 0.001$). Although it cannot be shown that grouse inhabiting bracken become infested with ticks as a direct result of utilising these areas, observations do show a positive association between bracken and ticks in vegetational comparisons within a particular grouse moor.

Bracken treatment, mat thickness and ticks

The control area was inadvertently sprayed in the summer of 1980 (Table 1) but there was an overall increase in the mean percentage cover of the sprayed ground. Vaccinium myrtillus was the

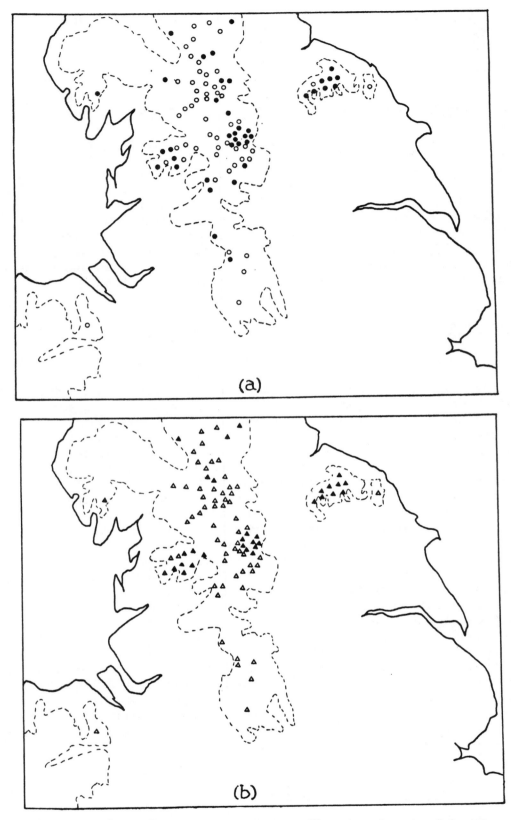

Figure 1 Location of grouse moors recording treatment of bracken (a) and presence of ticks (b). Solid symbols represent treatment and presence, open symbols represent no treatment and absence.

164

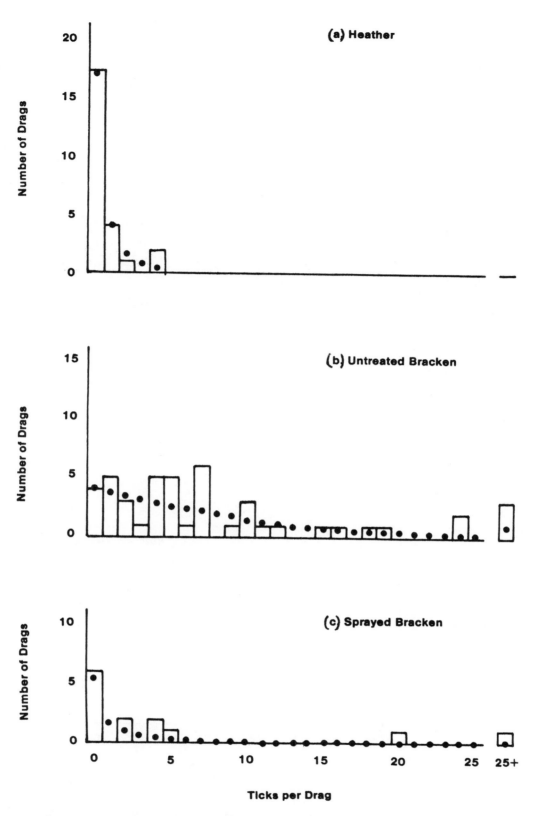

Figure 2   Frequency distribution of ticks per blanket drag. Points show the fit of the negative binomial for heather (a. mean = 0.6, k = 0.4), untreated bracken, (b. mean = 8.4, k = 1.1) and treated bracken (c. mean = 5, k = 0.3).

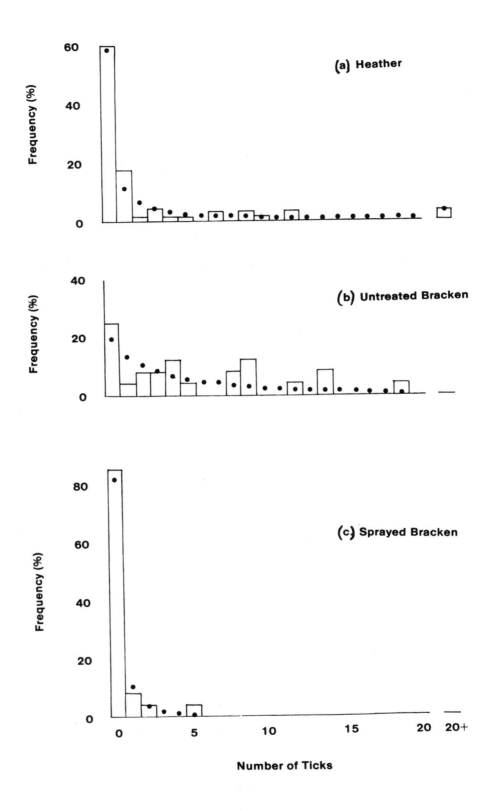

Figure 3   Frequency distribution of ticks per host.   Points show the
fit of the negative binomial for chicks caught in heather (a. mean =
2.7, k = 0.2), untreated bracken (b. mean = 4.8, k = 0.7) and treated
bracken (c. mean = 0.35, k = 0.2).

principle colonising species although <u>Empetrum nigrum</u> and various species of grass were also recorded. It is possible that heather may become established at a later date.

TABLE 1 Vegetation cover of ground in successive years after treatment of bracken with asulam. Figures show mean percentage cover for each plot

| Plot | Years after Treatment | | | |
	1	2	3	4
1	0	2		
2		41	43	59
3	23	42	27	
4	38	19		
Mean	20	26	35	59

Analysis of mat thickness found that in comparisons within each year since spraying, there was no difference between plots, except in the comparisons two years after spraying (ANOVA, F = 4.23, p < 0.05). Excluding the results from this second year, there was a significant difference between years since spraying (ANOVA, F = 7.58, p < 0.001) and a general decrease in mat layer thickness after bracken spraying (Figure 4a). Thus, even with the large variance in mat thickness measured in samples two years after spraying, these results indicate that there is a decrease in mat thickness after treatment.

Analysis of tick drags showed a large variance of ticks per drag within plots (Figure 4b), which prevented statistical comparisons, although the overall trend appears to be a reduction in ticks after spraying. The large variance within plots is perhaps not surprising, since it has already been shown that ticks are not distributed at random within bracken beds but are highly aggregated (Figure 2.)

DISCUSSION

On the heather-dominant moorlands of northern England, there is an association between the presence of sheep ticks and bracken. Furthermore, grouse chicks caught in bracken ground are more likely to be infested with ticks than chicks caught in heather or areas of bracken treated with herbicide. In some of our other studies (publication in preparation), we have found evidence that ticks alone do not reduce significantly the survival of grouse chicks, but, in areas where ticks transmit the Louping-ill virus, the survival of chicks is significantly lower[8], and this results in a reduced harvest and revenue for the land-owner. As chicks found in treated bracken were less likely to be infested than chicks from untreated

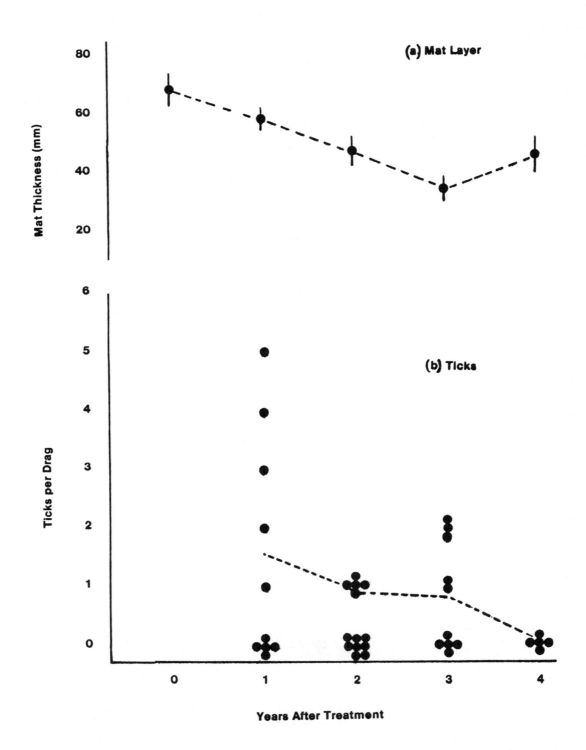

Figure 4   Change   in   mean   mat   thickness   (a)   and   number of ticks
per drag (b) after treatment of bracken with asulam (+1 standard error
indicated in (a)).

bracken, we can postulate that the removal of bracken will reduce the incidence of ticks, the prevalence of Louping-ill and, consequently, lead to an improvement in production.

The pilot experiment conducted in this study investigated the influence of bracken treatment on the mat layer and the tick population. This was not conclusive for two reasons. Firstly, in one of the four years after treatment, there was a significant difference between samples of mat thickness which prevented them being combined. Secondly, there was a large variation in the number of ticks sampled with blanket drags. It was not clear why the variance in mat thickness was so great in the one year referred to, unless there is a variation in the rate of breakdown between areas of bracken. Even so, when these findings were excluded from the analysis, there was a greater variation between than within the samples, and a general decline in mat thickness after spraying. In his study on ticks Milne[9] demonstrated that agricultural improvement of rough pasture brought about a reduction in bracken cover and a significant reduction in the tick population.

The large variation in the number of ticks sampled using blanket drags on the experimental plots is perhaps not surprising, since it was also found that ticks are highly aggregated on the moor and also on the chicks. This pattern of distribution is common for parasites in general[10] and has been recorded for other species of ticks[11]. The aggregated distribution can be related to three features of the tick-host relationship: firstly, to the adult female tick depositing her eggs within one place, so that emerging larvae are highly aggregated on the ground; secondly, to differential survival of ticks in relation to mat thickness[9]; and thirdly, to the variability in the behaviour of the many hosts that ticks infest. The use of blanket drags to sample ticks has its limitations since it collects only the questing ticks, individuals that have not successfully found a host. Thus, it may be possible to sample one piece of ground where ticks were abundant but are not available to the sampling technique since they have successfully found a host. As such, it is important that studies on ticks examine the intensity of infestation on the hosts.

CONCLUSION

In the experimental area the overall effect of bracken treatment has been beneficial to the owner and his grouse shooting, and also to the tenant farmers with grazing rights on the moor. The replacement of bracken principally with Vaccinium myrtillus has produced increased sheep feed and suitable habitat for grouse. The shooting on the sprayed area has improved from 5 to 10 birds a year to a crop of nearly 60 birds in 1984, although a longer time period will be needed to demonstrate an overall improvement in both grouse and sheep production.

This study has found an association between bracken and ticks, and the results indicate that the removal of bracken could result in a significant reduction of the tick population. To draw a more positive conclusion would require an intensive experiment with fenced plots and accurate monitoring of the tick population by regularly inspecting hosts kept within each plot.

ACKNOWLEDGEMENTS

I wish to thank Egton and Ramsgill estates for their kind co-operation during this study and, in particular, Bryan Nellist for conducting blanket drags at Egton. The subscribers of the North of England Grouse Research Project provided financial support and completed the questionnaires. May and Baker Ltd undertook the spraying of the study plots and provided a generous donation. David Newborn assisted with field work; and James Duncan and Dick Potts provided constructive discussion and comments throughout.

REFERENCES

1) North York Moors National Park (1982) The Future of the Moorland

2) Hudson P J (1984) Some effects of sheep management on heather moorlands in northern England. In D Jenkins (ed). Agriculture and the environment, 143-49, ITE: Cambridge

3) Hudson P J and Watson A (1985) The red grouse. Biologist, 32, 13-18

4) Evans W C, Patel M C and Koohy Y (1982) Acute bracken poisoning in homogastric and ruminant animals. Proc. Roy. Soc. Edin., 81B, 29-64

5) Jarrett W F H (1982) Bracken and cancer. Proc. Roy. Soc. Edin., 81B, 79-83

6) Milne A (1944) The ecology of the sheep tick, Ixodes ricinus L.: Distribution of the tick in relation to geology, soil and vegetation in northern England. Parasitology, 35, 186-196

7) Phillips J D P (1979) Tick research programme : 1978. Game Conservancy Annual Review, 9, 86-90

8) Duncan J S, Reid H W, Moss R, Phillips J D P and Watson A (1978) Ticks, louping ill and red grouse on moors in Speyside, Scotland. J Wildl. Manage., 42, 500-505

9) Milne A (1950) The ecology of the sheep tick, Ixodes ricinus L. Spatial distribution. Parasitology, 40, 35-45

10) Anderson R M (1978) The regulation of host population growth by parasitic species. Parasitology, 76, 119-157

11) Randolph S E (1975) Patterns of distribution of the tick, Ixodes trianguliceps Birula, on its hosts. J. Anim. Ecol., 44, 451-74

Biology and Environmental

Relationships of Bracken Communities

The strategies of Bracken as a permanent ecological opportunist

C N Page

INTRODUCTION

The bracken fern is either one of the world's worst weeds or one of the most successful pteridophytes ever, depending on one's point of view. A comparison of the natural attributes of bracken with those of many of the 15,000 or so other known species of ferns and fern-allies worldwide, shows bracken to have a number of fairly well defined and distinctive biological strategies (Table 1), some of which are shared, in varying degrees, by other ferns, and some of which are not.

THE MAIN STRATEGIES OF BRACKEN'S SUCCESS

1. High disease resistance

Field experience suggests it is seldom that severe diseases of ferns, including bracken, are met under natural circumstances[1-5]. One possible reason for this is that ferns have had at least 200 million years in which to evolve and perfect disease-resistance mechanisms. There is fossil evidence that bracken, or a very close relative, was present at least 55 million years ago[6]. Basic evolutionary trends and abilities, acquired over time-scales of this sort, are ones from which the plant is not likely to be easily deflected, and the benefits of this to the success of the bracken fern are obvious.

2. Low palatability

Over a similar time-scale, pteridophytes have been a continuous target for the herbivorous desires of grazing animals, including arthropods[7], allowing considerable time for defence mechanisms to evolve. A formidable array of biochemical weaponry has been

173

TABLE 1 The main strategies of bracken's biology

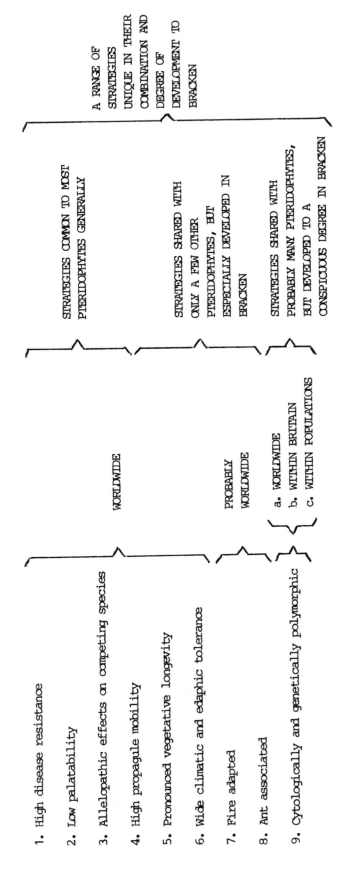

demonstrated in bracken[8-9], and the generally high levels of secondary plant metabolites in pteridophytes may have been facilitated[10] by the widespread evolution of polyploidy in the group as a whole[11-12].

In practical terms, bracken is seldom taken as a preferred substrate by many grazing animals, and this seems a general experience with almost all pteridophytes[13]. The tendency of man to try to maintain the same numbers of grazing stock on the ever smaller bracken-free areas has, undoubtedly, enhanced the rate at which the remaining areas have been lost to bracken in a steadily-accelerating vicious circle of events[13].

3. Allelopathic effects on competing species

There is accumulating evidence that allelopathic effects, whereby one plant can suppress the development of other species or individuals around it, is a phenomenon which is operative both at the gametophyte and sporophyte stage of the fern life cycle[5]. In the case of bracken, allelopathic compounds are not only released by the standing fronds, but also leached during the autumn and winter months from decaying ones[14-15], and these effects, plus the physical swamping of other vegetation by the rotting frond blanket[16], appear to be particularly effective in reducing vigour and species diversity of potential competitors. It may be significant in this respect that phenolic compounds have been reported from a wide range of ferns.[15]

In practice, the biochemistry of bracken proves to be particularly effective in despatching most herbaceous plants which might compete with it. In Britain, the areas where bracken occurs mostly indicate the occurrence of former forest[16], and bracken itself is a pioneer species, probably seral towards forest[19-21]. Tree seedlings such as birch or oak must, at some stage, be able to establish through it, and here resides one approach to natural bracken control, for forest ultimately shades and permanently reduces the success of bracken.

4. High propagule mobility

The minute, airborne spores of the bracken fern are released from each fertile frond by the million[5], and provide the plant with an unusually high mobility and reproductive capacity. In practical terms, the plant can invade initially by means of an unseen army of spores dispersing over very long distances[4]. Having no spore-bearing bracken in the immediate vicinity is not necessarily a handicap to the plant's initial arrival[4-5]. The ability of spores to arrive from multiple sources and over long distances, allows opportunity for environmental selection of genotypes best fitted to each specific environment. Furthermore, the haploid nature of its spores and the potential for self-compatibility of gametophytes, provide opportunity for a theoretical complete genetic homozygosity of isolated progeny. This is an ability shared by most ferns and, in this aspect, their genetics differs fundamentally from all flowering plants[5,11,12].

5. Pronounced vegetative longevity

Bracken appears able to establish new adult plants from spores in about three years[4,22]. Thereafter, spread by subterranean creeping rhizomes appears to be an indefinite process, whilst each portion of rhizome has the ability to come away to form a new plant and colony[23]. Regrowth from such fragments allows the plant to revert temporarily to a juvenile morphology, before returning eventually to adult form - a feature shared by a number of other pteridophytes[5,21].

The ecological implications of its longevity, regrowth ability and juvenile reversion are poorly understood. Some clones may be very young, others centuries old[24], and some may well be amongst the oldest living things in the contemporary landscape.

6. Wide climatic and edaphic tolerance

Worldwide, bracken is tolerant of an enormous range of climates, exposures and soil types[4,13,18,21-23,25]. Sensitivity of emerging fronds to spring frosts[23] seems to be its main climatic limitation in cooler areas and with increasing altitude, and this is particularly evident in many populations in Britain. Information about the sensitivity to climatic extremes of the gametophytes of different brackens is scant. Over a wide pH range[4,18,25], the main edaphic limitations of the sporophyte are probably soil depth and soil drainage[23,26,27], and factors such as water movement, oxygenation and duration of waterlogging are probably especially critical in sporophyte winter survival (and see Smith, herein). Such wide tolerances are unusual amongst most pteridophytes, so far as is known, where restriction to very much more specific conditions seems generally to be the rule[18,21].

7. Fire adapted

Bracken's adaptations to fire include its ability, as an established sporophyte, to withstand severe burning and to come away rapidly from rhizome growth before most competing vegetation has recolonised[4,28]. In addition, there is accumulating evidence of not only an ability, but probably even a requirement, of its spores, for fire-damaged sites in achieving the most widespread and rapid initial colonisation[13,18]. Furthermore, at an early stage of establishment, plants of British bracken are clearly base-tolerant, and numerous instances of its establishing on lime-rich mortar, are known[4]. It appears to switch to being acid-loving once the available bases, such as potash, released by an initial burn, have become leached out of the system[13]. As such, young bracken sporophytes appear to undergo a distinctive pH metamorphosis - a phenomenon matched, as far as is known, by no other pteridophyte, flowering plant, or other weed.

8. Ant associated

Observations made over a number of years on British bracken and subsequently on bracken in several overseas countries, have shown that the expanding fronds probably everywhere enjoy a cryptic, early-spring association with several species of the common terrestrial ant. Ants are regularly attracted by extra-floral nectaries sited in the axils of the pinnae and pinnules of bracken fronds. These nectaries are active only during the period when each frond is in its spring expansion phase[18,29,30]. The possession of nectaries is an extremely unusual feature amongst pteridophytes. Related genera (eg. Hypolepis and Paesia) do not have them, and we must conclude that they are an adaptation which has evolved within the genus Pteridium. Their presence is as yet poorly known and their ecological role is the subject of ongoing research at Edinburgh.

9. Cytologically and genetically polymorphic

Cytological and genetic polymorphism is an attribute which bracken almost certainly shares with numerous other pteridophytes, both temperate and tropical[18,21]. Polymorphy in bracken is manifested in considerable variability in the field as well as in certain biochemical traits[31-32]. A high opportunity for local environmental selection of favourably adapted ecotypes is consequent upon its dispersal mechanism. Indeed, the more I have studied the taxonomy of bracken[4], the greater I conclude its differences between various parts of the world to be. How much more might these differences, which we can see, be reflected in differences in its biochemistry and physiology, including susceptibility to herbicides, which we cannot see? The polymorphy of bracken in relation to its spread is again a field of ongoing research at Edinburgh, and evidence accumulated by the writer suggests that, even in Britain, we have not just one bracken, but two.

CONCLUSIONS

Bracken is, without doubt, an opportunistic pioneer of the disturbed types of sites created by man and his activities including the grazing of animals. Few would deny, too, that it has the endearing ability to become virtually permanent, once first allowed the slightest toe-hold. There has, consequently, been a tendency, by those who have attempted to control it, to regard the weed as a slowly spreading, green plague of an unwelcome but simple and uniform creature, which, wherever it occurs, will simply be destroyed by hitting it, once we have found the right implement with which to do so. This has, I respectfully suggest, been the general view of agriculturalists, not just for the last forty years, but for at least twenty centuries. Our implements may have changed and become more sophisticated but general philosophy concerning the plant has not!

My case is that our perception of the plant has been wrong. It is certainly not uniform. Nor is it in any way simple. Accumulating scientific evidence is that the plant is a highly complex, strategically diverse, rapidly responding, geographically mobile and genetically polymorphic organism. It also has a number of innate and poorly understood mechanisms of unusual environmental tolerance, insect mutualism and fire adaptation, enabling it to score strategic

177

advantages at otherwise vulnerable stages of its life cycle in ways which are so subtle that we have scarcely yet awoken to them. We need to know more about the subtle strengths of the enemy, if we are to exploit weaknesses, and hence better ways of control. Spraying with pteridocidal chemicals may be one method of proceeding towards a method of control. But such herbicides are bound to be confronted in their effectiveness by at least three major areas of pteridophyte biology:

1. The intrinsic variability of bracken

Others have discussed how effective are current herbicide sprays and application techniques from one locality to another and no further comments are necessary here.

2. The high susceptibility of other pteridophytes to bracken herbicides

All of the other 104 native pteridophytes in Britain[18], as well as totally unknown quantities overseas, are known or suspected to be totally killed-out by contact with herbicides such as asulam, although I can find no awareness of this in any of the reports in a previous symposium, relating to field trials[34-37]. In Britain, these extremely vulnerable plants include national and international rarities, specifically protected by law[18]. All of these and many others are in upland refuges, where there is often also plenty of bracken. Widespread aerial application of such broad-spectrum pteridocidal chemicals is bound to raise very considerable conservation concern.

3. The ability of bracken to return

Even if effective sprays could be developed which meet the above criteria, their application, no matter how locally effective, sometimes merely provides a temporary, energy-intensive and expensive breathing-space in the general progress of bracken's spread. Surrounding bracken retains the ability to return, so long as the same environmental conditions conducive to its success[13] remain.

We cannot afford to be complacement. Figures have been quoted for the acreage of land infested by bracken, and the rates at which it is still being lost[38-39]. What we must concertedly work towards, are better, and probably cheaper, ways to cure the cause of the problem - not just its symptoms - which are (i) effective against all variants of the plant, (ii) reasonably self-maintaining and hence effective in the long term, and (iii) sufficiently specific to bracken as not to cause widespread environmental concern. New thinking is certainly needed, and more detailed research on several unique aspects of the biology of this plant clearly has an important role to play.

ACKNOWLEDGEMENTS

It is a pleasure to acknowledge helpful discussion of this account with P Hadfield, Dr A F Dyer and Professor D M Henderson, and to thank the latter for his encouragement with this work.

178

REFERENCES

1) Gregor A J F Associations with fungi and other lower plants. In F Verdoorn (ed.) Manual of Pteridology, 141-158. The Hague: M Nijhoff

2) Hutchinson S A (1976) The effects of fungi on bracken. Bot. J. Linn. Soc., 73, 145-150

3) Bennell A P and Henderson D M (1985) Rusts and other fungal parasites as aids to pteridophyte taxonomy. Proc. Roy. Soc. Edinb. Pteridophyte Biology Symposium Volume: 86B: 115-124

4) Page C N (1976) The taxonomy and phytogeography of bracken - a review. Bot. J. Linn. Soc., 73, 1-34

5) Page C N (1979) Experimental aspects of fern ecology. In A F Dyer (ed.) The Experimental Biology of Pteridophytes, 551-589. London and New York: Academic Press

6) Zhen S -L and Zhang W (1983) A new genus of Pteridiaceae from late Jurassic, Heilongjiang Province. Acta Bot. Sinica, 25, 380-384

7) Cooper-Driver G (1976) Chemotaxonomy and phytochemical ecology of bracken. Bot. J. Linn. Soc., 73, 35-46

8) Cooper-Driver G, Finch S, Swain T and Bernays E (1977) Seasonal variation in secondary plant compounds in relation to the palatability of Pteridium aquilinum. Biochem, Syst. Ecol., 5, 211-218

9) Cooper-Driver G (1985) Anti-predation strategies in pteridophytes - a biochemical approach. Proc. Roy. Soc. Edinb. Pteridophyte Biology Symposium Volume: 86B: 397-402

10) Scott A C, Chaloner W G and Paterson S (1985) Evidence of pteridophyte-arthropod interactions in the fossil record. Proc. Roy. Soc. Edinb. Pteridophyte Biology Symposium Volume: 86B: 133-140

11) Manton I (1950) Problems of Cytology and Evolution in the Pteridophyta. London and New York: Cambridge University Press

12) Walker T G (1979) The cytogenetics of ferns, In A F Dyer (ed.) The Experimental Biology of Ferns. London and New York: Academic Press, 87-132

13) Page C N (1982) The history and spread of bracken in Britain. Proc. Roy. Soc. Edinb., 81B, 3-10

14) Gliessman S R and Muller C H (1972) The phytotoxic potential of bracken, Pteridium aquilinum (L.) Kuhn. Madrono, 21: 299-304

15) Gliessman S R (1976) Allelopathy in a broad spectrum of environments as illustrated by bracken. Bot. J. Linn. Soc., 73, 95-104

16) Frankland J C (1976) Decomposition of bracken litter. Bot. J. Linn. Soc., 73, 133-143

17) Bohm B A and Tryon R M (1967) Phenolic compounds in ferns. 1. A survey of some ferns for cinnamic acid and benzoic acid derivatives. Can. J. Bot., 45, 585-594

18) Page C N (1982) The Ferns of Britain and Ireland. London, New York, Sydney: Cambridge University Press

19) Levy E B (1923) The grasslands of New Zealand II. The Taranaki Buck Country. N.Z. J. Agric., 27, 138-156

20) Numata M (1974) Grassland vegetation, In M Numata (ed.) The Flora and Vegetation of Japan, 125-149 London and New York: Elsevier

21) Page C N (1979) The diversity of ferns - an ecological perspective. In A F Dyer (ed.) The Experimental Biology of Pteridophytes, 9-56 London and New York: Academic Press

22) Conway E (1949) The autecology of bracken (Pteridium aquilinum (L.) Kuhn). The germination of the spores, the development of the prothallus and the young sporophyte. Proc. Roy. Soc. Edinb., 63, 325-343

23) Watt A S (1976) The ecological status of bracken. Bot. J. Linn. Soc., 73, 217-239

24) Oinonen E (1967) The correlation between the size of Finnish bracken (Pteridium aquilinum (L.) Kuhn) clones and certain periods of site history. Acta For. Fenn., 83, 1-51

25) Dyer A F (1984) Personal communication

26) Poel L W (1951) Soil aeration in relation to Pteridium aquilinum (L.) Kuhn. J. Ecol., 39, 182-191

27) Poel L W (1961) Soil aeration as a limiting factor in the growth of Pteridium aquilinum. J. Ecol., 49, 107-111

28) Fletcher W W and Kirkwood R C (1979) The bracken fern (Pteridium aquilinum (L.) Kuhn); its biology and control. In A F Dyer. The Experimental Biology of Ferns, 591-636, London and New York: Academic Press

29) Darwin F (1877) An appendix on the nectar-glands of the common bracken fern, Pteris aquilina. J. Linn. Soc. Bot., 15, 398-409

30) Schremmer F (1969) Extranuptiale Nectarien. Beobachtungen on Salix eleganos Scop. and Pteridium aquilinum (L.) Kuhn. Ost. Bot. Zeit., 117, 205-222

31) Page C N (1982) Field observations on the nectaries of bracken, Pteridium aquilinum, in Britain. Fern Gaz., 12, 233-240

32) Cooper-Driver G and Swain A (1976) Cyanogenic polymorphism in bracken in relation to herbivore predation. Nature, 260, 604

33) Hadfield P and Dyer A F (1986) Polymorphism of Cyanogenesis in British populations of bracken. (This volume)

34) Cook G T, Stephen N H and Duncan H J (1982) Fundamental studies in bracken control - the use of additives to enhance herbicide uptake and translocation. Proc. Roy. Soc. Edinb., 81B, 97-109

35) Heywood B J (1982) Bracken control by asulam. Proc. Roy. Soc. Edinb., 81B, 111-116

36) Martin D J and Sparke C J (1982) Field trials in south-west Scotland. Proc. Roy. Soc. Edinb., 81B, 117-123

37) Scragg E B (1982) The bracken problem and its control in northern Scotland. Proc. Roy. Soc. Edinb., 81B, 125-134

38) Taylor J A (1980) Bracken: an increasing problem and a threat to health. Outl. Agric., 10, 298-304

39) Williams G H (1980) Bracken Control - A Review of Progress 1974-1979. West of Scotland Agricultural College Research and Development Publication No 12

Studies on the dynamics of Bracken in Breckland

R H Marrs and M J Hicks

INTRODUCTION

It is generally accepted by ecologists that bracken is primarily a woodland species and is therefore a component of climax communities. However, bracken now has an extensive distribution outside woodland and this spread is usually considered to be a consequence of the destruction of the climax community and its subsequent management by man[1]. Several simple models can be used to illustrate the types of vegetation succession that could occur after forest destruction, including: (1) A secondary succession leading back to a woodland climax community. (2) A secondary succession which is arrested either by changed biotic processes[2] or by man's intervention, for example using fire, grazing or cutting[3]. (3) A succession with bracken as a major component in the early stages. Bracken, as an aggressive species, may inhibit the invasion of shrubs and trees so that it could be considered a climax community in its own right.

Unfortunately, we do not know which of these three models is most appropriate for given situations, and we do not understand the underlying processes or the factors controlling them. Clearly, it is essential to understand the dynamics of bracken in relation to other communities if we are to manage our natural resources wisely. The study of dynamics of long-lived species such as bracken is extremely difficult, requiring detailed, long-term observations. In the Brecklands of East Anglia, a great deal of information on the ecology of bracken has been collected since the 1930s, by A S Watt. From these studies, Watt has proposed several hypotheses concerning bracken dynamics and its relationship with other communities, which may help us to understand the role of bracken in succession. Three hypotheses will be considered here:

(1) Bracken (<u>Pteridium aquilinum</u>) and heather (<u>Calluna vulgaris</u>) in adjoining areas may show phasic interdigitation, resulting in stability between the two communities[2].

(2) Bracken communities show cyclic changes between dense bracken

and grass heath [1,2,4,5,6,7].

(3) Trees do not invade dense bracken, but may invade once bracken degeneration occurs[1].

The aim of this paper is to review briefly the evidence for these three hypotheses, and to test them in relation to recent studies of vegetation change at Watt's major study site, Lakenheath Warren. Their relevance to land management will also be discussed.

HYPOTHESIS 1:   BRACKEN AND CALLUNA FORM STABLE RELATIONSHIPS

This first hypothesis concerns competition between bracken and Calluna in adjoining communities. Watt[2] showed, from a study of life histories and structural changes in both bracken and Calluna on a blowout at Lakenheath Warren, that there was some degree of phasic interdigitation between bracken and Calluna; with advance of bracken into pioneer and degenerate Calluna, but retreat from building and mature Calluna. The overall effect was stability, suggesting that biotic processes were sufficient to arrest the secondary succession. To test the validity of this hypothesis, changes in the vegetation of Watt's original plot between 1955 and 1984 will be considered.

Results

In 1955, Watt[2] described the study area in four parts:
(1) Callunetum with Calluna in all phases of its growth cycle, viz. pioneer (15-20%), building (37-49%), mature (26-28%), and degenerate (10-15%). By 1969 there had been a shift in the age structure, with 20% pioneer, 5% building, 13% mature and 62% degenerate[7] (Fig 1).
(2) Bracken-north (BN). Pure bracken on the higher ground, and mixed bracken/Calluna elsewhere.
(3) Bracken-east (BE). Bracken with occasional Calluna.
(4) Bracken-west (BW). Callunetum with sparse and occasional bracken patches.

In 1984, there was still a fairly sharp transition between the bracken and open heath on the eastern and northern boundaries, but bracken covered the rest of the area including BW where Calluna was dominant in 1954. The open heath outside the blowout (Callunetum in 1954) was mainly grass heath (Deschampsia flexuosa and Festuca ovina) intermixed with dead Calluna and a few pioneer Calluna plants. Bracken is prevented from invading this grass heath by the micro-relief interacting with frost. Very little Calluna remained in the understorey of the bracken communities across the central area. Apart from a very small patch of building/mature Calluna near the eastern front, no post-pioneer Calluna was found under bracken, and none in the area described by Watt as being Callunetum with sparse or occasional bracken (BW). A few individuals of pioneer Calluna were found in the sparse bracken and the open grass heath communities, with 20 and 50 plants/ha present respectively, but no pioneer Calluna was found under dense bracken.

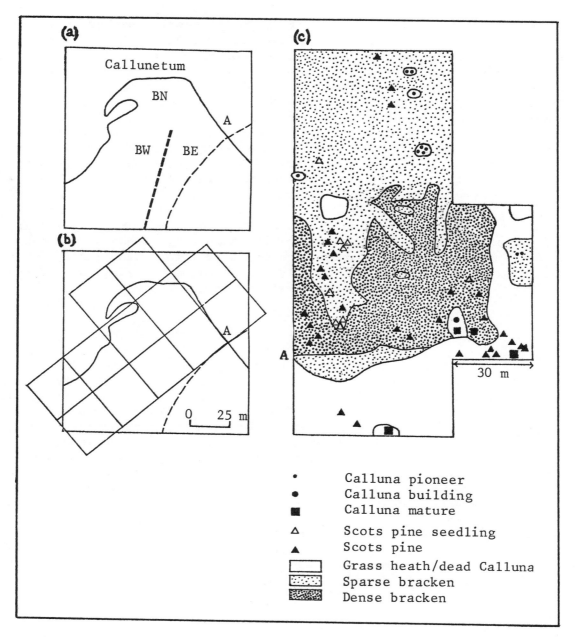

FIGURE 1   Maps of the bracken versus Calluna area: (a) Watt's 1955
            map; (b) area mapped in 1984; (c) 1984 vegetation map

Discussion

     The bracken and Calluna communities are clearly not in long-
term equilibrium in this area, and the situation described by Watt[2],
where the bracken and Calluna are in phasic interdigitation has broken
down in less than thirty years.   However, the phenomenon of
interdigitation can still be observed on a small scale elsewhere at
Lakenheath Warren (R H Marrs, unpubl.), and it is possible that the
apparent stability represented only a temporary check in the

succession from Calluna heath towards bracken. Nevertheless, the hypothesis that adjoining communities of bracken and Calluna can co-exist in the long-term must be rejected for this site.

Reasons for this breakdown in stability remain unclear. The bracken may simply have advanced into the Calluna and killed it. However, this has not been established and there are several other possible explanations: (1) that the small bracken population found in 1955 has increased along a similar cyclic succession proposed for bracken and grass heath; (2) that a reduction in competition from Calluna following a massive decline in Calluna numbers would allow bracken to increase. Large reductions in Calluna populations are quite common in Breckland following either cold winters (eg 1963[2]), or hot, dry summers (eg 1976) (R H Marrs, unpubl.). It is also possible (3) that grazing pressure may be an important complicating factor influencing the breakdown of stability. When Watt did his study in 1955, there was grazing pressure from sheep and rabbits, but sheep grazing was removed in 1956, and rabbit grazing was reduced following the introduction of myxomatosis in the 1950s[8].

HYPOTHESIS 2: BRACKEN COMMUNITIES SHOW CYCLIC CHANGES

From several detailed studies of the morphology of bracken fronds and rhizomes across bracken fronts, Watt postulated that bracken followed a cyclic succession (Figure 2), through building, mature and degenerate phases. The aim here is to test whether this cyclic succession can still be found at Lakenheath Warren, and to determine its scale. To do this a series of bracken distribution and density maps were produced[9] from aerial photographs taken in 1918/22 (composite for both years), 1946, 1968 (verified against a field survey in 1971[10]) and 1979 (updated by intensive field survey in 1984). Bracken densities were ranked on the following scale (calibrated 1984) (1) sparse bracken/grass heath < 1 frond/m^2, frond height 25 cm. (2) Intermediate bracken density 1-5 fronds/m^2, frond height 25-75 cm. (3) Dense bracken > 5 fronds/m^2, frond height 75 cm. (4) Mosaic of densities (3) interspersed with pockets of (1) and (2).

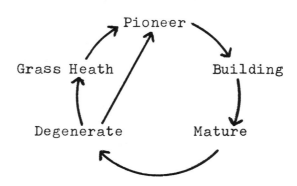

FIGURE 2   Watt's proposed cyclic succession in bracken

186

Results

There was little increase in the area occupied by bracken between 1918/22 and 1984 (Table 1) with a measured increase of only 24 ha (12% or 0.2%/year). Moreover, as part of the south-western boundary was not clearly visible in the 1918/22 photographs, this figure may be an overestimate of bracken advance. Between 1968 and 1984, there has only been an increase of 10 ha (4.5% or 0.5%/year). There have, however, been marked changes in bracken densities through time, the most striking being the dramatic reduction in dense bracken between 1968 and 1984, with a corresponding increase in the sparse bracken/grass heath category (Figure 3). The 1968 maps show small areas of sparse bracken/grass heath and intermediate density bracken in the middle of an almost complete cover of dense bracken. It is possible that these small patches have coalesced and enlarged. Similarly, the 1984 maps show that the sparse bracken/grass heath is often surrounded by bracken of intermediate density, and it is possible that degeneration to sparse bracken/grass heath will continue to spread outwards. It is important to note that this degeneration from dense bracken cannot be attributed to bracken control nor to errors in aerial photo-interpretation since the 1968 and 1984 maps were verified in the field.

TABLE 1   Changes in area (ha) and proportional status of bracken at Lakenheath Warren (512 ha) between 1918/22 and 1984

Bracken status	1918/22	1946	1968	1984
No bracken	2.0	1.6	12.8	5.3
Sparse/grass heath	28.5	9.8	7.8	91.7
Intermediate	52.6	64.4	6.2	27.2
Dense	98.7	138.3	179.4	86.5
Mosaic	24.2	-	13.8	19.3
Total	206	214.1	220	230

Discussion

Watt detected the cyclic changes in bracken on a relatively small scale, using transects up to 100 m long, and in one study all five phases could be mapped within a 30 m x 30 m grid[4,5,6]. The present study has shown that, in the absence of management, the entire central portion of the bracken patch present in 1968 has changed into sparse bracken/grass heath, showing bracken degeneration on a large scale (> 90 ha). Thus, the hypothesis that dense bracken degenerates to grass heath appears valid, and operates on a scale much larger than

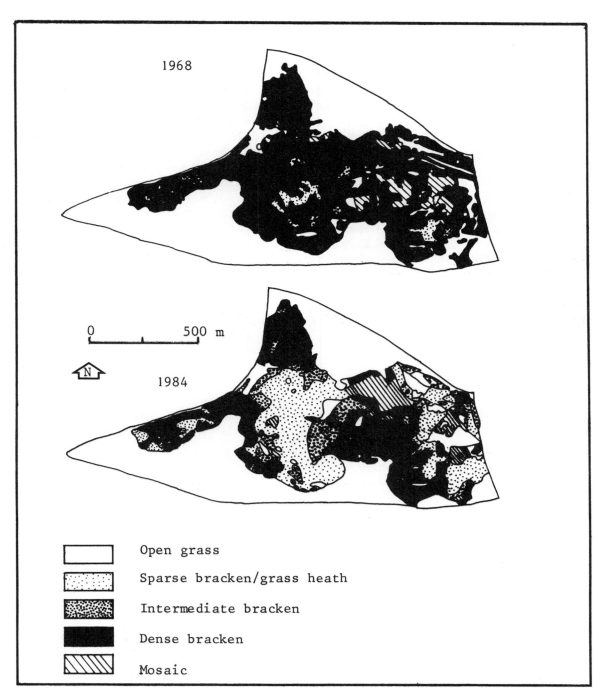

1968

0   500 m

N

1984

Open grass

Sparse bracken/grass heath

Intermediate bracken

Dense bracken

Mosaic

FIGURE 3   Distribution of different densities of bracken in 1968
            and 1984 at Lakenheath Warren

originally   thought.   However, it is important to note that the sparse
bracken/grass   heath phase is, as the description implies, not free of
bracken,   and   it   is   possible   that   its density in these areas will
increase   in   the future.   Further monitoring is required to test this
hypothesis.
        This massive degeneration of dense bracken to sparse bracken/

grass heath has significance for applied ecologists working in two main areas of bracken research. First, for assessing bracken encroachment, where usually only the distribution of fronds above ground is mapped. Failure to identify land in the degenerate phase may ·provide serious overestimates of encroachment rate once recovery occurs. For example, Watt[1] stated that "large areas of Calluna may have rare fronds, or none at all, but the presence and indeed, abundance of bracken is established by its remains under the Calluna mor". This presence of bracken at low abundance and its subsequent recovery may be one of the reasons for bracken densities to increase rapidly[11]. However, this is not true encroachment, where colonization must occur either from bracken fronts or from establishing prothalli, but regeneration of an already established bracken area. From a management point of view the result may be the same - dense bracken - but the biological and ecological interpretation is fundamentally different. It is essential, therefore, that when encroachment rates are calculated, historical information on bracken distribution, or present-day studies of the rhizome distribution in the area where bracken is encroaching, should be considered. Secondly, these findings have relevance for assessing the sustainable yield of bracken for use as biofuel[12,13]. Calculations of potential sustainable yields are usually based on short-term experiments ($\underline{c}$. 3-5 years) on dense bracken stands. These assume that the bracken system is in a steady-state, and does not degrade from a dense stand to a grassland ecosystem. Where cyclic succession to grass heath occurs, the calculated sustainable yield could not be achieved over the entire areas on a long-term basis. The loss of a large portion (c. 90 ha at Lakenheath Warren) of the most productive bracken must affect yield predictions. However, it is also possible that a rotational cutting system, which removes the litter layer, may rejuvenate the bracken by stimulating new frond buds[14,15], thus maintaining the stand in a more productive phase.

HYPOTHESIS 3: TREE INVASION DEPENDS ON BRACKEN DEGENERATION

If bracken is a step in succession to woodland, then trees must be able to invade dense bracken. However, it is often suggested that dense stands of clonal species inhibit succession[16,17]. Two questions therefore need to be answered. Firstly, is succession inhibited because trees are prevented from invading into dense bracken? Secondly, does cyclic bracken degeneration facilitate tree invasion? To answer these questions, two investigations were carried out. First, maps of Scots pine distribution were produced for 1971, based on the 1968 aerial photographs plus field survey in 1971[10], and 1984, based on 1978 photographs plus field survey in 1984. The canopy cover of Scots pine was assessed from the photographs, using a ranked canopy cover scale: 0, <10%, 11-30%, 31-60%, >60% and extended by field survey to include data on the distribution of small pines, invisible on the photographs; these data were included in the <10% canopy cover class. Second, the numbers of Scots pines were counted in plots established in four different communities, pioneer Calluna, building Calluna, sparse bracken and dense bracken.

Results

There has been substantial invasion by Scots pine since 1946, when the only trees were found around the Lodge (Point A; Fig 4) to

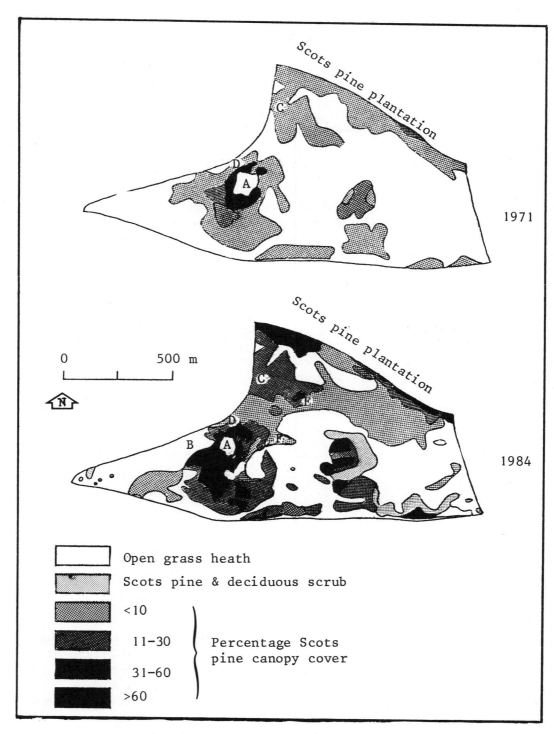

FIGURE 4   The distribution and canopy cover of Scots Pine at Lakenheath Warren in 1971 and 1984

190

286 ha or 56% of the site in 1984. The important point to note is that the Scots pine has invaded and grown to maturity in stands of dense bracken; for example, Point C at the north of the bracken patch, and Point D surrounding the Lodge. Both of these areas are near parent seed sources; Point C near the Scots pine plantation along the northern boundary and Point D near the shelterbelt around the Lodge. In 1971, both of these areas had abundant Scots pine seedlings, but as the pines could not be detected on the aerial photographs, they were presumably below the bracken canopy and detectable by field survey. By 1984, Scots pine was established, had overtopped the bracken, and achieved a canopy cover of at least 30%. Moreover, further invasion of dense bracken by pine had occurred by 1984 (Point E) as well as some spread into the sparse bracken/grass heath (Point F).

In the small study, no significant difference was found (ten observations) in frond density between the two bracken communities (dense = 12 $\pm$ 1.3/m^2; sparse = 15 $\pm$ 2.1/m^2; t = 1.2), but fronds in the dense community were taller (dense = 107 $\pm$ 5 cm; sparse = 65 $\pm$ 4 cm; t = 6.6, P = 0.001), and there was a greater litter cover (dense = 87 $\pm$ 5%; sparse = 42 $\pm$ 10%; t = 4.0; P = 0.01). Dead Calluna indicated its greater cover under both bracken communities in the past, but in 1984 its cover in the dense bracken community was very low (2%), and although greater in the sparse bracken community (18%), Calluna was mainly in the pioneer phase.

Scots pine of all size classes was found in each of these four plant communities (Table 2). There was no significant difference in the numbers of mature trees (>3.0 m tall) in each community but greater numbers of small trees (0.5-3.0 m) were found in the sparse bracken and pioneer Calluna than in the dense bracken and building Calluna. Scots pine seedlings were found in all four communities at low levels, the lowest in the building Calluna (2/m^2), and the highest in the sparse bracken community (5.5/m^2). No significant difference was found between seedling numbers in the sparse and dense bracken.

TABLE 2 Scots pine invasion at Lakenheath Warren

Community	Size Categories		
	<0.5 m* numbers/m^2	0.5-3.0 m numbers/300 m^2	>3.0 m numbers 300 m^2
Pioneer Calluna	2.0 $\pm$ 0.5	18	9
Building Calluna	3.0 $\pm$ 0.9	8	5
Sparse bracken	5.5 $\pm$ 2.1	25	7
Dense bracken	2.5 $\pm$ 1.1	4	17
x^2	-	20.2	2.1
		(P<0.001)	(ns)

*Mean values (n=10) $\pm$ standard error

Discussion

These results show that at Lakenheath Warren, Scots pine can invade and become established in dense bracken. Indeed, the limiting factor to Scots pine spread appears to be seed dispersal rather than the density of bracken canopy. The bracken at this site obviously does not inhibit succession to woodland so the initial hypothesis must be rejected. The model of inhibitory succession claimed as appropriate for certain dense clonal species is likewise not supported.

CONCLUSIONS

The results discussed here have profound implications both for theoretical studies of the role of bracken in succession and for the practical management of our natural resources. From a theoretical viewpoint, it has been shown that stability between bracken and Calluna may only be short-lived, bracken can degrade to grass heath, and succession to Scots pine woodland may proceed even in dense bracken. From a practical viewpoint, the degradation of bracken on a large scale is perhaps the most serious, as it may make the interpretation of bracken encroachment, and assessment of sustainable yield, more difficult. In addition, vegetation change brought about either by breakdown of stability along bracken fronts, or through succession to woodland, may have serious consequences for nature conservation.

ACKNOWLEDGEMENTS

We thank Mrs G Crompton and Mr R M Fuller for help with the interpretation of the aerial photographs, and Ms S Ide for drawing the figures. It is also a great pleasure to acknowledge the help of the late Dr A S Watt FRS, who provided access to his original data, and whose stimulating discussions led to most of this work. The work was supported by both Nature Conservancy Council and Suffolk Trust for Nature Conservation funds.

REFERENCES

1) Watt A S (1976) The ecological status of bracken. In F H Perring and B G Gardiner (eds) The biology of bracken, pp 217-240. London: Linnnean Society

2) Watt A S (1955) Bracken versus heather, a study in plant Sociology. J. Ecol., 43, 490-506

3) Gimingham C H (1972) Ecology of heathlands. London: Chapman and Hall

4) Watt A S (1945) Contributions to the ecology of bracken (Pteridium aquilinum). III. Frond types and the make-up of the population. New Phytol., 44, 156-178

5) Watt A S (1947a) Contributions to the ecology of bracken (Pteridium aquilinum). IV.. The structure of the community. New Phytol., 46 97-121

6) Watt A S (1947b) Pattern and process in the plant community. New Phytol., 35 1-22

7) Watt A S (1971) Factors controlling the floristic composition of some plant communities in Breckland. In E A Duffey and A S Watt (eds). The Scientific Managment of Animal and Plant Communities for Conservation, pp 137-152. Oxford: Blackwell Scientific Publications

8) Crompton G and Sheail J (1975) The historical ecology of Lakenheath Warren in Suffolk, England: a case study. Biol. Cons., 8, 299-313

9) Fuller R M (1983) Vegetation mapping of broadland using aerial photographs. Report to Broads Authority. Cambridge: Institute of Terrestrial Ecology

10) Crompton G (1972) Historical ecology of Lakenheath Warren: an historical study for ecologists. Report to the Nature Conservancy (typescript) 129 pp.

11) Taylor J A (1980) Bracken: an increasing problem and a threat to health. Outlook on Agric., 10, 298-304

12) Callaghan T V, Lawson G J, Scott R and Mainwaring A M (1984) An experimental assessment of native and naturalized plants as renewable sources of energy in Great Britain. Report to the UK Department of Energy. Cambridge: Institute of Terrestrial Ecology

13) Lawson G J, Callaghan T V and Scott R (1984) Renewable energy from plants: bypassing fossilization. Adv. Ecol. Res., 14, 57-114

14) Lowday J E, Marrs R H and Nevison G B (1983) Some of the effects of cutting bracken (Pteridium aquilinum (L.) Kuhn) at different times during the summer. J. Env. Man., 17, 373-380

15) Lowday J E (1986) The effects of pre-cutting on the performance of asulam on bracken. Weed Res. (In press)

16) Niering W A and Goodwin R H (1974) Creation of relatively stable shrublands with herbicides: arresting "succession" on rights-of-way and pastureland. Ecology, 55, 784-795

17) Finegan B (1984) Forest succession. Nature, 312, 109-114

Bracken on the Malvern Hills:
The influence of Topographic and Management Factors
on early-season Emergence and Biomass

T P Atkinson

INTRODUCTION

The Malvern Hills are a steep-sided ridge of Precambrian rocks which extend for 12km along a north-south axis. From an altitude of 425 km at the Worcestershire Beacon (SO 768452) there is a general descent of ridge top altitude southwards. In a previous study[1], plant communities were recorded at 293 sites along transects across the Hills. Of these sites, 70% were found to contain bracken (<u>Pteridium aquilinum</u> (L.) Kuhn) but at very different levels of abundance, especially in relation to altitude. Several features of the spatial pattern of bracken communities prompted further study. Firstly, bracken has a discontinuous distribution within its position intermediate between hill-top grasslands and hill-margin woodlands[2]; secondly, small-scale patterns, such as bracken rings, distinguish some interesting communities; and thirdly, the changing management of the Malvern Hills is a strong influence on the vegetation balance. The kaleidoscope of spatial patterns and seasonal changes in the bracken is a characteristic of the Malvern Hills, confirming the designation as an Area of Outstanding Natural Beauty (AONB).

BRACKEN AND ITS ENVIRONMENT

Alex S Watt studied the ecology of bracken in Breckland over many years[3]. By monitoring experimental and control plots, he established the effects of environmental variation through time on the morphology and behaviour of the bracken plant. He demonstrated the temporal and spatial characteristics[4] of bracken and the critical influence of frost[5] and drought episodes on its development phases[6]. Periodic disturbance of his permanent plots also enabled him to elucidate the influence of management[7] on bracken communities. Figure 1 is an attempt to relate Watt's conclusions to

195

the relationships expected between bracken and its natural and managed environment in the Malvern Hills AONB.

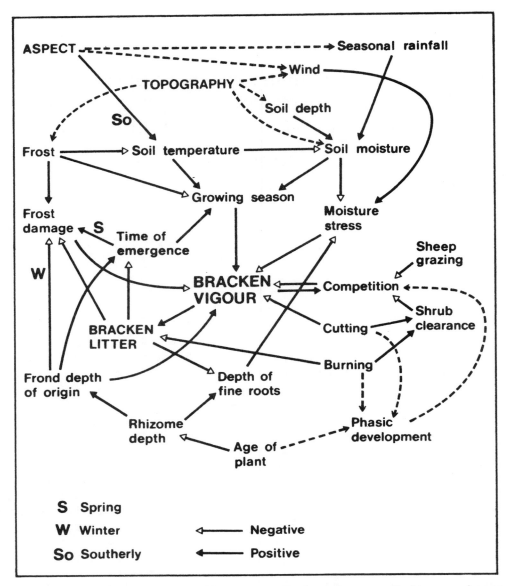

Figure 1   Interaction diagram of bracken and its environment. Relationships are shown by the arrows.

Topography and aspect

In the Malvern Hills many slopes are steep (Fig.2) and soils are thin, rich in angular stones, freely drained and leached. There are frequent rocky outcrops and nearby shallow soils are liable to moisture stress. In other localities, dense plant litter is moisture retentive, but moisture stress is induced by the strong winds crossing the isolated ridge of the Malvern Hills. Altitude influences the incidence and severity of frosts. Aspect, especially on steep slopes, affects soil temperatures via the receipt of direct solar radiation.

Bracken vigour

The response of bracken to its environment is influenced by the age and history of the plant. At the pioneer phase a deep set rhizome near the apex of a long shoot produces robust and early-emerging petioles (stems). At the building phase there is a greater density of rhizomes and petiole-bearing short shoots. Soil characteristics, especially soil volume, limit further increase of rhizome biomass in the mature phase with a tendency for the average depth of origin of petioles to decrease[8]. The development cycle may continue to the degenerate phase with senescence[9] of the plant leading to rhizome fragmentation, a decline of frond vigour and a decrease in the density of petioles. Where environmental conditions allow, re-invasion by pioneers may produce a stable, uneven-aged community.

The productivity of the bracken and the length of its growing season determine the annual production of bracken litter[10]. The rate of its decomposition[11] is slowed where a 'thatch' of dead, dry petioles is created by tall petioles snapping about mid-length in autumn. Litter provides a protective layer to frost, and may further reduce potential frost damage by inhibiting emergence, as it retards the rise of soil temperature in the spring. Late emergence, on the other hand, reduces potential photosynthesis. At the mature phase, many finer roots occupy the top of the mineral soil and extend into the bracken debris with a likely self-limiting effect on the nutrient status of the plant. Further, any disturbance, such as burning, exposes the shallow roots to frost or drought.

Bracken is an effective dominant on account of its competitive strategy[12] which includes its dense accumulation of persistent litter. Intraspecific competition between fronds and rhizomes is at a maximum at the mature stage of development and few competitors are likely to invade the community. The community can also rapidly recover from short term stress or damage through investment in storage rhizomes and dormant buds[13].

METHODS OF INVESTIGATION AND ANALYSIS

Sampling procedure

The 123 sites from the sample grid of the previous study covering the North Hill (397 m) - Worcestershire Beacon (425 m) - Perseverance Hill (325 m) areas (Fig.2) were visited from 11-15 May and 7-11 June 1985. In addition, sites along transects with southerly and south-easterley aspects that were otherwise poorly represented were visited, to provide a total sample of 136. Environmental factors such as slope and aspect were noted in May 1985, whilst the morphology and density of emerged petioles were recorded as identified in 1m square quadrats. Petioles (cut at their junction with the rhizome) were harvested from a 0.25 m square area and an F and L layer litter sample was taken from a quarter of that area. Pegs were placed to mark the position of quadrats. Similar petiole data were subsequently collected from an adjacent square in June. As soon as possible, and always within 60 hours of collection, the stems, stem bases and fronds were measured and weighed. Samples were sealed in plastic bags with as much air as possible removed and were stored in a cool place.

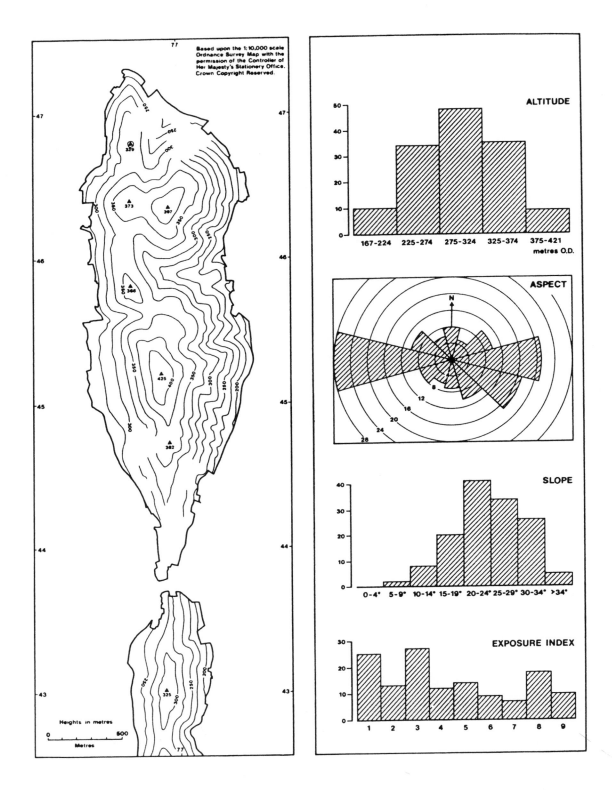

Figure 2   The northern Malvern Hills with the distribution of environmental variables across the sample of sites; vertical dimensions show the frequency of observations in each class.

Within a week of original collection, samples were dried at 110°C overnight and weighed.

Analysis

The analysis reported in this paper uses multiple correlation coefficients from a stepwise regression (SPSS). Dry and fresh biomass data and ratios of their components were entered as the dependent variables. Altitude and an index of exposure (Table 1) were estimated from 1:10,000 maps. Aspect was recorded on a 0-18 scale as 10° units from north. Aspect and slope values were entered as independent variables. Since biomass ratios cancel out the dependent relationship between litter and biomass, the analysis was also run with litter as an independent variable against each biomass ratio as a dependent variable.

TABLE 1   Derivation of the Exposure Index

Value	Qualifying site characteristics
1	Lower altitude valley; woodland
2	Lower altitude shallow slopes
3	Lower altitude steep slopes; mid-altitude valley
4	Upper valley; low altitude spur
5	Upper slopes (above 350 m)
6	Higher altitude valley head; below higher altitude spur
7	On higher altitude spur, or some way below main ridge
8	Below the main ridge
9	On the main ridge and above 330 m

RESULTS AND DISCUSSION

The effect of altitude on biomass, density and vigour

Negatively correlated with all May and June biomass components, including the vigour of the largest and average shoot, is altitude. This is commonly entered into the multiple regression at step 1 (Table 2). An increase in altitude produces a lower biomass with less vigorous vertical shoots. A similar but weaker trend in the biomass of persistent litter suggests that this relationship is present in the community throughout the year. Indeed, the effects are cumulative, as the relative increase of biomass from May to June is also negatively correlated with altitude. It is not necessarily expected that altitudinal constraints on photosynthesis, due to lower temperatures, will operate through the summer, but the shorter effective growing season at higher altitudes will have a persistent effect on biomass.

199

TABLE 2 Multiple correlation coefficients

Dependent variable	Independent variables					
	Step 1		Step 2		Step 3	
	Var	r1	Var	r2	Var	r3
June biomass (dry weight)						
Petiole base (a)	Alt	.40				
Petiole stem (b)	Alt	.49	Asp	.55		
Total petiole	Alt	.48	Asp	.53		
Frond (c)	Asp	.38	Alt	.49		
Total shoot	Alt	.44	Asp	.53		
Average shoot	Alt	.55	Sl	.59	Asp	.61
Heaviest shoot	Alt	.54	Sl	.56	Asp	.58
May biomass (dry weight)						
Total shoot	Alt	.43	Asp	.49		
Average shoot	Alt	.59				
Litter	Alt	.34				
Density						
Petioles/m^2 (June)	Asp	.31	Alt	.39		
Petioles/m^2 (May)	Asp	.35				
Biomass ratios (June)						
Frond: petiole stem	Sl	.22	Asp	.28		
Frond: total petiole	Asp	.29	Sl	.38		
Petiole: total petiole	Alt	.50	Sl	.56	Asp	.60
Frond: total shoot	Sl	.32	Asp	.41		
May: June ratios						
Total shoot	Alt	.39				
Petioles/m^2	Alt	.36				
Average shoot	Alt	.39				

All correlations are significant at 99% probability. Alt = Altitude, Asp = Aspect, Sl = Slope, Var = Variable.

The effect of aspect

The highest correlation with bracken density (shoots/m^2) is southerly aspect, moderated by altitude at step 2 of the regression. Since by early June not all bracken has emerged, especially at higher altitudes, aspect may primarily be affecting rates of emergence, and so it can be postulated that bracken density will be explained more fully by altitude later in the season. On the other hand, an increase in shoot density may be an alternative competitive strategy to an increase in shoot robustness. Other variables in the analysis clarify some of the relationships between density, production and rate of emergence. The first point to note is the one exception to the primacy of altitude in the explanation of biomass variables, that is, the role of aspect in the explanation of frond biomass. This may be taken as the effect of fronds unfurling relatively early so that at a given time a higher proportion of the shoot biomass is concentrated in the photosynthesing pinnae. This is confirmed by the frond: total petiole ratio. Whether this early, aspect-related advantage will be maintained through the summer season of peak production is uncertain, since factors such as moisture stress are likely to be correlated with aspect to limit production. Where moisture stress operates in drier months, a high density of less robust shoots may prove a viable strategy, by maintaining the capture of photosynthates in the favourable early part of the growing season.

The effect of slope and shelter/exposure

The vigour of bracken shoots as measured by average shoot biomass and maximum (individual) shoot biomass is primarily negatively correlated with altitude and secondarily with slope. The single correlation coefficients show that the general relationship of shoot biomass with slope is positive. Because of the association of steeper slopes with mid-altitudes, this relationship is expected, but was not predicted after removal of the altitudinal effect at step 1 in the regression. As many of the steepest slopes are in hillside valleys, it is postulated that the increase of bracken vigour is associated with these steep-sided valleys and is accounted for by their greater shelter. This effect is not distinguished by the exposure index used in this study (Table 1), because the high correlation of the index with altitude reduces its efficacy. The situation is described further by the incorporation of aspect at step 3 of the regression. This is interpretable as the favourable influence of southerly aspect on the more sheltered localities at a given altitude.

This interpretation may be extended to each of the frond biomass ratios. Favourable shelter and aspect thus account for the early concentration of biomass into the frond component and lead to an early season advantage in resource capture by photosynthesis. Confirmation of these results requires a more precise index of shelter/exposure, and measurements of microclimate at a later date are proposed to this end. These and soil moisture measurements should clarify the effects of altitude, aspect and slope on environmental variation.

The effect of litter

Litter, as an independent variable, only influences one variable, the petiole: total petiole ratio, with a correlation of .59. While the petiole: total petiole ratio increases with earlier emergence and growth (as do other ratios), the distinctive position of litter may be attributable to its association with the mature phase of bracken communities where the base of the vertical shoot is at a shallow depth. The result is a greater petiole: total petiole ratio at a given stage of emergence.

The effect of management

The success of bracken is often attributed to habitat opportunities created by man[14]. The removal of woodland cover on the Malvern Hills has been a gradual and incomplete process. It had started at least by the Iron Age when hilltop camps were constructed on Midsummer Hill and the Herefordshire Beacon. Through the Middle Ages, Malvern Chase was protected for deer, with common rights permitting the grazing of pigs and cattle. Sheep grazing was illegal before Elizabethan times. Common rights remained after the area's deforestation in 1664[15].

Although few commoners exercise grazing rights today, their flocks of sheep maintain grassland communities. Rabbit populations are also recovering following the myxomatosis pandemic. Traditional commonland management included the removal of bracken litter for animal bedding and composting. This practice had ceased by 1940 and local people report an increased bracken dominance in recent years.

The Malvern Hills Conservators actively manage the vegetation. Controlled burning is practised in selected areas to the end of March, given sufficiently dry weather. The aims are to reduce the likelihood of summer fires and to control invasive scrub. A mowing policy is being developed which demands an increased investment in machinery and man-hours. The edges of hillside paths are cut in summer, while the creation of fire breaks and more general clearance and mowing of selected slopes is performed in late autumn and winter.

Bracken recovers well from burning. Its competitor, rosebay willow herb (Chamaenerion angustifolium) spreads on burnt ground. Interestingly, it tends to invade the older stages of bracken rings at lower altitudes. This is in contrast to the grass infilling of such rings that accentuates their prominence at higher altitudes. On burnt ground, bracken petioles emerge earlier and fronds unfurl earlier, the blackened, litter-free soil leading to a more rapid warming of soil in spring. Bracken fronds are dwarfed in the short term, but after 2-3 years the community produces robust petioles at relatively low density in a community with a carpet of creeping soft-grass (Holcus mollis). The summer fire in Wide and Firs valleys (SO 7740 NW) in July 1984 produced a notable response: weak petioles emerged and rapidly unfurled in the late summer. Fronds remained green in mild weather to the beginning of November, in marked contrast to the bronzed fronds of unaffected areas.

Mowing reduces bracken thatch while comminuting its litter. For reasons not yet understood, bracken emergence is often retarded. There is also evidence of greater damage by trampling in mown areas.

202

CONCLUSIONS

The semi-natural vegetation of the Malvern Hills is determined by the environmental variation of different topographic habitats. Bracken communities exemplify this variation. Altitude and aspect are important controls on the morphology and biomass of emergent and early-season bracken. Slope, exposure and shelter are locally important. Not all the recorded variation is explained by the general parameters analysed. Subsequent study will focus on the effects of temperature, moisture and management as well as the seasonal cycle of the bracken community.

The Malvern Hill Conservators are confronted by difficult decisions over the most effective means of managing such common land in an Area of Outstanding Natural Beauty. On the one hand the area must be managed so as both to safeguard common rights of grazing and to prevent invasion by woody scrub species. On the other hand, dry persistent bracken litter is, according to local experience, an asset in the management of vegetation by fire while bracken itself contributes in a major way to the natural beauty of the area. No policy of progressive bracken control is therefore currently envisaged.

ACKNOWLEDGEMENTS

I am most grateful to the Malvern Hills Conservators for permission for the field studies and for the friendly assistance of their staff. Jean and John Mobbs kindly accommodated me and my laboratory at Rock House. My thanks are also due to David Lawes who drew the figures, Nicola Pope who typed my manuscript, Dr Paul Burrin, Dr Richard Gulliver and my wife, Carol, who made helpful comments on the text.

REFERENCES

1) Atkinson T P (1984) Plant communities on the Malvern Hills. Trans. Worc. Nat. Club N.S., 1 (4), 237-246

2) Salisbury E J and Tansley A G (1921) The Durmast oakwoods of the Silurian and Malvernian strata near Malvern. J. Ecol., 9, 19-38

3) Watt A S (1964) Some factors affecting bracken in Breckland. J. Ecol., 52, 63-77

4) Watt A S (1947) Contributions to the ecology of bracken (Pteridium aquilinum). IV. The structure of the community. New Phytol., 46, 97-121

5) Watt A S (1950) Contributions to the ecology of bracken (Pteridium aquilinum). V. Bracken and frost. New Phytol., 49, 308-327

6) Watt A S (1945) Contributions to the ecology of bracken (Pteridium aquilinum). III. Frond types and the make-up of the population. New Phytol., 44, 156-178

7) Watt A S (1956)   Contributions to the ecology of bracken (Pteridium aquilinum).   VII. Bracken and litter. 1. The origin of rings. New Phytol., 55, 369-381

8) Watt A S (1969)   Contributions to the ecology of bracken (Pteridium aquilinum). VII. Bracken and litter. 2. Crown form. New Phytol., 68, 841-859

9) Watt A S (1971)   Contributions to the ecology of bracken (Pteridium aquilinum). VIII. The marginal and the hinterland plant: a study in senescence. New Phytol., 70, 967-986

10) Watt A S (1976) The ecological status of bracken. Bot. J. Linn. Soc., 73, 217-239

11) Frankland J C (1976) Decomposition of bracken litter. Bot. J. Linn. Soc., 73, 133-143

12) Grime J P (1979)   Plant strategies and Vegetation Processes. Chichester and London: John Wiley and Sons

13) Williams G H and Foley A (1976)   Seasonal variations in the carbohydrate content of bracken. Bot. J. Linn. Soc., 73, 87-93

14) Page C N (1982) The history and spread of bracken in Britain. Proc. Roy. Soc. Edinb., 81B (1-2), 3-10

15) Smith B S (1964)   A History of Malvern. Leicester: Leicester University Press

The structure of a grazed upland bracken (Pteridium aquilinum L. Kuhn) community

H C Lee, J A Cooke and T J Bines

INTRODUCTION

Established bracken in grazed upland pasture is regarded as a weed or pest species because it is associated with lower grazing potential[1] and toxicity[2]. In terms of the structure and dynamics of grazed upland bracken, various attributes may be regarded as favouring the establishment of bracken dominance (Table 1). This paper describes a field study on the structure of a grazed upland pasture in Teesdale, County Durham and seeks to investigate the

Table 1.

Biotic attributes tending to lead to an increase in bracken dominance of upland pasture.

1.   Decrease in competitive ability of underlying turf species.

1.1   Shading by bracken fronds

1.2   Direct shading and smothering by litter

1.3   Indirect effects of litter through increased acidification of

       soils and build up of organic surface horizons.

2.   Decrease in bracken frond mortality.

2.1   Unpalatability of bracken fronds relative to other plant

       species.

2.2   Litter build up to protect young emerged fronds from frost

2.3   Low grazing pressure minimising the physical damage of fronds by

       livestock through trampling.

relative importance of some of the biotic interactions implied by the attributes summarized in Table 1.

THE STUDY AREA

The study area covered approximately 90 hectares and lay within Woolly Hills Farm (National Grid Reference NZ 044 249) which is situated on Woodland Fell, County Durham at an altitude of 348 m. The area is used as open grazing for sheep and has a documented history of sheep farming for at least 150 years. A general survey of the vegetation (Fig.1) showed it to consist of a mosaic of Nardus stricta and Juncus squarrosus - dominated communities, with bracken on better-drained, mainly south-east facing slopes. In poorly-drained, low-lying areas Juncus effusus - Sphagnum spp. were dominant. There were 13 separate stands of bracken with a wide range of frond densities from $1-2/m^2$ to >100. This discontinuity of bracken cover is thought to be long established. A more extensive site description is given elsewhere[3].

FLORISTIC COMPOSITION AND STRUCTURE

The relative frequency of plant species was compared with bracken frond characters and soil factors. Eight bracken stands were selected to cover the range of frond densities found at the site. A transect was selected randomly to traverse each stand, comprising 0.5m square quadrats, 10 m apart. Bracken frond densities, and height (to the uppermost branch of the petiole), rooted frequencies of other plant species, soil surface pH and organic matter content, were measured in each quadrat during August.

The soils were acidic (pH 2.9 - 4.8) and showed a wide range of organic matter content (9 - 94%); bracken frond density (8 - $100/m^2$) and heights (13 - 155 cm) also covered a wide range. A total of 21 plant species were recorded; those with the highest frequencies (Deschampsia flexuosa, Agrostis tenuis, Festuca ovina, Anthoxanthum odoratum, and Nardus stricta) are grasses characteristic of species - poor, acid grassland. The data from the 57 quadrats were further examined by rearrangement of species and samples in tabular form[4]. This indicated that the vegetation was a continuum between two relatively distinct groups of quadrats at either extreme. These two groups can be considered separately and are designated Nodum 1 and Nodum 2. Nodum 1 was characterised by the relatively high rooted frequency of A. tenuis, F. ovina, A. odoratum and N. stricta. These were associated with relatively short, sparse bracken fronds on a soil of medium organic matter content. Nodum 2 generally contained high frequencies of D. flexuosa and showed an absence of the species characteristic of Nodum 1. Bracken cover for Nodum 2 was dense and tall, with a deep litter layer overlying soil of higher organic matter content and lower pH.

Figure 2 shows a simple ordination of these quadrats using dissimilarity coefficients based on the rooted frequency of species[5]. The distribution of quadrats in two dimensions can be over-layed by various factors which allows the vegetational and environmental pattern to be compared. The highest percentage rooted

206

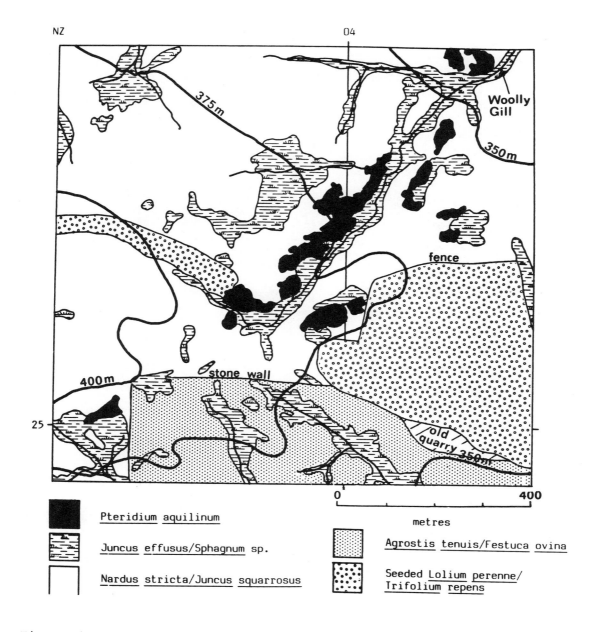

NZ   04

375 m

Woolly
Gill

350 m

fence

stone wall

400 m

25

old
quarry 350 m

0   400

metres

■ *Pteridium aquilinum*

Juncus effusus/Sphagnum sp.

Nardus stricta/Juncus squarrosus

Agrostis tenuis/Festuca ovina

Seeded *Lolium perenne/Trifolium repens*

Figure 1   Vegetation Map of the Study Area.

frequency for *D. flexuosa* was associated with low frequency of *F. ovina*, low pH values and high soil organic matter. Surprisingly, frond density and frond height did not seem to determine the pattern shown in the major grass species and could suggest that soil factors are ultimately more important in determining the floristic composition of this community.

THE BIOMASS STRUCTURE

Fourteen, 0.5 m square quadrats were chosen, on a subjective

207

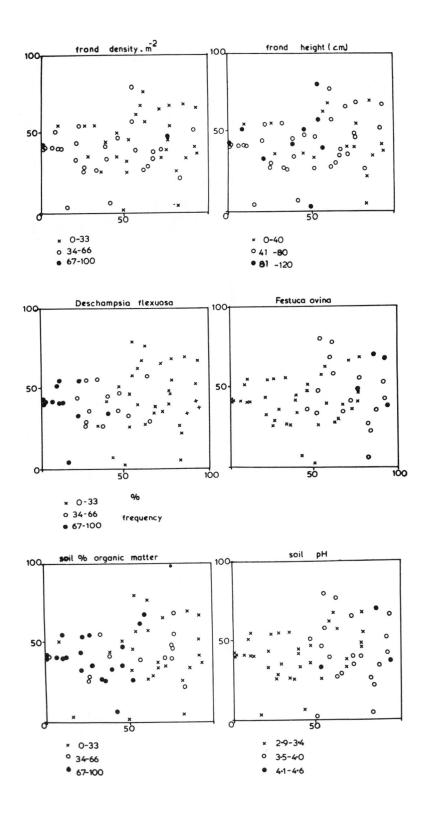

Figure 2   Polar Ordination.   Quantitative distribution of characteristics for bracken frond, other species and soil.

basis, to be representative of the range of bracken frond densities and heights. In each quadrat, all above-ground and below-ground biomass was excavated in August. A summary of the data is shown in Table 2.

TABLE 2   Means and ranges for compartments of biomass and other measurements
(n = 14)

	Measurement	Range			Mean (with standard error)
FROND	density (m^{2})	2	-	65	36 (6)
	height (cm)	19	-	73	48 (5)
	lamina dry wt g.m^{-2}	8.5	-	551.9	282.0 (52.7)
	petiole dry wt g.m^{-2}	1.5	-	216.0	94.6 (21.3)
	individual frond wt g.	19.0	-	72.6	47.7 (4.5)
	litter dry wt g.m^{-2}	0	-	4100	1082 (344)
SHORT-SHOOT RHIZOME	dry weight g.m^{-2}	8.0	-	495.8	208.7 (44.0)
	length m.m^{-2}	4.4	-	213.4	73.6 (17.2)
	no. unem. fronds .m^{-2}	0	-	42	6.7 (2.9)
	no. live buds .m^{-2}	5	-	132	82.2 (22.3)
	no. bud scars .m^{-2}	30	-	1358	471.6 (113.0)
LONG-SHOOT RHIZOME	dry weight g.m^{-2}	40.0	-	1421.4	684.4 (118.5)
	length m.m^{-2}	17.6	-	537.6	259.0 (48.6)
	no. unem. fronds .m^{-2}	0	-	16	3.5 (1.1)
	no. live buds .m^{-2}	0	-	88	24.7 (7.2)
	no. bud scars .m^{-2}	6	-	312	74.0 (22.2)
ASSOCIATED VEGETATION	shoot dry wt g.m^{-2}	76	-	4840	1735 (390)
	root dry wt g.m^{-2}	89	-	1210	504 (85)
SOIL	pH	3.1	-	4.1	3.6 (0.1)
	% organic matter	21	-	90	47 (7)

(BRACKEN)

Considering the mean value for each variable, a number of points can b made. The largest component of the bracken biomass was the litter, about three times the weight of the green fronds (lamina and petiole) which suggests a slow rate of decomposition. The amount of long and short-shoot rhizome below ground was considerable (> 300 m/m^2). Short-shoot rhizome accounted for 80% of frond production, as shown by the number of bud scars indicating the history of frond production. In terms of overall mean values the above-ground biomass of associated vegetation, mainly grasses, was considerably larger than that of bracken fronds. These data were analysed further by assessing the degree of correlation between the variables. The correlation matrix was simplified and summarized using Principal Components Analysis[6]. Collectively, components one and two account for 74 per cent of the variation (Table 3). One of the most surprising aspects of these data was that most variables, including frond density, were not significantly correlated with short-shoot rhizome variables. Thus, even though the majority of fronds developed on short-shoot rhizome, frond density was only significantly correlated with long-shoot rhizome characteristics. This paradox may be due to factors adversely affecting frond development and emergence from short-shoot rhizome. An analysis of the data comparing the total number of emerged and below-ground, unemerged but potential fronds ($x = 46.2/m^2$) with the total number of live buds ($x = 106.9/m^2$) and bud scars, ($x = 545.6 /m^2$) gave significant positive correlations ($r = 0.70$, $P < 0.01$; $r = 0.65$, $P < 0.01$ respectively). Thus, the total number of fronds is proportional to the number of live buds ie. the reservoir of recruitment to the frond population. It is still, however, difficult to make any conclusions about bud mortality as the category 'live buds' may represent an age group of more than one year. Thus if the buds took two or more years to develop, the mortality would appear to be low.

TABLE 3   Principal Components Analysis on a correlation matrix for partitions of biomass and other measurements.

		Component	1	2
		percentage of variation accounted for	45.7	27.9
BRACKEN		frond density .m^{-2}	0.36	0.05
		frond litter wt (g.m^{-2})	0.36	-0.07
	short-shoot rhizome	length (m.m^{-2})	0.06	0.49
		no. unem. fronds m^{-2}	-0.03	0.46
		no. live buds m^{-2}	0.04	0.50
		no. bud scars m^{-2}	0.05	0.48
	long-shoot rhizome	length (m.m^{-2})	0.33	0.09
		no. unem. fronds m^{-2}	0.29	0.07
		no. live buds m^{-2}	0.33	-0.05
		no. bud scars m^{-2}	0.30	-0.01
	Associated vegetation	shoot wt (g.m^{-2})	-0.34	-0.03
		root wt (g.m^{-2})	-0.19	0.18
	Soil	pH	-0.34	0.13
		% organic matter	0.25	0.07

Turf biomass was negatively, but significantly correlated with frond density $r = 0.9$, $p < 0.001$). Opposite signs between eigen vectors within component one (Table 3) indicate that this reduction in turf biomass is related to increasing frond density, litter weight, soil organic matter and long-shoot rhizome length. Turf biomass is also significantly positively correlated with soil pH ($r = 0.84$, $p < 0.01$).

SOME EFFECTS OF SHEEP ON BRACKEN COMMUNITY STRUCTURE

The presence of sheep in the study area may increase frond mortality and thus affect the dominance of bracken. A study of the mortality of fronds in fixed populations in the presence or absence of sheep was therefore carried out in one stand of bracken with a frond density of about $40/m^2$. A 15 x 15 metre area was enclosed by Flexi-Net electrified fencing, to prevent access by sheep. 15, one metre square quadrats were randomly chosen from a grid of 25 one metre square quadrats inside the exclosure and another similar grid outside. The latter was established to avoid any small areas used by sheep as overnight 'camp' sites[7] or which showed a concentration of faeces. In each quadrat, all emerging fronds were tagged from June onwards and periodically the number of surviving fronds and their heights were recorded. Frond mortality was consistently higher in the presence of sheep (Table 4). Measurement of height for tagged fronds which subsequently disappeared, indicated that in late June to early July, those in the presence of sheep were about half the height of those in the absence of sheep (Table 5). The shorter fronds which disappeared in the presence of sheep indicates that they were more likely to have been damaged as sheep pushed their way through the canopy. Frond damage and loss of tall fronds in the absence of grazing was probably due to the effect of high winds.

TABLE 4   Mortality for fronds in the presence or absence of livestock.

		Date and month of measurement			
		20.6	4.7	18.7	28.9
% mortality between dates of measurements	livestock present		14.2	22.0	11.0
	livestock absent		2.5	3.4	4.6

If such damage were an important factor affecting bracken vigour then some observable changes might be expected in the pattern of frond bud production on the rhizome. Six, 0.25 m square quadrats, linearly spaced 1 metre apart, were set up within the exclosure and another six were set up approximately 10 metres outside, where there was free access by sheep. In July, 15 months after the exclusion of sheep, each quadrat was excavated and the rhizome and aerial parts collected and measured for frond density, number of unemerged fronds, number of live buds, number of bud scars and total length of live and dead rhizome. The number of unemerged fronds and bud scars was the same in the presence or absence of sheep but the densities of live buds and unemerged fronds on short-shoot rhizome were significantly lower ($p < 0.01$) in the absence of sheep. This suggests a similar frond production history prior to the start of the treatment but that the exclusion of sheep may have reduced mortality during frond emergence so that fewer frond buds maintained the same population of emerged fronds.

TABLE 5   Mean frond height (mm) (with standard errors) at
          which fronds appear most likely to suffer damage.

(for n, see below)	Measurement interval (day and month)		
	20.6 to 4.7	4.7 to 18.7	18.7 to 28.9
Livestock present	318 (49)	574 (49)	599 (34)
Livestock absent	640 (16)	670 (93)	594 (52)
Effect due to livestock	***	N.S.	N.S.

N.S.   p>0.05 non significant

***   p<0.001

sample n for each interval, respectively : livestock present - 158,151,154

livestock absent - 118,152,147

DISCUSSION

These results show the overall decline in species richness and pasture grass biomass associated with increases in bracken frond density from <25 to <50 fronds/m^2. The species present in Nodum 1 are typical of species - poor upland grassland recorded for many other sites in Britain where bracken is absent[8,9] or of low density[10]. The changes with increasing bracken density recorded in this study are similar to those suggested for upland bracken communities in Scotland[11]. Species found in such communities are generally well adapted to acid, nutrient-deficient soils. It is, however, difficult to explain the differences in distribution of D. flexuosa and F. ovina, in terms of soil factors, as both are good competitors and able to grow at low nutrient levels[12,13]. It may be that D. flexuosa is favoured at high frond densities because of its greater ability to tolerate shade[14], caused particularly by the frond canopy. Bracken fronds and litter have been shown to have an allelopathic effect on underlying turf[15] and the relative magnitude of the effect of any such toxin release may affect the species composition of the underlying sward. From the data presented in this study it is difficult to separate the relative importance of the effects of the bracken canopy, litter deposition and soil factors. Competition, particularly for nutrients, by bracken long-shoot rhizome[16] may also be important in explaining the changes in the floristic structure and biomass of the underlying sward.

A maximum of 1400 sheep (3.2 sheep/ha) grazed the farm during the summer, constituting moderate grazing pressure[17]. Although direct grazing of fronds is well known[18], it was never observed in this study and the mortality of short fronds during the early stages of frond emergence (Table 4 & 5) was probably caused by sheep snapping or causing sufficient vascular damage to the frond petioles while in search of underlying pasture for grazing. It may be that the presence of sheep contributes to the maintenance of the two nodal extremes of

212

the floristic continuum and this is shown in schematic form in figure 3. The most attractive grazing was beneach sparse bracken which would encourage sheep and lead to an increased rate of frond mortality. While in the short term it would seem that bracken can compensate for such mortality by increasing frond bud production, it may be that in the long term, the effect on bracken vigour will be adverse.

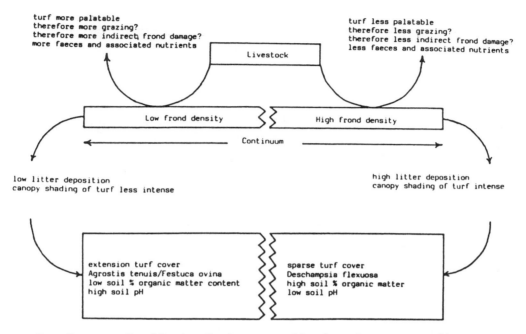

Figure 3   Proposed effect of sheep on the bracken community.

It is difficult to speculate from a single time-specific survey about how the present bracken community structure on this site has arisen. However, it would seem that there has been very little spatial change over at least the last 35 years in the discrete areas of bracken shown in Figure 1. Thus the model of cyclic vegetational change from pioneer to degenerate phases shown for Breckland[19] seems unlikely for this site. It may be, however, that such dynamic changes are occurring very slowly within each bracken stand.

REFERENCES

1) Tivy J (1973)   The bracken problem.   In J Tivy (ed) The organic resources of Scotland.   Edinburgh: Oliver and Boyd

2) Evans I A and Mason J (1965)   Carcinogenic activity of bracken. Nature, 208, 913-914

3) Lee H C (1982)   Aspects of the ecology of bracken removal from upland pasture.   Unpubl. PhD thesis.   Sunderland Polytechnic

4) Mueller - Dombois D and Ellenberg H (1984)   Aims and methods of vegetation ecology.   USA: John Wiley and Sons

5) Bray J R and Curtis J T (1957) An ordination of the upland forest communities of southern Wisconsin. Ecological Monographs, 27, 325-349

6) Jeffers J N R (1978) An introduction to systems analysis: with ecological applications London: Edward Arnold

7) Hilder E J (1964) The distribution of plant nutrients by sheep at pasture. Proceedings of the Australian Society of Animal Production, 5, 241-248

8) Tansley A G (1985) The British Isles and their vegetation London: Cambridge University Press

9) Birse E L and Robertson J S (1976) Plant communities and soils of the lowland and southern upland regions of Scotland. Aberdeen: The Macaulay Institute for Soil Research

10) Horrill A D, Dale J and Thomson A (1979) Effects of asulam on selected plant communities and animals. ITE/NCC Research Report No 174

11) Nicholson I A and Paterson I S (1976) The ecological implications of bracken control to plant/animal systems. Botanical Journal of the Linnean Society, 73, 269-283

12) Mahomud A and Grime J P (1976) An analysis of competitive ability in three perennial grasses. New Phytologist, 77, 431-435

13) Jarvis P G (1964) Interference by Deschampsia flexuosa (L) Trin. Oikos, 15, 56-78

14) Grime J P and Jeffrey D W (1965) Seedling establishment in vertical gradients of sunlight. Journal of Ecology, 53, 621-642

15) Gliessman S R (1976) Allelopathy in a broad spectrum of environments as illustrated by bracken. Botanical Journal of the Linnean Society, 73, 95-104

16) Mitchell J (1973) Mobilisation of phosphorus by Pteridium aquilinum. Plant and Soil, 38, 489-491

17) Welch D (1968) Sheep grazing in Northern England. Some ecological considerations. In I V Hunt (ed) Hill-land productivity. Proceedings of a Symposium of the European Grassland Federation No 4, 173-176

18) Garrett Jones R (1958) Grazing of bracken by sheep in South Wales. Proceedings of 4th British Weed Control Conference, 194-197

19) Watt A S (1947) Contributions to the ecology of bracken (Pteridium aquilinum). IV. The structure of the community. New Phytologist, 46, 917-921

Opportunistic behaviour of bracken (Pteridium aquilinum L. Kuhn) in moorland habitats: Origins and Constraints

R T Smith

ECONOMIC AND SOCIAL CHANGE

Bracken is an aggressive competitor and its spread since prehistoric times has been attributable to successive shifts in land use type and intensity (Fig.1.)[1,2]. I would like firstly to present a case study which gives insight into the forces at work in bracken expansion earlier this century. The area is that of Ilkley Moor, some 15-20 miles north west of Leeds. The results of repeated vegetation surveys (Fig.2.) show that a remarkable expansion of bracken had occurred from the early years of this century up until 1959 - a bracken distribution which broadly persists to the present. This expansion occurred on the lower slopes of the moor, on land previously classed as 'grass heath with heather'. The vegetation maps show that crowberry had also become virulent by the time of the later survey.

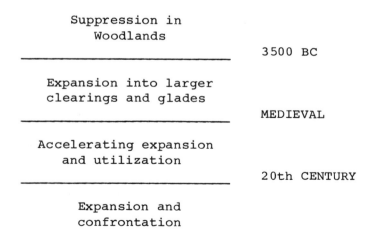

Suppression in
Woodlands

3500 BC

Expansion into larger
clearings and glades

MEDIEVAL

Accelerating expansion
and utilization

20th CENTURY

Expansion and
confrontation

Fig.1.   Bracken: phases of expansion

215

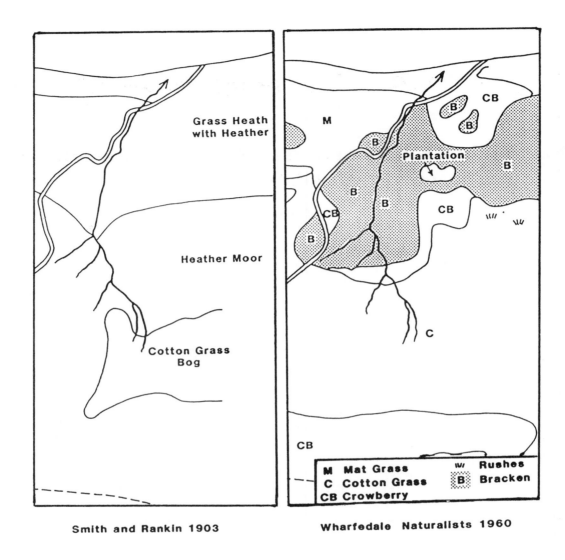

Grass Heath
with Heather

Heather Moor

Cotton Grass
Bog

M Mat Grass   w/ Rushes
C Cotton Grass   B Bracken
CB Crowberry

Smith and Rankin 1903   **Wharfedale Naturalists 1960**

Fig. 2.   Vegetation changes, Ilkley Moor, West Yorkshire

        Why might such dramatic changes have taken place? Clearly one
must allow for interpretive differences between vegetation surveys but
we know that the moor passed from private ownership in 1893 to
become an urban common and amenity. During two world wars the area
was chronically overgrazed with stories of sheep dropping into the
town for a bite to eat. It was also used for military purposes. The
period of the 1930s was also a critical time, for horses were
decreasingly used for transport and farm work, and so bracken was no
longer cut from the moor for their bedding. In the interests of
brevity it may be said that these were probably the major factors
leading to ecological instability and change. I have also argued
elsewhere[3] that as bracken expanded on the better grazings at lower
elevation, increasing grazing stress would have been applied to the
heather at higher levels paving the way for a quite extraordinary
expansion of crowberry, the latter continuing to expand until the late

1970s[4]. It is therefore my judgement that the progress of both bracken and crowberry, occupying ecologically distinct areas of the moor, represents a related floristic response to a quite exceptional period of economic and social change. Ilkley Moor may seem to be a severe case to take but I do believe it points to the origins of the bracken problem this century in many other less well documented areas and serves to emphasise the particular plight of common lands[5].

DEFORESTATION AND ITS IMPLICATIONS

For purposes of developing insight into the ecology and opportunistic success of bracken its emergence in prehistoric times will now be considered. In the earlier Holocene, bracken can be visualised as having been present as a dispersed species, spatially limited and substantially suppressed by the all-embracing woodlands (Fig.1). It is not until widespread and sustained forest clearances of the Neolithic and Bronze Age that bracken was allowed its first major bid for freedom[6]. Let us consider the processes at work here. In the first place, more favourable lighting conditions in clearings would inevitably have led to enhanced photosynthetic rates and to a larger exchange of moisture and nutrients by the bracken. Bracken's association with freely-draining soils, commonly on valley-side slopes, has led ecologists more often to emphasise its drainage requirements rather than its water needs while current research confirms the sizeable transpirational losses from bracken which appear to be enhanced in more open habitats with increased air circulation[7-11].

Forest clearance, however, increases water yields from river basins - often by more than 25 per cent[12] - through reduced transpirational consumption and interception, so it may be of some significance that the rise of bracken should accompany increases in available soil moisture. In like manner, this century, it is worth considering whether the periodic degeneration of heathland communities through lack of appropriate management has similarly invited bracken to exploit increasing levels of available soil moisture.

THE SEARCH FOR LIMITING FACTORS

So, no matter how important we may claim land use practices to have been in causing the present widespread infestations of bracken, the plant must also operate on its own terms. Equally, the fact that ecotypes of Pteridium tolerate a wide range of environments[13,14] does not seem to me to adequately explain its dominance in a few of them. One has perhaps to distinguish between the basic requirements for survival or replacement of a species - factors which operate over a broad spectrum and determine its overall range, and those which form a foundation for its expansion and dominance in given contexts. The latter would probably identify moisture criteria as well as certain traits of past and present land use. In the case of such a cosmopolitan species as bracken the search for genuinely limiting factors is obviously more challenging. In British moorland environments the chief constraints appear to be those of soil water regime and frost incidence. It is these key factors which arguably interact to determine stand density (Fig.3). The term soil moisture regime is here used to include the requirements of water availability and adequate drainage during the growing season. Sites with shallow soils are unlikely to satisfy the former while those with a tendency to waterlogging will fail in respect of the latter. Soil moisture regime and frost incidence are both conditioned by relief characteristics and I am increasingly of the opinion that exposure - readily offered as a primary factor limiting bracken populations - is a spurious and misleading concept. The significant properties of the local climate operate through moisture and frost stresses while the resulting stand density remains as the key factor influencing wind stress on the population at large. Poor growth performance in any stand will therefore merely reinforce the effectiveness of the prevailing moisture and frost stresses.

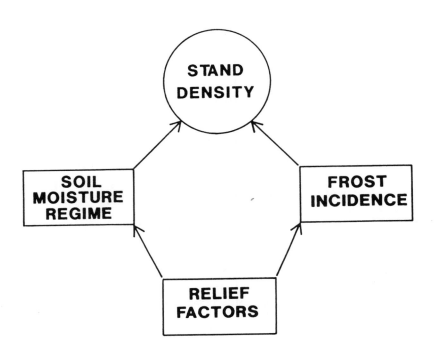

Fig. 3. Factors affecting the vigour and density of bracken stands

BRACKEN VIGOUR AND SOIL MOISTURE

Spatial variations

Field observations of moorland bracken stands, and in particular, closer study of a site near Pateley Bridge in North Yorkshire over the past 15 years, show the influence of ground water on the status and vigour of bracken (Fig.4). Deep-litter bracken occupies the more elevated positions yet is underlain by a water table subject to marked fluctuation. Variations in phenology are noted, with later emergence in the marginal zone associated with a higher

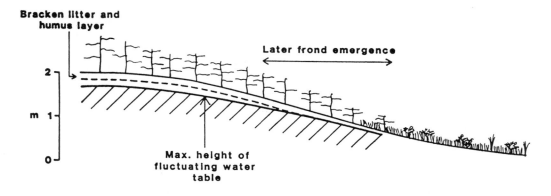

Fig. 4. Generalised hydrological relationships in moorland bracken

water table. Dip wells were used to check water table depths in two
successive years (1975-6) and the results showed that the empirical
limit of bracken broadly coincided with sites having at least 30 cm of
unwaterlogged surface soil horizons[15] (Fig.5). This growth pattern,
and especially the realisation that bracken will grow effectively on
sites subject to short periods of waterlogging, suggests that
widespread moorland drainage over the last 150 years has been a
significant stimulus to bracken invasion. Other coincident factors
such as the abandonment of many upland small holdings following the

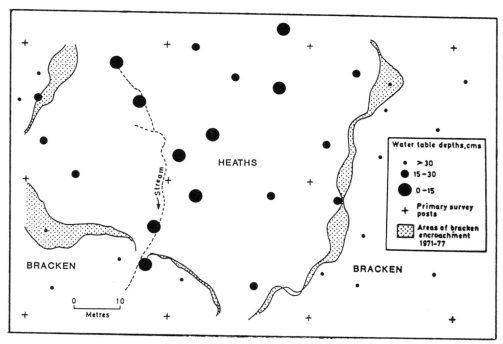

Fig. 5. Moorland bracken: maximum water table levels during
the growing season

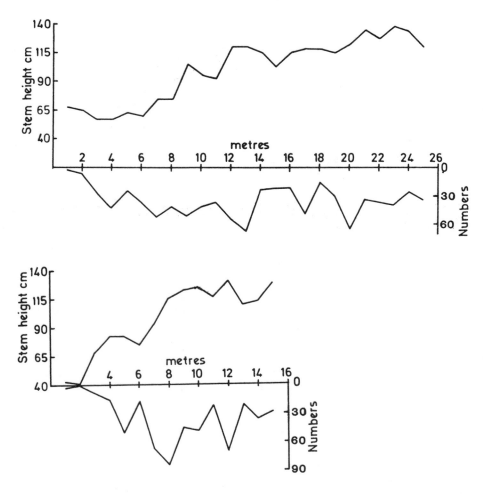

Fig. 6.   Relationship between bracken stem numbers and average
heights along two transects

cessation of base metal mining and the collapse of cottage textile
industries will merely have reinforced the more favourable context for
bracken.

        Turning to consider data collected along transects (Fig.6) we
see how bracken stem numbers and heights (measured in early August)
vary from the margin into the centre of the bracken-dominated areas.
There is a tendency for the greatest height to be attained in areas
more elevated from the water table and for the greatest frequency of
stems to occur some distance behind the pioneer marginal zone. In
view of the fact that this bracken population has remained largely
stable for the last 15 years it might better be described as in an
equilibrium condition rather than 'building phase' and thus on the way
to a temporally more mature state. This denser condition may partly
depend upon access to subsoil water, for while parts of these same
areas may be later in emergence, the proximity of subsoil water and
nutrients may be a positive stimulus to the production of frond buds

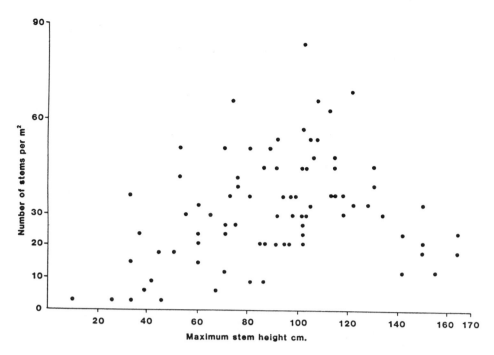

Fig. 7.   Relationship between bracken stem numbers and maximum heights

in the upper rhizome and to the maintenance of greater stem density throughout the growing season. On the other hand, frequency of soil wetness clearly restricts depth of rhizome and root development which is likely to be a major factor leading to more limited growth potential of individual petioles. By contrast, as we move to positions more elevated from water table influence into the bracken hinterland there are fewer, but taller, petioles. This latter trend is illustrated in Fig.7 based on a larger sample of belt quadrats and has been confirmed by research carried out in the current field season (not illustrated). It must be noted that such a presentation as Fig.7, while revealing structural attributes of a bracken population, has validity in numerical terms only for a given year, locality and site.

A recognized feature of mature bracken stands is their very uneven stem density over quite small areas. This was especially evident in our 1984 estimations of leaf area index based on systematic harvesting. Aside from obvious patterning imposed by sheep walks and other trampling, such variations also seem likely to be influenced by available subsoil moisture reserves. Such is the rampant growth of bracken over many sites that the original microrelief of the ground is largely lost and the possibility must remain that concealed boulders and gross variations in the local character of subsoils explain this irregularity of cloning. However, only detailed studies of small areas over several years are likely to determine whether such fixed attributes are really so important.

221

Temporal variations

There is I believe another important issue which points to the importance of subsoil moisture in relation to deep-litter bracken and one which bears upon the ideas of Watt that bracken can eventually bring about its own decline[16]. The issue primarily concerns water stress. At full growth in late July and August with a multilayered and interpenetrating canopy, supported by some 50 stems per square metre, values of the leaf area index can often exceed 4 (or 400% ground cover) while if the surfaces of stems are included the value is increased by some 10 percent. It is clear that under such circumstances the majority of summer showery activity can have little effect on moisture recharge in the soil layers. Furthermore, this live canopy is underlain by an open layer of dry litter (overlying the bracken humus horizon), commonly some 5-10 cm in thickness with dead stems projecting above it. I recently carried out a laboratory experiment on a representative sample of this litter using a m^2 container on wire mesh and with measured amounts of water applied by a garden sprayer (Fig.8). The practicalities and repeatability of such experimentation (based here on 3 separate sets of determinations) are reflected by the error bars, yet in relation to magnitude and trend the implications are clear enough. In the experimentation, rainfall intensity was kept as nearly constant as practicable. As expected, with larger amounts of artificial rainfall the proportion of intercepted rainfall diminishes despite the tendency for the litter to absorb water the longer the duration of the wetting. At lower rainfall intensities there will similarly be a tendency, up to a certain limit, for water to be absorbed by dead biomass rather than be transmitted to the succeeding horizon. Added to the effects of canopy interception these experimental results merely serve to emphasise that only the heaviest or most prolonged rainfall will be effective in soil moisture recharge during the growing season. Two mechanisms provide some slight compensation, first, that of stem flow water with more direct access to the soil and second, the insulating effect of dry surface litter in reducing evaporative loss from the soil surface. Nevertheless, it would seem that successful bracken growth on deep litter sites must depend on access to subsoil moisture reserves and, no doubt, to a substantial rhizome storage.

Let us at this point consider the biomass and water content of bracken rhizomes. A variety of estimates on different sites in Britain give dry weight values from 300 to over 4000 g/m^2. Moorland bracken normally has a shallower layer of rhizomes than typically characterises bracken in lowland areas; the Breckland, for example. Even so, research conducted in the summer of 1985 at the field site near Pateley Bridge indicates that the dry weight of rhizomes lies between about 750 and 1300 g/m^2, depending on the density of the stand. The calculated water content was consistently around 87 percent with the fresh weight of rhizomes in mature, deep-litter areas towards 8000 g/m^2. It would appear, then, that the equivalent of at least 6 mm of water is contained within the rhizome system and while the plant tops will only be able to utilize a proportion of this living store its importance as a buffer against moisture stresses must be recognized. So indeed must the existence of thin roots extending to observed depths in excess of 50 cm from the base of the rhizome layer, for with transpiration rates likely to be exceeding 4

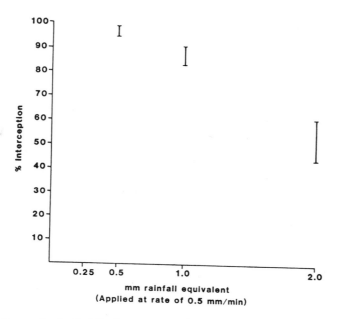

Fig. 8. Rainfall interception by dry bracken litter

mm/day on many days during the summer (other factors permitting), bracken clearly does have a very efficient means of replenishing moisture losses.

But in years and at times when water stress is excessive it seems that in addition to stomatal controls the plant undergoes premature senescence, a process leading to some general bronzing and to the early death of a proportion of stems. As superficial layers deepen it is probable that periodic moisture stresses will increase in frequency and lead to a depletion of rhizome vitality, a mechanism which may in time cause degeneration of the stand. That bracken in moorland areas demonstrates a reluctance to follow this path seems likely to be due to the more general accessibility of subsoil moisture in these cooler and wetter environments.

CONCLUSION

It is my contention therefore, that while changing land use and management have been strong determinants of bracken expansion, the attainment and maintenance of local dominance in the British uplands has depended on the plant's ability to utilize subsoil moisture and nutrients during the short but highly productive growing season. In this respect bracken stands in marked contrast to other moorland species, a fact which is reflected in the farmer's perception of hill soils for, to quote an earlier saying, "under heather - copper; under gorse - silver; under bracken - gold".

223

REFERENCES

1) Taylor J A (1986) (This volume)

2) Taylor J A (1985) The relationship between land use change and variations in bracken encroachment rates in Britain. In The biogeographical impact of land use change ed. R T Smith. Biogeographical Monographs No 2, 19-29. Geo-Books, Norwich

3) Smith R T and Atherden M A (1985) Recent vegetative change and the management of Ilkley Moor, West Yorkshire, In The biogeographical impact of land use change ed. R T Smith. Biogeographical Monographs No 2, 39-50, Geo-Books, Norwich

4) Dalby M et al (1971) The vegetative changes on Ilkley Moor, The Naturalist 49-56

5) Hughes E and Aitchison J W (1986) This volume

6) Rymer L (1976) The history and ethnobotany of bracken. Bot. J. Linn. Soc. 73 : 151-176

7) Roberts J M et al (1980) Seasonal changes in leaf area, stomatal and canopy conductances and transpiration from bracken below a forest canopy. J. Appl. Ecol. 17 : 409-422

8) Roberts J M (1986) This volume

9) Lockwood J G et al (1986) This volume

10) Pitman J and Pitman R M (1986) This volume

11) Hollinger D and Evans G (1985) Forest Research Institute, Christchurch N.Z. Personal Communication

12) Moore P D (1975) The origin of blanket mires. Nature 256 : 267-269

13) Page C N (1976) The taxonomy and phytogeography of bracken - a review. Bot. J. Linn. Soc. 73 : 1-34

14) Page C N (1986) This volume

15) Smith R T (1977) Bracken in Britain II : Ecological observations of a bracken population over a six-year period. Working Paper 190 School of Geography, University of Leeds

16) Watt A S (1976) The ecological status of bracken. Bot. J. Linn. Soc. 73 : 217-239

Sward changes following bracken clearance

C J Sparke and G H Williams

INTRODUCTION

The suppression of bracken growth is only the first step in improving the grazing value of hill land. In many cases, what is revealed is not the lush sward which some farmers imagine lies below their bracken, but a mixture of grass, mainly Agrostis spp., which tends to turn brown in dry weather, bracken litter and obvious weeds (Cirsium spp., Digitalis purpurea and Urtica dioica). Most of the bracken-infested land in the West of Scotland is either too steep or too rocky to plough, while the addition of phosphate alone has little effect[1,2]. This paper summarises the results of a number of investigations designed to study the changes in the sward which occur in the absence of any deliberate post-spraying follow-up treatment, and whether sward composition and output could be improved by various methods which did not involve ploughing.

SWARD CHANGES IN THE ABSENCE OF FOLLOW-UP TREATMENT

Asulam (4.5 kg/ha ai) and glyphosate (2.0 kg/ha ai) are equally effective in controlling bracken, but glyphosate has a wider spectrum of activity with few species showing any degree of resistance[3]. The sward which develops following frond control depends partly on the herbicide employed and partly upon the species present[4]. The survival of clumps of unaffected vegetation is important for recolonisation, as it has been found that, unless cultivations are undertaken, the buried viable seed bank plays little part in sward recovery[5].

The initial effect of overall spraying in the West of Scotland, even onto a closed canopy of fronds which could be expected to provide some protection, is to cause sward damage which is greater if glyphosate is used, and if treatment is carried out in August rather than in July. Agrostis species are especially susceptible while Festuca rubra tends to be resistant. The recolonisation of areas of litter or killed vegetation after spraying is primarily by Holcus mollis, Anthoxanthum odoratum, Galium saxatile and Potentilla erecta. If Digitalis purpurea, Urtica dioica or Cirsium arvense are present initially, heavy infestations can develop following the use of asulam, with smaller increases after glyphosate spraying[4].

In the longer term, the composition of the vegetation depends on whether the grazing pattern changes or whether bracken becomes re-established. In the absence of either, it seems that the higher proportion of dicotyledonous species produced as a result of spraying, is reduced as grass becomes re-established, but that changes in proportions of grasses present may persist. Table 1 shows sward analyses carried out in July each year on an area which was treated with glyphosate in August 1976. Grazing has continued to be by sheep and cattle, and bracken recolonisation has been minimal[6]. Agrostis species have never recovered the dominance which they had when frond cover was present, while the proportion of Festuca rubra has increased greatly. This does not appear to be a simple effect of frond removal, since other sites which have been treated with asulam have re-established[4] with Agrostis species.

The increase in grass dry matter yield achieved after frond control varies from site to site. Some large percentage increases have been quoted[2,7] but these depend on the amount of grass present originally. Actual yields obtained have ranged from 700-1600 kg/ha DM in the year after spraying asulam, and from 1800-3000 kg/ha DM two years after spraying[2,8,9].

TABLE 1 Changes in sward composition (% cover) following glyphosate spraying in August 1976

Species	1976	1977	1978	1980	1982	1984
Agrostis spp	33.8	1.0*	3.2	17.6*	21.0	16.3
Anthoxanthum	8.4	17.2*	15.9	12.1	17.4	11.5*
Festuca rubra	9.8	4.0	29.1*	33.7	25.8	43.1*
Holcus mollis	3.4	2.1	3.0	6.2	8.5	10.5
Poa spp	7.0	1.2*	1.5	1.9	2.9	5.6
Carex/Luzula spp	7.5	1.4*	2.8	4.3	2.7	3.3
Potentilla/Galium	13.7	11.6	18.3	15.0	9.6	2.3*
Other	4.7	3.1	4.5	3.7	4.9	2.8
Litter/Bare ground	11.7	58.4*	21.7*	5.5*	7.2	4.6

* Value significantly different (P < 0.05) from preceding figure

CHANGES FOLLOWING SURFACE TREATMENT

Cadbury[10] has indicated that colonisation and the subsequent spread of perennial species is influenced by the depth of bracken litter and species with the ability to rapidly form dense, prostrate growth.   Thus   <u>Holcus mollis</u>, <u>Anthoxanthum odoratum</u>, <u>Galium saxatile</u> and <u>Potentilla erecta</u>, can quickly establish in a <u>moderate litter</u> layer[4].

TABLE 2   Effect of method of litter removal during the previous winter on sward composition (% cover)

| Species | Assessed | Litter | | | |
		Intact	Raked	Burnt	Incorporated
Holcus	April 1980	21	28	3	2
	July 1980	36	44	51	18
	Oct 1980	49	45	68	46
	Sept 1981	28	32	61	30
Other Grasses	April 1980	6	22	<1	1
	July 1980	29	37	6	5
	Oct 1980	25	23	12	10
	Sept 1981	23	19	12	34
Dicots	April 1980	4	8	1	<1
	July 1980	12	17	34	61
	Oct 1980	23	32	18	43
	Sept 1981	45	49	25	34
Bare Ground	April 1980	69	42	96	97
	July 1980	23	2	9	16
	Oct 1980	3	0	2	1
	Sept 1981	4	0	2	2

Asulam applied August 1979

The effects of various methods of litter removal on the subsequent development of the sward have been investigated[9] and the results are summarised in Table 2.   Following frond control with asulam, litter was removed by raking, burning or incorporation, or left <u>in situ</u> as a control.   Removal of the litter and surface vegetation by burning resulted in rapid recolonisation by <u>Holcus mollis</u>.   Holcus also recolonised where the litter and surface vegetation had been incorporated by surface cultivation but, in addition, many of the buried weed seeds known to be present in the seed bank[5] were stimulated to germinate and several established themselves, including <u>Polygonum spp.</u> and <u>Digitalis purpurea</u>.   These species held the spread of Holcus in check and they were replaced in the second year by Agrostis and Poa species.   Removal of the litter by raking enabled <u>Ranunculus repens</u> in particular to spread.   There was an indication that burning or incorporation of the litter and surface vegetation gave rise to swards with fewer herbaceous species.   Whilst the total proportion of grasses in the sward was little different, burning resulted in a sward dominated by <u>Holcus mollis</u> and incorporation favoured Agrostis and Poa species.   In terms of grass DM production, no benefit was derived over two years from removal of the litter by raking, burning or incorporation.

In a further trial (Table 3), the surface treatments were followed by application of lime (2 t/ha $CaCO_3$), phosphate (60 kg/ha P_2O_5) and seed of <u>Lolium perenne</u> and <u>Festuca rubra</u> at 14 kg/ha of each, in order to allow for variations in soil fertility. The sown grasses established and spread most successfully where the surface litter layer and competition from the existing indigenous species had been removed by incorporation. Competition from existing species and the presence of the litter layer prevented a good initial establishment and spread on the control treatment. Competition from the indigenous species resulted in poor establishment on the raked treatment. Burning to remove the litter and surface vegetation provided an intermediate response. The sown grasses were better able to respond to the lime and phosphate than were the indigenous species, so that by the end of the second year, the proportion of sown grasses was little different on the four treatments.

TABLE 3 Effect of method of litter removal on establishment of sown grasses (% cover) after fertiliser, lime and seed application in April 1980

| Species | Assessed | Litter | | | |
		Intact	Raked	Burnt	Incorporated
All	April 1980	22	37	4	4
Grasses	Oct 1980	81	72	76	79
	Sept 1981	61	56	74	76
Sown	April 1980	0	0	0	0
Grasses	Oct 1980	6	11	23	58
	Sept 1981	31	35	41	59

Although soil disturbance during the incorporation of the litter enabled many weedy dicotyledonous species to establish, their development was gradually suppressed by the sown species. Their presence was more unsightly than detrimental to grass DM yield[4]. It was in the second season that total grass DM production on the burnt and incorporated treatments significantly exceeded that on the plots where no surface treatment had taken place (Table 4).

TABLE 4 Total grass production (kg/ha/yr DM) following various surface treatments

| Litter | Without FLS | With FLS | | |
	Intact	Intact	Burnt	Incorporated
1980	1372	1672	1915	1740
1981	2037	2661	3315*	2974*

FLS Fertiliser, lime and seed
*   Significantly different ($P < 0.05$) from Intact without FLS

DISCUSSION

This paper has dealt with sward changes which have occurred following overall bracken spraying on hill land which is used for agriculture in the West of Scotland. Under these conditions, long-term changes in the proportions of major sward components as a result of spraying, even with glyphosate, are fairly small and, in most cases, limited to changing the proportions of grasses present. As the seed bank apparently plays little part in recolonisation, species which occur less frequently may disappear if the original population is killed. Where individual components of the sward are important, such as in nature reserves, a more directed application of herbicide by rope-wick applicator is likely to give adequate control of bracken with no sward damage[11]. The rope-wick applicator is unsuitable for clearing dense bracken stands but may be used on agricultural land for preventing recolonisation by bracken. It therefore seems that any changes in vegetation which do result from the original spraying will be maintained.

Whilst increases in the proportion of grasses in the sward and in DM production are important, equally so, is the quality of the herbage[12]. Many native grasses have low inherent digestibility and their maximum period of productivity tends to be concentrated between mid-May and mid-July. In order to extend the effective grazing season and to improve the quantity and quality of the sward, it may be necessary to replace some of the existing species.

Surface seeding of land where bracken control has been achieved has not always been successful. Bracken has been found to have an allelopathic influence on associated species[13,14] but this is not thought to be important under West of Scotland conditions[1]. One of the problems may be that of sowing seed into a layer of litter and dead, or living, vegetation. Some authors[15,16] have suggested that the presence of a layer of litter is necessary as cover to maintain moisture and humidity and to reduce variations in temperature and exposure, but Martin and Sparke[1] found that the establishment of surface-sown seed was reduced when the litter depth exceeded 1 cm. The use of stock has been advocated[17-19] to break up the vegetation mat and to bring seed into contact with the soil, while the importance of suppressing the growth of indigenous species for long enough for the introduced plants to become established, has also been stressed[20,21,22]. This work has shown that while litter removal alone has little effect on grass DM production, burning or incorporation, followed by application of lime and phosphate, improve initial establishment of sown grasses, and there are significant production increases in the second year. Burning may therefore be an acceptable alternative method of removing bracken litter, prior to reseeding, if cultivation of any sort is not possible.

REFERENCES

1) Martin D J and Sparke C J (1982) Field trials in South-West Scotland. Proceedings of the Royal Society of Edinburgh, 81B, 117-123

2) Williams G H and Fraser D (1979) The effect of asulam, frond

cutting and ground mineral phosphate on the yields of swards dominated by bracken (Pteridium aquilinum (L) Kuhn). Grass and Forage Science, 34, 95-100

3) Williams G H (1980a) Bracken control: a review of progress, 1974-1979. West of Scotland Agricultural College Research and Development Publication No 12

4) Williams G H (1977) Qualitative effects of asulam and glyphosate on swards dominated by bracken (Pteridium aquilinum (L) Kuhn). Journal of the British Grassland Society, 32, 149-155

5) Sparke C J (1982) Factors affecting the improvement of hill land dominated by bracken (Pteridium aquilinum (L) Kuhn). PhD Thesis, University of Glasgow

6) Williams G H (1980b) Follow-up treatments for the control of Pteridium aquilinum. Proceedings of the 1980 British Crop Protection Conference - Weeds, 423-428

7) Farnworth J and Davies G M (1974) The response of hill bracken and the associated pasture to applications of picloram and dicamba. Weed Research, 14, 401-404

8) Davies G E, Newbould P and Baillie G J (1979) The effect of controlling bracken (Pteridium aquilinum (L) Kuhn) on pasture production. Grass and Forage Science, 34, 163-171

9) Sparke C J (1985) The effect of after-treatments on sward composition and the establishment of introduced species following the control of bracken (Pteridium aquilinum (L) Kuhn). Grass and Forage Science, (in press)

10) Cadbury C J (1976) Botanical implications of bracken control. Botanical Journal of the Linnaean Society, 73, 285-294

11) Lowman J W (1985) Asulam applied by rope-wick applicator for controlling scattered bracken on a grassland nature reserve. Tests of Agrochemicals and Cultivars, 6, 90-91

12) Newbould P (1981) The potential of indigenous plant resources. In The Effective Use of Forage and Animal Resources in the Hills and Uplands. Occasional Symposium No 12 of the British Grassland Society, 1-15

13) Gliessman S R (1976) Allelopathy in a broad spectrum of environments as illustrated by bracken. Botanical Journal of the Linnaean Society, 73, 95-104

14) Gliessman S R and Muller C H (1978) The allelopathic mechanisms of dominance in bracken (Pteridium aquilinum) in Southern California. Journal of Chemical Ecology, 4, 337-362

15) Blackmore L W (1957) Chemicals as an aid to oversowing and crop establishment. Proceedings of the 10th New Zealand Weed Control

Conference, 18-23

16) Evans R A and Young J A (1970) Plant litter and establishment of alien annual weed species in rangeland communities. Weed Science, 18, 697-703

17) Copeman G J F and Roberts H W (1960) The development of surface seeding. Journal of the British Grassland Society, 15, 163-168

18) Davies J, Edwards D E and Rowlands A (1968) Some aspects of hill-land improvement in Wales. In Hill-land Productivity. Occasional Symposium No 4 of the British Grassland Society, 47-50

19) Rowlands A (1966) Reseeding and surface treatment - a comparison of two methods of improving hill grazings. Journal of the British Grassland Society, 21, 174-180

20) Campbell M H (1968) Establishment, growth and survival of six pasture species surface sown on unploughed land infested with serrated tussock (Nassella trichotoma). Australian Journal of Experimental Agriculture and Animal Husbandry, 8, 470-477

21) Davies G M (1968) The use of fertilisers and paraquat on a hill sward. In Hill-land Productivity. Occasional Symposium No 4 of the British Grassland Society, 141-145

22) Hughes R and Nicholson I A (1961) Herbage varieties for surface seeding. In 2nd Report of the Hill Farming Research Organisation, 1958-1961, 61-65

Restoration of Calluna heathland following bracken clearance

J E Lowday

INTRODUCTION

The conservation of wildlife on lowland heaths in Britain and Western Europe currently faces three interrelated problems. Firstly, the area of heathland has declined rapidly in response to powerful economic forces. Advancing agricultural technology has provided unprecedented opportunities for sustaining high levels of productivity on light heathland soils. Many heathlands have changed to a high input : high output agricultural system, either arable or intensive pasture. Elsewhere, coniferous forestry has proved to be an economic alternative. Secondly the traditional low input : low output agricultural systems, which created and maintained heathlands, have become uneconomic. Often, rather than being put to an alternative use, heathlands have been abandoned or neglected. Because most British and European heathlands are plagioclimax communities, abandonment has allowed succession to woodland to occur on disused sites. Indeed, many former heathlands now more closely resemble the woodland from which they were created by prehistoric forest clearance. On other heathland sites, bracken occupies large areas and has spread[1] (although usually not as rapidly as scrub encroachment), often forming pure, dense stands with little else growing underneath the canopy amongst the accumulation of bracken litter. Thirdly, as a result of both land-use and vegetation changes, remaining areas of heathland are smaller, more fragmented and isolated, leading to concern about preserving populations of rare or interesting species which are dependent on the heathland habitat.

Although agricultural interest in lowland heaths has virtually ceased, society has increasingly valued heathlands for recreational and educational purposes as well as for wildlife conservation. However, if examples of heathland ecosystems are to be retained for these purposes for future generations, then it is essential that active management programmes are introduced on our remaining heaths. Weed control will often be the first step in a heathland management programme, and, for bracken, cutting and herbicides may be used for

233

control. However, restoration of heathland vegetation where bracken was formerly present is the most important long-term objective. Where light infestations of bracken are controlled on established heathland, the former presence of bracken may have minimal effect on the subsequent development of the vegetation. However, where dense stands of bracken occur, there is often a deep accumulation of litter underneath the canopy, with heathland flora sparse or absent. After removal of a dense stand, restoration of heathland vegetation will be more difficult and is likely to require further management.

This paper reports on an experiment to remove at least two of the possible constraints on restoring heathland vegetation after the control of dense bracken with asulam; firstly, by the dispersion of accumulated bracken litter and secondly, by sowing locally collected Calluna seed.

MATERIALS AND METHODS

In August, 1978, 0.1 ha of dense, uniform bracken at Cavenham Heath, Suffolk (GR TL 755725) was sprayed with asulam (Asulox, 4.4 kg a.i/ha) using a motorised mist blower. Later, in February 1979, a split-plot randomised block experiment was arranged on the treated area, investigating four main plot litter dispersal treatments: (i) untreated, (ii) burnt, (iii) raked off, (v) rotavated, with each main plot being split to investigate (a) untreated and (b) sowing 20,000 Calluna seeds/m^2. Four replicate blocks were used. Pathways 1 m wide separated the split-plots which measured 4 x 3 m.

The plots were burnt when the underlying, peaty component of the litter was moist, but the loose litter from more recent fronds was dry and combustible. Hand rakes were used to remove all the litter to expose the mineral soil. The rotavating treatment was applied with two passes of a Howard Gem rotavator. The Calluna seed was collected locally in October 1978 and sown after the main litter dispersal treatments had been applied. All experimental treatments were applied during February-March 1979. Any bracken regrowth was hand-weeded three times each year from 1979 onwards. The overall vegetation cover and the cover of Calluna were recorded annually in early July from 1979 to 1984.

RESULTS

Calluna seedlings were first observed on the experimental site in spring 1980, approximately 14 months after the start of the experiment. They were nearly all confined to seeded plots where the litter had been dispersed. Elsewhere, very few seedlings were observed, either on the unseeded plots or on seeded plots where the litter remained undisturbed. In subsequent years, the greatest cover of Calluna was observed on the seeded plots where the litter was raked off (Table 1). On seeded plots where the litter remained undispersed, development of Calluna was slower and had attained a maximum of only 13% cover by July 1984. Establishment of Calluna from naturally occurring seed (the unseeded plots) was slow, attaining 7-11% cover in 1984 where the litter was dispersed but remaining below 1% where the litter was undispersed.

234

TABLE 1 The effects of litter dispersal (main treatment n=8) and seeding with Calluna (sub-treatment n=4) on the % cover of Calluna, Cavenham Heath, 1981-1983.

a) Main treatment

Litter dispersal		1981	1982	1983	1984
Untreated		0.5	2.0	5.5	6.8
Burnt		2.5	8.8	16.4	26.0
Litter removed		9.4	21.3	36.5	35.5
Rotavated		7.9	21.1	28.4	27.9
LSD ($p \leq 0.05$)		5.6	5.8	10.6	15.6

b) Sub treatment

Litter dispersal		1981	1982	1983	1984
Untreated	unseeded	0.1	0.3	0.9	0.8
	seeded	0.9	3.7	10.1	12.9
Burnt	unseeded	0.1	1.5	3.8	6.8
	seeded	4.9	16.1	29.0	45.3
Litter removed	unseeded	0.3	1.7	4.6	7.5
	seeded	18.5	40.9	68.4	63.5
Rotavated	unseeded	0.5	1.7	5.5	11.0
	seeded	15.3	40.5	51.3	44.9
LSD ($p \leq 0.05$) between any two sub-treatments		7.4	8.7	16.0	21.6

TABLE 2 The effects of litter dispersal (main treatment n=8) and seeding with Calluna (sub-treatment n=4) on the overall % vegetation cover at Cavenham Heath, 1979-1983

a) Main treatment

Litter dispersal		1979	1980	1981	1982	1983	1984
Untreated		9.7	19.5	42.9	50.7	69.4	66.0
Burnt		7.1	13.6	42.4	54.4	66.8	70.6
Litter removed		6.4	16.7	44.4	60.7	77.9	74.6
Rotavated		2.5	5.7	33.1	59.0	76.2	81.7
LSD ($p \leq 0.05$)		NS	NS	NS	NS	NS	NS

b) Sub treatment

Litter dispersal		1979	1980	1981	1982	1983	1984
Untreated	unseeded	11.7	22.0	38.0	47.1	67.3	65.1
	seeded	7.6	17.0	47.8	54.3	71.5	66.9
Burnt	unseeded	11.4	20.3	53.3	63.8	68.8	70.3
	seeded	2.8	6.8	31.5	44.9	64.8	70.9
Litter removed	unseeded	10.2	18.9	48.3	60.4	72.1	68.0
	seeded	2.6	14.5	40.4	60.9	83.7	81.3
Rotavated	unseeded	2.9	7.2	37.3	59.4	70.6	80.8
	seeded	2.0	4.2	28.8	58.5	81.7	82.6
LSD ($p \leq 0.05$) between any two sub-treatments		NS	NS	NS	NS	11.7	NS

Development of vegetation from natural sources occurred readily on the experimental site, even where the litter remained undispersed. The principle, naturally occurring species were Rumex acetosella and Agrostis spp., although Calamagrostis epigejos, Aira praecox and Dicranum scoparium all increased. These species were present, but not abundant, at the start of the experiment. Betula pendula successfully established on the experimental plots either from buried seed or nearby mature trees.

Although the overall vegetation cover was broadly similar on all plots regardless of litter dispersal or seeding sub-treatment (Table 2), there were major differences in vegetative composition. Where the cover of Calluna was highest, ie. on seeded plots receiving litter dispersal treatments, the natural development of vegetation was suppressed. Elsewhere, on unseeded plots and where the litter remained undispersed, the vegetation was dominated by Rumex acetosella and Agrostis spp. with Calluna occupying less than 11% overall cover.

DISCUSSION

The control of bracken and other weeds such as Betula pendula and Pinus sylvestris, will often be the first objective of a management programme for the conservation of lowland heaths. The subsequent objectives will then be to restore an open heath community to the treated areas, before imposing a maintenance management regime to optimise the value of the site for wildlife[2]. Although the results of bracken control, either by spraying or cutting, are relatively predictable, the vegetation that develops after the control of dense bracken, is less certain. Indeed, vegetation development depends on the interaction of several factors, some of which are beyond the control of the manager, for example: (i) survival of vegetative propagules underneath the bracken canopy; (ii) buried seed; (iii) seed rain; (iv) depth of the litter layer; (v) climate; and (vi) grazing pressure and future management.

Successful control of dense bracken by a herbicide causes a massive and rapid change in the structure of the vegetation, transforming a dense, often pure stand to an ecosystem typically dominated by an accumulation of bracken litter. Removal of the dominant species in a plant community creates opportunities for colonisation, and may initiate rapid changes in the vegetation compared to an enclosed or established community. Provided that the accumulation of litter is not too severe, typically one or two opportunistic species grow rapidly after bracken control, although in common with other coloniststhey maynot persist in the community. Examples of such early colonists are:- Rumex acetosella, Epilobium spp., Urtica dioica, Betula pendula, Agrostis spp., Aira praecox, Deschampsia flexuosa, Holcus mollis, Helictotrichon pubescens and Carex arenaria.

At Cavenham Heath the principle natural colonisers were Rumex acetosella and Agrostis spp., which grew rapidly following bracken control even where the bracken litter was undispersed. In contrast, undispersed accumulations of bracken litter suppressed the establishment of Calluna, from either natural buried seed or an introduced source. However, litter dispersal either by burning, raking off or rotavating encouraged the establishment of Calluna, either rapidly from introduced seed or more slowly from the natural buried seed pool. Where rapid establishment of Calluna occurred (on seeded areas where the litter was dispersed), the development of natural colonisers, such as Rumex acetosella and Agrostis spp., was suppressed.

Germination of Calluna is encouraged both by light at ground level and fluctuating temperatures, two qualities which are characteristics of disturbed, cleared or burnt areas as distinct from closed communities[3]. Germination and establishment of Calluna is poor on its own litter, especially when fresh and loose, but is more vigorous on litter that is partly decomposed or compacted. It is not certain whether the rapid growth of Calluna after litter dispersal is due to the elimination of a physical or allelopathic constraint on germination and establishment. However, when all the litter was physically removed by raking off, the development of Calluna was more rapid compared to incorporating the litter by rotavation or its partial removal by burning (only the loose dry strawy litter was burnt).

Estimates of the buried seed populations in the litter and soil beneath two bracken canopies show that post-asulam vegetation may potentially develop in several ways[4]. Seeds of heathland species and relict components of a former grass heath are clearly beneficial for heathland restoration, and are an important mechanism for floristic recovery. However, weed seeds may also be present in or below the bracken litter, eg Betula spp., Urtica dioica and Epilobium spp., and may be capable of rapid establishment and growth in the open condition created by bracken clearance.

Vegetation development should be closely monitored after bracken control, and, if necessary, further management carried out to remove any undesired colonists in order to manipulate the vegetation development in a desired direction. If colonisation by tall weeds or bracken regrowth occurs after an initial application of herbicide, then there may be a problem in respraying, if species sensitive to herbicide are present in the developing heathland vegetation. This may be overcome by using a differential height herbicide applicator, which smears concentrated herbicide onto the taller target vegetation, avoiding the possibility of spray drift harming non-target species[5]. The manager must be aware that it may be necessary to allocate as many, if not more, resources for subsequent vegetation management as were used for bracken control. After successful weed control and restoration of heathland vegetation, it is important to establish a maintenance management regime which will minimise the risk of the recurrence of a weed problem.

ACKNOWLEDGEMENTS

This work was commissioned by the Nature Conservancy Council as part of its programme of research into nature conservation. J D and R Cheesman, D Malins and G B Nevison gave valuable assistance on field work.

REFERENCES

1) Marrs R H and Hicks M J (1986) Studies on the dynamics of bracken in Breckland. (This volume)

2) Marrs R H and Lowday J E (1985) Management of lowland heaths. Peterborough: Nature Conservancy Council

3) Gimingham C H (1972) Ecology of heathlands. London: Chapman and Hall

4) Lowday J E (1984) The restoration of heathland vegetation after control of dense bracken by asulam. In: Weed control and vegetation management in forests and amenity areas, 283-290. Aspects of Applied Biology 5; Wellesbourne: Association of Applied Biologists

5) Lowday J E (1985) Asulam applied by rope wick applicator for controlling scattered bracken on a grassland nature reserve. Tests of Agrochemicals and cultivars No 6, Annals of Applied Biology 106, Supplement, 90-91

Bracken as an energy resource

G J Lawson, T V Callaghan and R Scott

INTRODUCTION

The majority of contributions to the bracken problem concentrate on the negative side of bracken infestation, and elaborate on aspects of control. Our contention is that bracken has advantages as well as hazards. In the past, its uses included potash for glass and soap making, fuel for brick-making, baking and brewing, roofing-thatch and bedding for animals[1]. It is also a potential source of chemicals, including insecticides.

It seems foolish to pay dearly to attempt to control a weed which could be regarded as a resource. Bracken is opportunistic, prolific, and resists predation. These features ensure its success as a weed, and also suggest that bracken could be an ideal opportunity crop for conversion to fuel. The potential unreliability and the cost of petroleum imports has stimulated the development of indigenous fuel supplies. Countries like Brazil, Sweden, New Zealand and the USA now accept that biomass is a realistic and versatile source of energy, especially when carefully planned and integrated with existing supplies of food, timber and organic residues. It has advantages in the provision of power to remote areas, creating rural employment and utilizing surplus agricultural land or produce.

In the UK, a bioenergy resource equivalent to 10% of the current energy requirements may be available without significantly reducing the production of food and timber[2]. If present trends continue, 9 million ha in Europe will be producing food surpluses by the year 2000. These areas could be used for energy crops, and it is theoretically possible that around 30% of the European Community's energy needs could be derived from biofuels[3]. Bracken is one component of the biomass resource.

EXPLOITING BRACKEN AS AN ENERGY RESOURCE

Extent

There are over 3,000 km^2 of bracken in Britain, though estimates vary widely[1,4-9]. Bracken may be expanding[7] at up to 100 km^2/year but other accounts claim its extent is locally contracting[10]. Confusion over the true area of this important species is explained by differences in methodology, extrapolation to a national scale from small samples, and imprecision in accounting for sparse cover. Clarification may result from improved remote sensing but difficulties will remain in distinguishing bracken areas at a realistic scale for national surveys. Useful pilot studies have, however, been conducted in Eastern Scotland[4] and the North Yorkshire Moors[5].

Yield

Until recently, only two papers[11,12] gave reliable estimates of bracken yield. A study in 1979[13] and results from field plots over a period of years[14] showed a range of frond yield from 4 to 9 t/ha in closed stands in different areas and communities. Weight is lost as the fronds senesce in autumn, and yields at this time are around 60% of the summer peak (Fig.1).

Values for the standing crop of rhizomes and rhizoids are rare in the literature. Studies on the feeding value of rhizomes[15] quoted data which convert to dry weights of around 28 t/ha. Podzol and brown earth soils in the Breckland[12] yielded 14.4 and 10.6 t/ha, respectively, and dense swards in Northern England[13] had below-ground yields between 11.2 and 16.7 t/ha, with little seasonal variation. A more detailed study[16] demonstrated significant increases in rhizome weights from March to September, particularly on deep soils, and below-ground biomass ranged from 2.5 to 38.2 t/ha. Unlike frond yield, these data represent more than one year's production.

Field plots were established in 1980 to assess the effect on aerial yield of repeated harvesting, fertilizers and weather. The split-split plot design covered 0.17 ha on a 26° east-facing slope at Lindale, South Cumbria. Results are briefly summarized here and detailed elsewhere[13].

The effect of weather on yield

The main climatic variables influencing yield are summer temperature, drought and late frosts. Watt[12] presumed that spring air frosts in 1957 were responsible for frond yields being 48% lower in a Breckland area than they were following the mild spring of 1958. Another study[17] in East Anglia implicated frost damage to explain yield variation from 4.1 t/ha in 1978 to 8.1 t/ha in 1982. The effect of frost was particularly severe[18] on harvested plots where the litter layer insulation had been removed.

The effect of repeated harvesting on yield

Perennial species like bracken offer advantages as energy crops

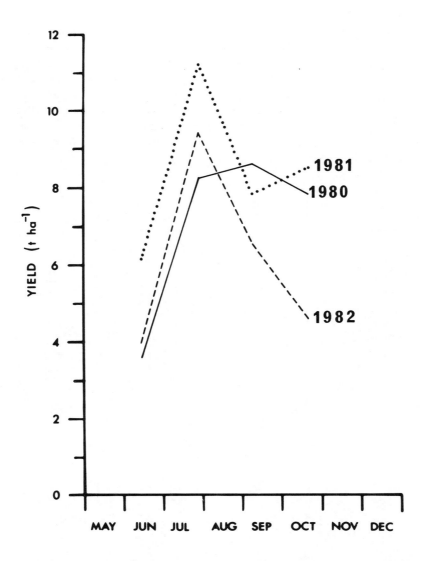

Figure 1   Seasonal development of frond biomass in three successive years at Lindale, Cumbria

since planting and management costs are minimal. However, they must demonstrate resilience to harvesting. Measurements between 1980 and 1983 showed that the combination of frost and harvesting reduced yield, because of the removal of the litter layer. The season in which harvests are taken also affects subsequent yields. Repeated cuts in spring and summer are a recognised method of bracken control, but single annual harvests bring a gradual reduction in yield in subsequent years because of loss of nutrient and carbohydrate reserves. Autumn harvesting has little effect on regrowth in subsequent years while mean autumn yield is maintained in excess of 7 t/ha/yr. This confirms the wisdom of ancient bye-laws[19] existing when bracken was exploited as a resource, which precluded harvesting before September 29th.

The effect of fertilizers on yield

Fertilizers (20:10:10, N,P,K,granules) were applied to bracken to see if yields could be increased and to investigate the level of nutrient replacement necessary to stop yields being depleted by removal of nutrients in harvested biomass. Surprisingly, yields decreased (Fig.2A) at the high application level (2t/ha). Damage may have been caused to young fronds by concentrated nutrients, especially K. Analysis of variance of treatments showed no significant yield response to spring applications, although luxury levels of nutrients were found in frond tissues (Fig 2 B-D), which suggests that N,P and K were not limiting at the study site.

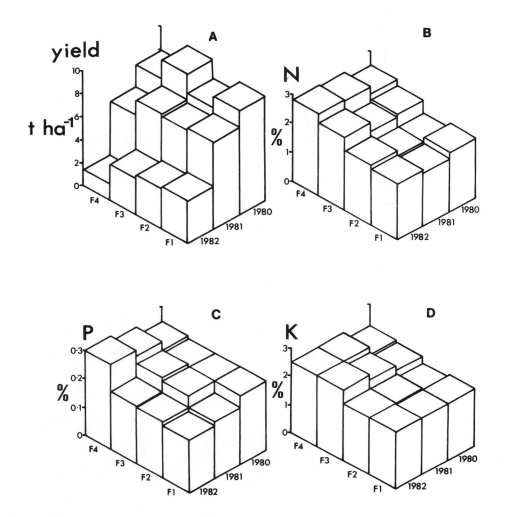

Figure 2 Bracken frond yield (A) as t/ha, in field plots at Lindale. Tissue concentrations of nitrogen (B), phosphorus (C) and potassium (D) are percentages of dry weight. F1 - F4 are 0, 0.5, 1.0 and 2.0 t/ha applications of 20:10:10 NPK fertilizer.

It is often lamented that bracken infests the most fertile hill land, but it seems more likely that bracken makes these areas fertile. Leaching experiments show[20] that bracken rhizomes mobilize mineral phosphate, and a study of nutrient cycling in an area where bracken is advancing into heather[21] similarly indicate that bracken brings larger amounts of N, P and K into circulation. Measured rates of uptake in the bracken sward (N 13.4, P 1.0, K 21.3 g/m^2) equal those observed in a Scots Pine wood[22], and exceed those from other woodland types.

THE CONVERSION OF BRACKEN TO FUELS

Anaerobic digestion of bracken

Laboratory-scale digestion trials[23] on chopped bracken gave 40% recovery of energy as biogas after 100 days. Because of problems in providing year-long supplies of feedstock to an anaerobic digester, bracken could supplement other digestable organic materials, like animal slurry and other organic wastes, including herbaceous weeds.

Conversion to solid fuel

Bracken of low moisture content (10-20%) can be compressed into solid fuel blocks of different bulk densities. Chopped bracken could be used in fluidized-bed furnaces. Conventional bales would fuel farm-based burners, and there could be domestic use of compressed briquettes in stoves and fires. A density of 240 kg/m^3 is needed for efficient use of both volume and weight in transport[24]. Briquettes of 450-960 kg/m^3 and pellets of 800-1120 kg/m^3 are necessary for home use or small-scale gasification. Dense briquettes have the advantages of (1) cheapness of transport, (2) ease of handling (eg. by hopper feeding), (3) amenability for long-term storage and (4) versatility of use.

Conversion to liquid fuel

Until the synthesis of lignases and cellulases is perfected[25], ethanol production from plants such as bracken, which are low in starch and sugars, is unlikely to be efficient or profitable. Methanol synthesis could be economic[26]. The gasification stage involves partial combustion under high pressure to give synthesis gas (mainly hydrogen and carbon monoxide) with an efficiency of up to 77%. Further reactions can produce substitute natural gas, methanol, ammonia or even petroleum[27]. Finely-chopped biomass clogs fixed-bed grates, so new fluidized-bed reactors are being designed[28]. Briquetting prior to gasification would add to the product cost.

METHODS AND COSTS OF BRACKEN EXPLOITATION

Harvesting scenarios

Three scenarios are envisaged[24] for cropping bracken as a fuel:

(1) Harvest in summer when biomass is at its peak. Fresh material could be digested to methane gas or dried in the field for briquetting. Yields will drop and continued harvesting is justified only if control is an aim.

(2) Periodic harvests at peak biomass in summer. This would

neither control bracken nor maximise energy production. Nevertheless, it may be a cost-effective use of hill land.

(3) Harvest in autumn. A sustained yield is achieved, of around 60% of summer yield. Fronds will have undergone some drying, but more drying will be required before compaction into briquettes or bales.

Costings

Exploratory costings have been made for three energy conversion routes, based on preliminary estimates for the various stages involved (Table 1). The yields assumed are high, but harvesting would initially proceed on the more productive bracken areas. No allowance has been made for the cost of replacing nutrients removed during harvesting. If full replacement cost of fertilizer for removed nutrients is included, then costs would increase by £12.3/t and £8.8/t for summer and autumn harvests, respectively. Cutting and collection costs in summer and autumn are similar; higher summer yields are balanced by a slower working rate and high moisture content.

Costings, which assume the use of conventional farm tractors and operating rates, were based on cutting trials in the 1950s[29]. Of the six systems assessed, the cheapest in summer is a combination of 4 tractors and men, 2 trailers, a flail harvestor and a buckrake. In autumn, a system is suggested using a modified Unimog 4-wheel drive truck/tractor with side mounted flail harvester, carrying and tipping loads of around 1 t into high-sided trailers for transport to the farm. Alpine tractors with front mounted flail mowers and self-loading forage wagons are designed for use on steep slopes[30] and would be best for this work.

Financial return

Because of the complexity of bracken control grants, especially after revision in 1980, it is difficult to extrapolate from grant payments to a total cost for bracken control. However, figures for 1983 (DAFS pers comm) give an estimate of £160/ha. Only with particularly successful bracken control on fertile land might stocking rates be increased by 1 ewe/ha, which might generate £40/ha (including further subsidies). This compares with the profit which a farmer could make harvesting and baling bracken at a cost of £13/t, and selling bales for pelletizing or combustion at £20/t.

Bracken solid fuels could be financially justified in the domestic market either in the form of bales or high quality pellets. Methanol from bracken is not competitive with pre-tax motor spirit, but relief of tax on petrol/methanol blends would encourage its use. In any case, bracken is not likely to be a major source of methanol since it needs more expensive preparation than wood. Methane is competitive with bottled propane but not with natural gas.

CONCLUSION

The use of bracken as an energy crop is feasible on biological, environmental and technological grounds. It is also close to financial viability and is likely to become more competitive in the future. Bracken, in conjunction with other sources of biomass, could be considered for local supplies of heat and power in rural areas,

TABLE 1 Costings per tonne of bracken (20GJ or 3.4 barrels equivalent) assuming yields of 6 t/ha/yr for direct burning and gasification, or 8t/ha/yr for anaerobic digestion

Basis of Costing	Direct burning	Gasification to methanol	Anaerobic digestion to methane
Cutting and collection	£13.00	£13.00	£12.80
Crop drying	£ 9.00	£ 9.00	£ 0.00
Densification	£26.20	£ 8.00	-
Storage (1 year)	£ 2.00	£ 6.00	£32.00
Transport (20 km)	£ 3.00	£ 3.00	£12.00
Conversion costs	£ 0.00	£54.00	£30.00
Total cost	£53.20	£93.20	£76.80
Conversion efficiency	70%	50%	45%
Total cost per GJ	£ 3.80	£ 9.32	£ 8.53

particularly if economic benefits were also obtained from bracken control. There are, however, significant barriers to the acceptance of this heterodox view of bracken as a resource, the most significant being that few of the assumptions have been tested on a commercial scale. It is difficult to see these trials being financed before another increase in oil prices brings clearer financial advantages to biofuels in general.

Nevertheless, pressures in the EEC are considerable to reduce the subsidies to uneconomic agriculture. Support to UK agriculture[31] in 1983 comprised: less favoured area grants £121 million, capital and other improvement grants £197 million, price guarantees £14 million and market regulation £1536 million, making a total of £1868 million. Since net farming income in the same year was only £1690 million, an arguable conclusion is that exploitation of weeds like bracken may be more profitable than some sectors of UK agriculture!

ACKNOWLEDGEMENTS

This work was partly funded by the UK Department of Energy and the Commission of the European Communities, whom we thank, but the views expressed in this paper are ours alone. We also thank those who assisted with field and laboratory work, notably Alison Mainwaring. Chemical analyses were carried out by the analytical service at ITE Merlewood. Holker Estates Ltd and Mr R Atkinson kindly allowed the use of their land in Cumbria for the field experiments.

REFERENCES

1) Rymer L (1976)   The history and ethnobotany of bracken. Bot. J. Linnean Society, 73, 151-176

2) Lawson G J and Callaghan T V (1983) Primary productivity and prospects for biofuels in the UK.   Int. J. Biomet., 27, 197-218

3) Giraud A (1985) La biomasse dans la compétition énergetique. In W Palz, J Coombs and D O Hall (eds). Energy from biomass - 3rd EC Conference. London, Applied Science Publs

4) Birnie R V, Ritchie P F S and Stove G C (1983) Mapping the distribution of bracken in Scotland by remote sensing techniques. Pilot Study Report; Aberdeen: Macaulay Institute for Soil Research

5) Weaver R E (1984) Integration of remote sensing data for moorland mapping in Northern England.   Presented at 18th International Symposium on Remote Sensing and the Environment, Paris

6) Best R H (1959) The major land uses of Great Britain. Wye College

7) Taylor J A (1985) Bracken encroachment rates in Britain. J. Soil Use and Management, 1, 53-56

8) Bunce R G H, Barr C J and Whittaker H A (1981) A stratified system for ecological mapping. In R H Fuller (ed.) Ecological mapping from ground, air and space. 39-46, Cambridge: ITE

9) Hendry G F (1958) The size of Scotland's bracken problem. Scot. Agric. Econ. 9, 25-28

10) McKelvie A D and Scragg E B (1973) The control of bracken by asulam. Scot. Agric. 51, 474-480

11) Pearsall W H and Gorham E (1956) Standing crops of natural vegetation. Oikos, 7, 193-201

12) Watt A S (1964) Some factors affecting bracken in Breckland. J. Ecol., 52, 63-77

13) Callaghan T V, Scott R and Whittaker H A (1981) The yield, development and chemical composition of some fast-growing indigenous and naturalised British plant species in relation to management as energy crops. Report to UK Department of Energy. Cambridge: ITE

14) Callaghan T V, Scott R, Lawson G J and Mainwaring A M (1984) An experimental assessment of native and naturalized species of plants as renewable sources of energy in Great Britain. I. Bracken (Pteridium aquilinum). Report to UK Dept of Energy. Cambridge: ITE

15) Hendrick J (1919) Bracken rhizomes and their food value. Trans. Roy. Highland Agric. Soc., 31, 227-236

16) Chen L-Z and Lindley D K (1981) Primary production and nutrient

cycling in a bracken grassland ecosystem. <u>Merlewood R & D Paper</u> 80. Cambridge: ITE

17) Lowday J E (1984) The effects of cutting and asulam on the frond and rhizome characteristics of bracken. <u>Asp. Appl. Biol.</u>, 5, 275-281

18) Lowday J E (1984) Frost damage to emerging fronds during bracken cutting experiments. <u>Trans. Bot. Soc. Edinb.</u>, 44, 151-155

19) Davies-Shiel M (1972) A little-known Late Mediaeval industry. I. The making of potash for soap in Lakeland. <u>Trans. Cumb. Westmld. Antiq. Soc.</u>, 62, 85-111

20) Mitchell J (1973) Mobilization of phosphorus by <u>Pteridium aquilinum</u>. <u>Plant and Soil</u>, 38, 489-491

21) Sponder P M (1979) <u>Nutrient cycling in heather and bracken ecosystems</u>. Unpublished PhD Thesis, University of Hull

22) Ovington J D (1965) Organic production, turnover and mineral cycling in woodlands. <u>Biol. Rev.</u>, 40, 295-336.

23) Stafford D A and Hughes D E (1981) Fermentation to biogas using agricultural residues and energy crops. In W Palz, P Chartier and D Hall (eds) <u>Energy from Biomass 1st EC Conference</u>. 400-410. London: Applied Science Publishers

24) Callaghan T V, Lawson G J and Scott R (1982) Bracken as an energy crop? In D O Hall and J Morton (eds) <u>Solar World Forum</u>, 1239-1247. Oxford: Pergamon Press

25) Milgrom L (1985) Lignase: biotechnology's new moneyspinner. <u>New Scientist</u>, 1456, 16-17

26) Energy Technology Support Unit (1982) Strategic review of the renewable energy technologies. Vols I and II. London: HMSO

27) Ader G, Kent A V, Bridgwater A V and Hatt B W (1981) Techno-economic evaluation of thermal routes for processing biomass to methane, methanol and liquid hydrocarbons. In W Palz, P Chartier and D O Hall (eds) <u>Energy from Biomass</u>, 598-606. London: Applied Science Publishers

28) Van den Aarsen F J, Beenackers A A C M and van Swaij W P M (1982) Performance of a rice husk fluidized bed pilot plant gasifier. In <u>Proc. Producer Gas Conference</u>, Sri Lanka. Stockholm: The Beijer Inst

29) McCreath J B and Forrest J D (1958) Bracken control. <u>West of Scotland Agricultural College Research Bulletin</u> 24

30) Lawson G J, Callaghan T V and Scott R (1980) Natural vegetation as renewable energy crop. Rep. to UK Dept of Energy, Cambridge: ITE

31) MAFF, DAFS and DANI (1984) <u>Annual Review of Agriculture 1983</u>. London: HMSO

Stomatal conductance and transpiration from a bracken understorey in a pine plantation

J Roberts

INTRODUCTION

The major habitat type for bracken studies reported in this volume is the open situation of hillslopes or lowland heaths. The results reported here were obtained in forest plantations but because bracken is often regarded as a species of wooded habitats[1,2] the results can be considered as defining the baseline behaviour of the species, to which its physiology and growth in open situations can be referred. Concern has been expressed over the spread of bracken in open habitats but little information exists on its status in wooded habitats. The areas planted to forest have increased in the United Kingdom particularly in the west and north of the country but these recent plantings consist almost entirely of densely-stocked spruce, pine or larch on wetter, less well-aerated soils which would not particularly favour the growth of bracken. Although the future management and resulting structure of these newer forests may well not favour bracken invasion it is nevertheless a very common understorey species in drier well-established forest and often achieves complete dominance of the field layer.

Very few studies have made a separation of transpiration contributed by different layers in forests. Models of water use by forests which neglect forest components may be insensitive to management changes which influence the amount of understorey. The principle objective of the studies reported in this paper was to examine the contribution of the understorey component to total forest transpiration. The bracken understorey which was the subject of this investigation was typical of bracken growing within woods and plantations in the UK and therefore the results and conclusions can be regarded as representative of its behaviour in these situations.

This paper describes results obtained on stomatal conductance and its control, leaf area development and transpiration from bracken in a Scots pine (<u>Pinus sylvestris</u>) plantation in Thetford Chase, East

Anglia, and examines some aspects of understoreys as they influence forest transpiration.

SITE DESCRIPTION AND METHODS

The Scots pine stand in which the study was conducted was in Thetford Chase (NGR TL806835), East Anglia and was planted in 1931. At the time of the studies, made in 1976 and 1977, there were 600 trees/ha, which were about 16 m tall. During 1976 the site of this bracken study was also the location of an intensive micrometeorological study of the profiles, both within and above the forest canopy, of temperature, humidity, radiation and windspeed[3,4]. These latter papers also give the formulae used to calculate forest evaporation from the micrometeorological data and a representative range of results are also presented later in this paper. In addition to the more detailed studies, two Automatic Weather Stations[5] were located on a tower at a level above the top of the trees and operated continuously throughout 1976 and 1977.

A full description of the plant physiological measurements has already been given[6,7]. In the abnormally dry year of 1976, measurements were made of stomatal conductance (g_s) with a diffusion porometer (Mk 2, Delta-T Devices, Burwell, Cambridgeshire) on up to four pinnae levels. Leaf area index (LAI) was determined by clipping ten 1 m^2 plots on several occasions throughout the growing season and separating the clipped plants into component pinnae levels. Aerodynamic conductance (g_a) was determined from a wetted replica of a bracken plant made of blotting paper whose weight loss was determined at intervals while the wet surface temperature and the absolute humidity of the air above was known. g_a was calculated from the following expression

$$g_a = \frac{E}{\chi_1 - \chi}$$

where E is the water loss rate, χ_1 is the absolute humidity of air saturated at leaf temperature and χ is the absolute humidity of the ambient air.

Transpiration of the bracken canopy was calculated from the Monteith[8] version of the Penman equation given below.

$$\lambda ET = \frac{sA + \rho C_p D g_a}{s + (C_p/\lambda) \{1 + (g_a/g_c)\}}$$

where A = 0.13 of the available radiative energy above the forest canopy,

C_p = specific heat of air at constant pressure
E_T = transpiration rate
g_a = aerodynamic conductance
g_c = canopy conductance
D = specific humidity deficit
s = rate of change of saturated specific humidity with temperature

λ = latent heat of evaporation of water and

ρ = density of air

The canopy conductance (g_c) was calculated from stomatal conductances (g_s) and leaf area indices (LAI) using the formula

$$g_c = \sum_1^n LAI(P_i)(g_{s_i}^L + g_{s_i}^U)$$

where $LAI(P_i)$ is the leaf area index at a given pinna location, $g_{s_i}^L$ and $g_{s_i}^U$ being the stomatal conductances of the lower and upper pinnae surfaces respectively. Leaf area indices were obtained by interpolation between harvest dates immediately prior to and following the stomatal conductance sample day.

In 1977 an investigation was made into the responses of g_s in three treatments established in bracken plots in the forest. One of these treatments was watered frequently ($\simeq$ every 7 days) to prevent the development of soil moisture deficits, another plot had a transparent shelter to exclude all rainfall and a third plot was untreated.

RESULTS

From several previous years of study in this forest a large amount of information was available on the radiation, temperature, humidity and windspeed conditions in profiles from immediately above the bracken canopy to the free air above the tree tops. Stewart[9] calculated that, when averaged over daylight periods, 13% of the above-canopy solar radiation reached the upper level of the bracken canopy. In comparison with the above-canopy windspeeds, those measured at the bracken level were usually around one tenth of these values[10]. Examples of the profiles of temperature and humidity deficits measured from just above the bracken canopy to above the tree crowns are given in Table 1. These data show very small gradients of temperature and humidity deficit. Because of these small gradients it was considered justifiable to use uncorrected temperature and humidity deficit data from Automatic Weather Stations located at the top of a tower above the tree canopy to represent the conditions at the understorey level for the studies reported. Solar radiation measured in these weather stations was multiplied by 0.13 to provide estimates of conditions at the understorey.

The leaf area index rose from 0 in late May to above 1 by early July (Figure 1). There was a slight but significant decline followed by a rise in mid-September. The green leaf area fell to zero by the end of October.

In comparison with other crops and vegetation, the stomatal conductances were fairly low with maximum values around 4 mm/s. These values were observed in the early parts of the days on the lower surfaces of the foliage. The conductance of the upper surfaces was always less than half of these values. No clear differences emerge in stomatal conductance on pinnae at different locations on a frond.

251

TABLE 1.   Differences in temperature (ΔT) and specific humidity deficit (ΔD) above and below the forest on 22 September 1976. Measurements are referenced to those made at 27.8 m, tree top height was at 16.5 m and the top of the bracken canopy at about 1.2 m.

Time (GMT)	0600		0800		1000		1200		1400		1600	
Height (m)	$\Delta T(^\circ C)$	$\Delta D(g\ kg^{-1})$	$\Delta T(^\circ C)$	$\Delta D(g\ kg^{-1})$	$\Delta T(^\circ C)$	$\Delta D(g\ kg^{-1})$	$\Delta T(^\circ C)$	$\Delta D(g\ kg^{-1})$	$\Delta T(^\circ C)$	$\Delta D(g\ kg^{-1})$	$\Delta T(^\circ C)$	$\Delta D(g\ kg^{-})$
27.8	0	0	0	0	0	0	0	0	0	0	0	0
24.8	0.02	-0.02	0	-0.13	0.02	-0.04	0.02	0.02	0	-0.01	-0.01	-0.01
20.5	0.02	-0.01	0.01	-0.18	0.07	0.02	-0.10	0.05	0.01	0.03	-0.03	0.02
17.4	0.03	-0.03	0.02	-0.01	0.21	0.05	0.04	0.07	0.04	0.05	-0.05	0.02
10.2	0.09	-0.01	0.01	-0.55	0.24	0.14	0.11	0.17	0	0.19	-0.14	0.07
7.3	0.10	-0.01	0.08	-0.52	0.13	0.14	0.07	0.20	-0.04	0.21	-0.15	0.08
3.2	0.10	-0.01	0.09	-0.71	-0.06	0.24	-0.09	0.33	-0.16	0.39	-0.20	0.24
1.2	0.07	-0.01	0.03	-0.72	-0.35	0.39	-0.03	0.54	0.08	0.60	-0.29	0.56

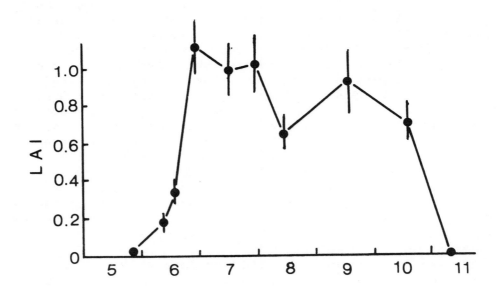

Figure 1   Changes in leaf area index (LAI) of bracken during 1976. Vertical bars indicate one standard error either side of the mean.

Conductances fall fairly sharply by mid-morning (Figure 2) but then fall only slowly through the rest of the day. The aerodynamic

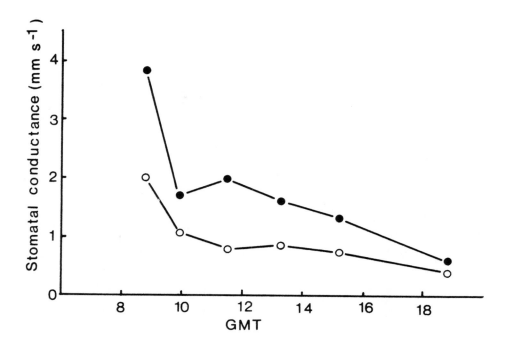

Figure 2   A comparison of stomatal conductance of upper (o) and lower (•) surfaces of bracken pinnae on 4 August 1976.

conductance ranged from 9 to 13 mm/s with a mean of 12 mm/s. These values are low compared with many field crops but this is to be expected in the low windspeed conditions experienced at the forest floor.

The values of stomatal conductance and leaf area index in canopy layers were used to calculate the canopy conductance and these values, in turn, were used with the aerodynamic conductance and climatic data to calculate transpiration. Daily values of transpiration from the bracken, and total transpiration from the forest measured by the micrometeorological equipment, is shown in Table 2. The percentage contribution from the bracken understorey rose from about 20 per cent in June to nearly 60 per cent in July but fell again from September.

The experiments carried out in 1977 involved irrigated, droughted and natural plots but the effects of soil moisture conditions on stomatal conductance were not dramatic. Statistically significant differences in stomatal conductance measured on bracken in the irrigated and droughted plots only occurred from late July onwards, and then, only on days of high specific humidity deficit and radiation. No significant differences in leaf water potential were observed on the irrigated and droughted plots.

The relationships of stomatal conductance to ambient radiation and specific humidity deficit were examined. In comparing stomatal conductance with radiation, data were classified according to specific humidity deficit (0-4 g/kg and 4-8 g/kg). Similarly the relationship of stomatal conductance with specific humidity deficit was examined after the data had been separated into groups defined by the radiation conditions. Data were separated into those occurring in two trunk

TABLE 2. Comparison of total transpiration from bracken and forest
(trees plus bracken) for 15 days in 1976

Date	Forest (mm)	Bracken (mm)	Bracken/Forest %	Monthly mean (%)
9 June	2.1	0.51	24	
11 June	1.8	0.38	21	21
14 June	1.8	0.41	23	
15 June	1.8	0.35	19	
6 July	1.9	0.97	51	
9 July	1.1	0.72	65	57
13 July	1.1	0.66	60	
15 July	1.3	0.70	54	
4 August	2.6	0.57	22	
6 August	1.3	0.56	43	33
9 August	1.5	0.45	30	
11 August	1.6	0.58	36	
16 September	0.9	0.19	21	26
22 September	1.3	0.41	31	
12 October	1.1	0.21	19	19

space radiation classes (0-50 W/m^2 and 50-100 W/m^2). Table 3 presents the statistical relationships of these comparisons. It can be seen that a significant positive correlation exists between conductance and radiation under all conditions and is none of the data was there evidence of a flattening out of this relationship under the radiation conditions measured. On the other hand stomatal conductance was negatively correlated with specific humidity deficit but only in the data taken when radiation exceeded 50 W/m^2 in the trunk space.

DISCUSSION

A somewhat surprising result emerging from our studies on bracken in forests is the high percentage contribution from the bracken understorey to the total forest transpiration which was observed on several occasions during the summer period in 1976. Canadian workers have also shown[11,12] that the understorey in a Douglas fir forest, can contribute over 70 per cent of the forest transpiration and this effect occurred when substantial soil moisture deficit conditions prevailed. However, the decreased percentage transpiration from the trees suggested from our study is thought to be related much less to the low soil moisture conditions than to the

TABLE 3.   Regression equation and correlation coefficient (r) for the
relationships between (1) stomatal conductance (y) and radiation in the
trunk space (x) in two specific humidity deficit categories and (2)
stomatal conductance (y) and specific humidity deficit (x) in two
radiation classes

(1)		(2)	
Stomatal conductance		Stomatal conductance	
versus radiation		versus deficit	
$0 - 4$ g K g^{-1} :	$4 - 8$ g Kg^{-1}	$0 - 50$ W m^{-2} :	$50 - 100$ W m^{-2}
:	:		:
$y = 1.77 + 0.012X$:	$y = 1.23 + 0.017X$	NO :	$y = 3.38 - 0.151X$
$r = 0.51$:	$r = 0.51$	RELATIONSHIP :	$r = 0.42$
$p > 0.01$:	$p > 0.01$	:	$p > 0.01$

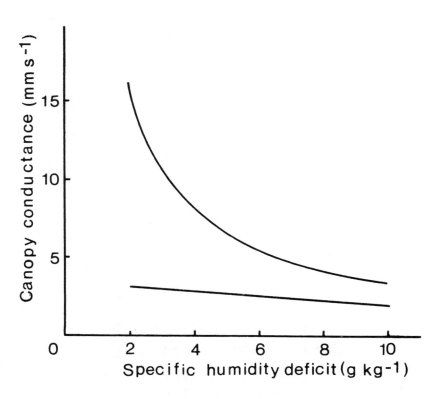

Figure 3   The change in canopy conductance with specific humidity
deficit of a Scots pine forest (upper line) and the bracken
understorey (lower line).

higher atmospheric deficit conditions which prevailed during the
drought conditions and the differing response of bracken and the trees

255

to these atmospheric deficits. Reports for a wide range of species, particularly trees, have shown decreasing stomatal conductances with increasing vapour pressure deficits. The response of Scots pine to increasing vapour pressure deficit has been reported for seedling and mature plants and this effect has also been observed in this particular forest using micro meteorological techniques[13] (Figure 3). Stomatal conductance, and therefore the canopy conductance, of bracken also declines with increasing specific humidity deficit (this paper) but the rate of change is much less. Using these conductance and vapour pressure deficit relationships to calculate transpiration for forest and bracken (Figure 4), shows that, with increasing vapour pressure deficit, forest transpiration rises slightly at first but then remains constant over a wide range of deficit. Transpiration from the bracken would continue to rise and therefore the ratio of bracken transpiration to forest transpiration rises under higher vapour pressure deficit conditions. These relationships would explain the results observed in 1976.

Additionally we have seen that stomatal conductance of bracken is limited by radiation levels in the forest but the stomatal conductance of the trees would have reached a plateau in response to light at the tree canopy level. Therefore, a period of weather in which high radiation and dry atmospheric conditions prevailed would favour an increase in bracken transpiration, while the transpiration of the trees would remain largely unaffected. It is only under more severe conditions of soil moisture deficit that the stomatal conductances of the bracken[7] or trees[13] is affected.

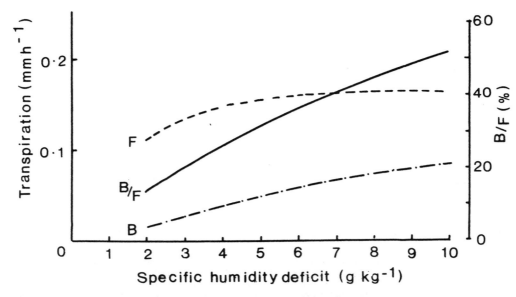

Figure 4   Effect of increasing specific humidity deficit on forest transpiration (F) bracken transpiration (B) and their ratio (B/F).

The presence of an understorey may have the effect of eliminating some water use differences between different tree species in plantations. Roberts, Pitman and Wallace[14] compared the transpiration in a Corsican pine and a Scot pine stand in Thetford Chase, East Anglia. No bracken grew in the Corsican pine stand but a vigorous understorey grew below the Scots pines which had a more open canopy. Although differences in transpiration were noted when only the trees were compared, the contribution from the bracken in the Scots pine stand was sufficient to equalise these differences and similar total forest transpiration therefore resulted.

The stomatal conductance of bracken shows an increase in relation to elevated levels of radiation at the understorey level but no evidence of a light-saturated response was observed. Clearly it will be necessary to examine more closely the photosynthetic response of bracken to increased lighting but it now seems unlikely that bracken will show the light-saturated response regarded as typical of plants from shaded habitats[15].

The well-ventilated nature of the forest site in this study meant that humidity deficits at the understorey level closely matched the values measured outside the forest and it is also evident that the stomatal conductance of bracken is not greatly limited by these humidity deficits. There is evidence[15] that fern species from shaded habitats have generally low stomatal conductances and that these show large reductions in response to increasing humidity deficits with the net effect of preventing excessive transpiration.

The responses observed here in forest bracken suggest that the plant is able to fully utilize non-forest habitats precisely because its stomatal conductance, photosynthesis and growth do not appear to show a light-saturated response at low levels. The plant is, furthermore, not restricted by humidity deficit, to which open habitats are especially subject.

REFERENCES

1) Rymer L (1976) The history and ethnobotany of bracken. Bot. J. Linn. Soc., 73, 151-176

2) Watt A S (1976) The ecological status of bracken. Bot. J. Linn. Soc., 73, 217-239

3) Stewart J B and Thom A S (1973) Energy budgets in a pine forest. Q. J. R. Met. Soc., 99, 154-170

4) McNeil D D and Shuttleworth W J (1975) Comparative measurements of the energy fluxes over a pine forest. Boundary Layer Meteorology, 9, 297-313

5) Strangeways I C (1972) Automatic Weather Stations for network operation. Weather, 27, 403-408

6) Roberts J, Pymar C F, Wallace J S and Pitman R M (1980) Seasonal changes in leaf area, stomatal and canopy conductances and transpiration from bracken below a forest canopy. J. Appl. Ecol., 17, 409-422

7) Roberts J, Wallace J S and Pitman R M (1984) Factors affecting stomatal conductances of bracken below a forest canopy. J. Appl. Ecol., 21, 643-655

8) Monteith J L (1965) Evaporation and Environment. In State and movement of water in living organisations. 19th Symposium of the Society for Experimental Biology

9) Stewart J B (1978) A micrometeorological investigation into the factors controlling the evaporation from a forest. PhD Thesis, University of Reading

10) Oliver H R (1971) Wind profiles in and above a forest canopy, Q. J. R. Met. Soc., 97, 548-553

11) Tan C S (1977) A study of stomatal diffusion resistance in a Douglas fir forest. PhD Thesis, University of British Colombia.

12) Tan C S, Black T A and Nnyamah J U (1977) Characteristics of stomatal diffusion resistance in a Douglas fir forest exposed to soil water deficits. Can. J. For. Res., 7, 595-604

13) Stewart J B and de Bruin H A R (1985) Preliminary study of dependence of surface conductance of Thetford forest on environmental conditions. In, The Forest - Atmosphere Interaction, B A Hutchinson and B B Hicks, (eds) D Reidel Publishing Company. 91-104

14) Roberts J, Pitman R M and Wallace J S (1982) A comparison of evaporation from stands of Scots pine and Corsican pine in Thetford Chase, East Anglia. J. Appl. Ecol., 19, 859-872

15) Nobel P S, Calkin H W and Gibson A C (1984) Influence of PAR, temperature and water vapour concentration on gas exchange by ferns. Physiologia Plantarum, 62, 527-534

Transpiration and evaporation from bracken (Pteridium aquilinum L. Kuhn) in open habitats

J I Pitman and R M Pitman

INTRODUCTION

Bracken (<u>Pteridium aquilinum</u> L. Kuhn) is the dominant or co-dominant species over large areas of upland Britain, lowland acid heaths and degenerate and abandoned pasture[21]. Vegetation of these open habitats prior to invasion of bracken is usually Festuca-Agrostis-Molinia grassland and acid ericaceous heathlands, of low stature, limited leaf area and shallow rooting habit[5]. Whilst considerable data now exists on changes in the hydrological cycle resulting from the replacement of short grass by forest[7,16], or heather moorland by forest[2,8,24], little data is currently available on the hydrological effects of the replacement of grass and heather moorland by bracken[11,13].

This paper presents data on the hourly, daily and seasonal rates of water loss by evaporation and transpiration from a pure stand of bracken in a lowland habitat, and it utilizes the resistance/conductance approach of the Penman-Monteith equation[9]. Comparison is also made with transpiration losses determined by an independent soil water balance.

THEORY

The combination model of Penman-Monteith[14] is written as

$$\lambda E = \frac{\Delta' R_n + \rho C_p (e_s - e_z) k_a + I (1-c)}{\Delta' + \gamma (1 + k_a/k_s)} \tag{1}$$

in which I is a model calculation or field measurement of canopy interception loss by evaporation[3,16], R_n the flux density of net radiation, C_p the specific heat of air at constant pressure, γ the psychrometric constant, Δ' the slope of the vapour pressure-temperature curve at air temperature T, e_z the vapour pressure at height z above the surface, e_s the saturation vapour pressure at air temperature, k_s and k_a the stomatal and aerodynamic conductances, and c, a variable calculated from[18]

$$c = \frac{\Delta' + \gamma}{\Delta' + \gamma(1+k_a/k_s)} \qquad (2)$$

which compensates for including transpiration losses in wet conditions.

The aerodynamic conductance, $1/r_a$, in this paper has been estimated from the expression

$$r_a = \frac{1}{k^2 u}\left[\ln\left(\frac{z-d}{z_o}\right)\right]^2 + r_b \qquad (3)$$

where k is von Karman's constant, d the zero plane displacement, z_o the roughness length, u the widespread at height z, u* the friction velocity, and r_b the 'excess resistance' term of Thom[22], to allow for pressure or bluff-body effects which have no counterpart in heat or mass transfer. The value of r_b is estimated from the expression

$$r_b = 6.266u*^{-2/3} \qquad (4)$$

derived by Thom, the friction velocity being derived from u, d and z_o.

MATERIALS AND METHODS

The data in this paper were collected during the growing seasons of 1980, 1981 and 1982 from an open heathland site located at West Heath Common, near Rogate, West Sussex (NGR SU72 786228)[16]. The experimental plot, of 0.25 ha, was centred within an extensive mature bracken stand developed as a result of the burning of senile Calluna heathland during 1976 and 1977. Soils developed over the Lower Greensand are ferro-humic podzols of the Shirrel Heath Series[10].

An automatic weather station (AWS)[20] located within the enclosure recorded values of solar radiation, net radiation, air temperature, wet bulb depression, windspeed and wind direction at 2.2m, and rainfall at five minute intervals on a Microdata logger. This data was stored as hourly averages after quality control[12].

Seasonal variation of bracken biomass, height, frond density, leaf area index (LAI) and area per frond was determined by harvesting four $1m^2$ quadrats at weekly and monthly intervals during 1980 and 1981. LAI was determined by laboratory measurement on a Li-Cor area measuring instrument. Allometric regressions were also developed from the LAI and growth data for both the 1981 and 1982 seasons.

Interception was measured by determining stemflow and throughfall together as net runoff, from two $2m^2$ sealed quadrats. Throughfall was measured by two 15m lengths of PVC guttering (area $2m^2$) suspended beneath the canopy. Both systems were logged at two minute intervals.

Soil moisture was monitored at weekly intervals down to a depth of 200 cm, at 10 cm intervals, by three sets of six neutron probe tubes, using a Wallingford Neutron Moisture Probe.

Soil water potentials ψ_s were determined with tensiometers down to a depth of 180 cm at 20 cm intervals, and by gypsum electrical resistance blocks; these were read weekly, and on every porometry day.

Bracken water potentials ψ_e were determined in the field on all pinnae levels using a small pressure bomb[22], usually within one minute of collection.

Stomatal resistances (rs) were measured on both the abaxial and adaxial surface of bracken pinnae, between the lowest and highest pinnae levels, using a Delta-T Devices Mk II diffusion porometer. Pinna conductance was estimated from

$$ks = \frac{1}{rs} = \left(\frac{1}{rs_{ad}} + \frac{1}{rs_{ab}} \right) \qquad (5)$$

and canopy conductance, kc, calculated from this and the LAI of each frond, summed over the whole frond:

$$kc = \sum_{i}^{n} \left[LAI\ (Pi) \cdot \frac{1}{rs} \right] \qquad (6)$$

A non-dimensional sensitivity coefficient[1] was calculated by differentiating the Penman-Monteith equation with respect to each of the input variables: Rn, rs, ra, T and e in turn, and calculating the function

$$Si = \frac{\delta \lambda E}{\delta Pi} \cdot \frac{Pi}{\lambda E} \qquad (7)$$

so that Si represents that fraction of the change in variable Pi that is transmitted to change Et.

RESULTS

Growth and development of leaf area

Seasonal changes in the development of the bracken canopy are shown in figure 1. Several allometric growth parameters were statistically tested against LAI measurements using the Li-Cor. Best fit regression equations were obtained between pinnae length (cm) and the square root of LAI (cm). For 1980 data Y = -0.92 + 0.59 X, (R = 0.93, n= 100), whilst for 1981 data Y = -0.49 + 0.47 X, (R = 0.94, n = 30). The first three pinnae levels contributed > 80% of the LAI; vertically integrated profiles of LAI showed that the median (50%) LAI point was 0.64 to 0.7 of frond height. The lowermost pinnae (level 1) were between 0.3 and 0.5 frond height. Die back of bracken fronds always started at the lowermost pinna level, and was particularly severe in 1981, due either to low ambient humidity or low soil water levels. Measurements of stomatal conductance were made at all pinnae levels, including those that were rapidly yellowing.

Approximately 91% of the bracken biomass (6 kg/m^2) is underground. About 64% of the root system was located within the top 50 cm of the soil profile, and no rhizomes penetrated as far as the Bh horizon.

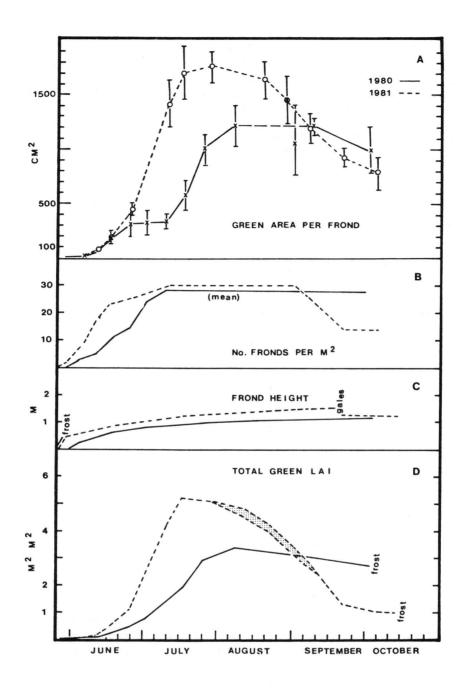

Figure 1   Seasonal variation of measured bracken stand parameters at West Heath Common, West Sussex

Climatic parameters

The summer of 1981 was the warmest and driest since 1976, whereas that of 1980 was close to normal. Average annual rainfall for 1980-1982 was 950 mm, and potential evaporation 550 mm. During the period June to 15th September, rainfall totalled 139 mm in 1981, compared to 330 mm in 1980 and 254 mm in 1982. Mean temperatures for the period June-September averaged 18°C, with maximum monthly values averaging 23.7°C.

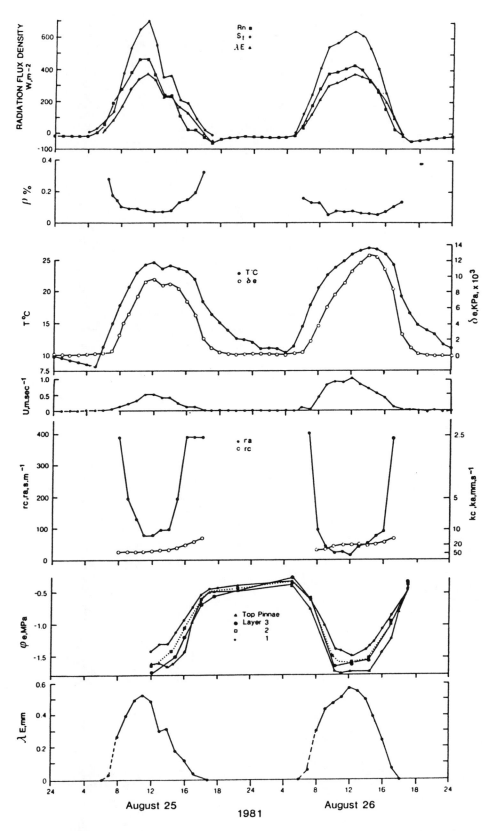

Figure 2   Diurnal   variation   of   plant and atmospheric variables for
the mature bracken stand at West Heath, August 25 and 26, 1981

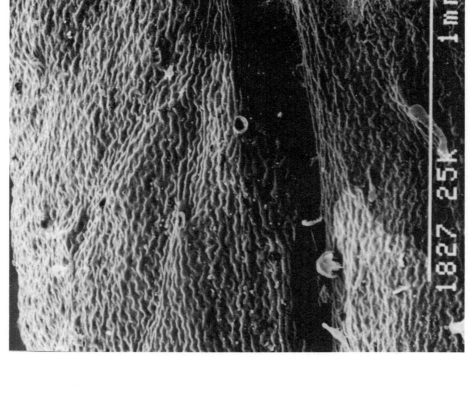

Figure 3b Upper, adaxial, surface of bracken pinna. No stomata observed. Pits and apertures seen are probably basal scars of pinna hairs.

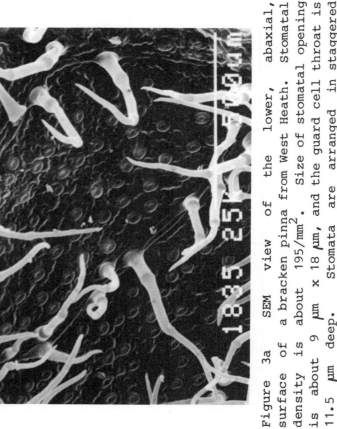

Figure 3a SEM view of the lower, abaxial, surface of a bracken pinna from West Heath. Stomatal density is about 195/mm². Size of stomatal opening is about 9 μm x 18 μm, and the guard cell throat is 11.5 μm deep. Stomata are arranged in staggered columns about 75 μm apart, at 70-75 μm intervals.

Aerodynamic resistance

Values of aerodynamic resistance, rav, calculated from (3) reflect the changing height of the bracken during the season. Roughness length, zo, and zero plane displacement, d, were calculated from the empirical functions d = 0.63 h and zo = 0.13 h. Using these functions for d and zo, and a calculated u* from (4), rav = 73.8/u when h = 75 cm to rav = 44.5/u when h = 155 cm. The 'excess resistance' term contributed about 34% and 42% of rav when h = 75 and 155 cm respectively. The diurnal variation in u (Fig. 2) resulted in minimum values of rav of 20-40 s/m around midday, for h = 155 cm, to early morning and late evening values > 100 s/m. Resistances for the shorter pioneer canopy (h = 75 cm) were about twice these values.

Stomatal conductance

The distribution and abundance of stomata on bracken pinnae is shown in the photographs, Figures 3a and 3b. Very few stomata are present on the adaxial surface.

Diurnal variations of stomatal conductance (1/rs) show a characteristic pattern (Fig.4) common to both seasons' data from pioneer and mature bracken communities. Highest conductances occur on the abaxial (lower) surface, are at a maximum shortly after sunrise (gs 10-12 mm/s), and fall during the day to values between 2-4 mm/s. Adaxial (upper) surfaces show little variation, and average 2-4 mm/s throughout the day. When under water stress, however, abaxial conductances are reduced to 4-6 mm/s.

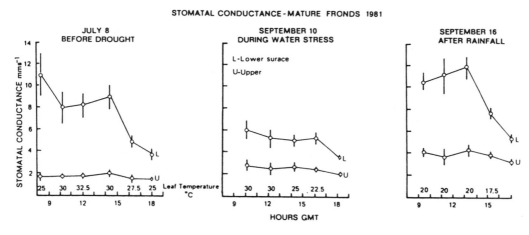

Figure 4 Response of bracken stomatal conductance to changes in soil water potentials, showing depression of ks and its subsequent recovery after rainfall. Soil water potentials were -0.01 MPa, -0.84 MPa and -0.02 MPa on each of the three days respectively

Seasonal variations of stomatal conductance show this phenomenon very clearly (Fig.5). Minimum values are similar for both seasons'data. Maximum values, however, show a very marked difference, with the 1981 values exhibiting a severly reduced ks in late August-early September, associated with large soil water deficits. 1980 maximum values tended to increase as the season progressed.

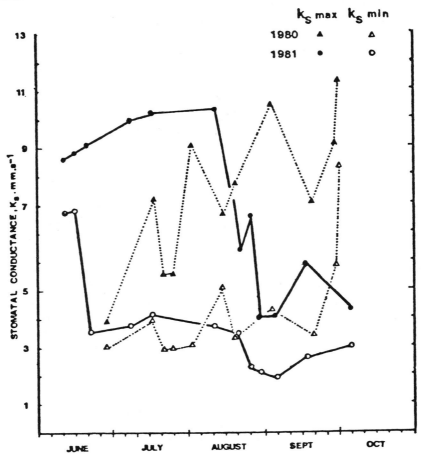

Figure 5   Seasonal variation of stomatal conductance, 1980-1981

Seasonal changes in canopy conductance, kc, reflect this difference in stomatal behaviour, with the combined effects of enhanced die-back and reduced conductance being clearly evident (Fig.6).

The major finding of importance here is that bracken growing in open habitats responds to soil water deficits by reducing stomatal conductance of its abaxial surface, and by die-back[16]. Other factors affecting stomatal conductance are discussed more fully elsewhere[11,14,6].

Transpiration

Rates of transpiration from both the mature bracken and pioneer bracken were calculated for all days on which porometry data was collected. Maximum daily rates are close to the available Rn for the mature bracken, although for the pioneer bracken values are lower. In both the 1980 and 1981 seasons, the effect of water stress was more apparant on the pioneer community, with rates under these conditions being only 60% of the mature bracken plants.

266

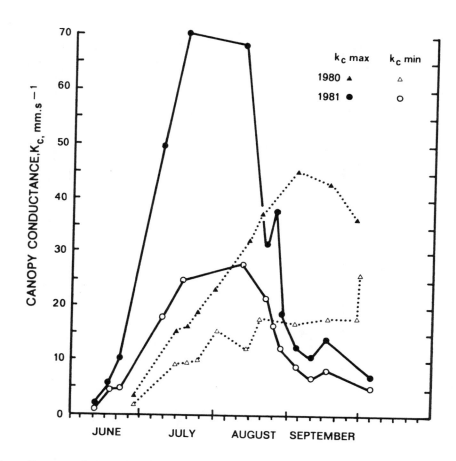

Figure 6   Seasonal variation of canopy conductance, 1980-1981

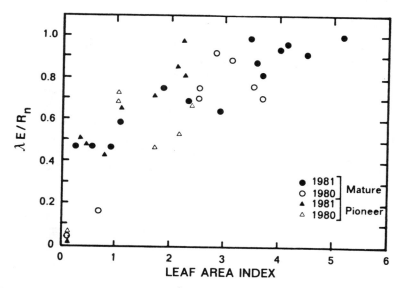

Figure 7   Dependence of λ E/Rn on LAI for all data when AWS was operational.

        Seasonal values of the ratio λ E/Rn (Fig.7) show that the ratio is highly correlated with the green LAI of the bracken, for both pioneer and mature plants, and is close to unity when LAI equals 5.

However, when ψs is more negative than -0.1 MPa, the ratio λE/Rn is better related to ψs than LAI, which for the 1981 data showed a large decrease at this time (Fig.1).   Figure 8 shows the very high correlation existing between the actual to potential evaporation rate (with ks = 0) ratio and ψs, indicating the very real effect of reduced soil water potentials on transpiration.

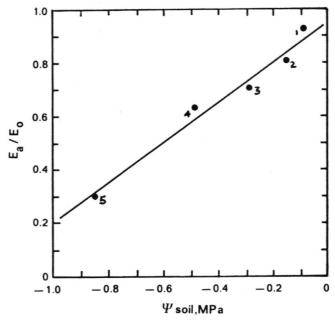

Figure 8   Ratio of actual to potential rates of evaporation (ks = 0) between 25.8.81 (point 1) and 10.8.81 (point 5).

Estimates of evaporation on a daily basis for the bracken growth period were made by interpolating daily values from the field-measured ks, LAI and hourly AWS parameters in equation 1, with ka calculated from the AWS u values. These values were then used to calculate a cumulative total evaporation for the two seasons. Net precipitation was measured directly by the interception plots; in the 1981 season, interception losses accounted for 40.1% of the gross precipitation.   Figure 9 shows the plot of cumulative (λ E-net precipitation) and the measured total soil water in the top 180 cm as determined by neutron probing. Agreement between the two methods is very good, and within the standard error of determination of soil moisture change.   It suggests that the measured and estimated values of kc are realistic, although they differ significantly from bracken data obtained in woodlands and forests.

Sensitivity analysis

The most important controls over transpiration when soil water is not limiting are, in order of importance, Rn, kc, ra, e, and T. When soil water is limiting, kc becomes the most important variable (Skc ranges from -0.16 to -0.87 diurnally).
These results are similar to those described for grass[1], and

268

reflect the dominant role of Rn and ra in determining transpiration.

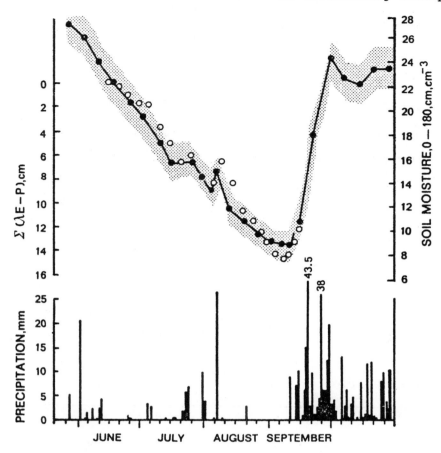

Figure 9   Measured soil moisture in top 180 cm of soil profile, and
cumulative   transpiration   minus   measured   total   throughfall   plus
stemflow.   Shaded   zone is standard deviation of soil moisture probe
determinations for six tubes.

DISCUSSION AND CONCLUSIONS

The measured adaxial and abaxial conductances presented in this
paper   form a natural continuum of the data for understorey bracken at
Thetford   Forest[13,14].   However,   because of the very much larger LAI
of   open   habitat   bracken   compared   to   forest   bracken,   values of the
canopy   conductance   are   between 5 and 15 times larger.   This, combined
with   the   higher   Rn   and   e   values   of   open   habitats,   results   in
evaporation   and   transpiration   rates   which   averaged 1.98 mm/d in 1980
and   2.74   mm/d   in 1981, on porometry days; the overall mean was 2.44
mm/d.   Daily   maximum   rates   exceeded 5mm/d.   These rates are about 5
times   those   recorded   at   Thetford   Forest.   Unlike the Thetford data,
bracken   in   open   habitats   responds to soil water deficits by reducing
stomatal   conductance.   The most likely controls on this are soil water
potentials   and atmospheric vapour pressure deficits.
What   hydrological   effects   can   therefore   be   expected   when
invasion   of other open habitats takes place?   Table 1 gives a summary
of data pertinent to three typical habitats which are commonly invaded
by bracken: pasture, heather moorland, and cleared woodland.   From the

Table it can be seen that the canopy conductances for lowland bracken are higher than those of heather by a factor of two, and are coincident with data for coniferous trees. The most important variable influencing this is the value of LAI.

TABLE 1 Comparison of canopy parameters in different vegetation

Vegetation type	Maximum LAI	Conductance, mm/s ks	kc	ka	Evaporation, mm/d mean	max	median	Ref No
Bracken								
Forest	1.0	1-4	1-4	9-13	0.51	-	-	13,14
Heathland	5.0	3-12	20-60	5-100	2.5	5.49	2.43	This
Heather								
N Yorks	?	-	6-20	10-100	2.3	0.25	1.0	24
Scotland	?	-	3.5-20	-	2.0	0.30	1.0	8
Pasture	?	-	5-100	10-100	2.1	2.9	-	15
Barley	?	-	5-67	5-100	2.1	3.2	-	15
Forest								
Fetteresso	8-10	1-8	8-32	80-500	-	-	-	26

This paper has concentrated on losses by transpiration; however, long term interception losses are known to be closely controlled by the ratio rc/ra[2,14,21]. If the function rav = 144/u is taken to be a reasonable average for heather, and say rav = 50/u average for bracken, then values of 1/ra will be about twice those for the heather community for the same values of u. In the bracken stand, values of rc ≤ ra occur throughout the period mid July to late August, when the canopy resistance rapidly rises in response to decreasing soil moisture. Similarly, early season rc values are high (>100 s/m). Thus, for this canopy, values of rc ≫ ra occur for two months at either end of the growing season, and, obviously, after the stand has died back in October. At this time windblow commonly forms a canopy of broken fronds 0.5-0.75m high, and rc is zero. The ratio of evaporation of intercepted water to transpiration under these circumstances is commonly between 0.5 and 0.8[16].

ACKNOWLEDGEMENTS

This study was supported by the Emsee Fairbain Trust and by a postdoctoral award from NERC (GR3/4531) to JIP, which we gratefully acknowledge. Logistical support from the Institute of Hydrology, and particularly John Roberts, made this project possible.

REFERENCES

1) Bevan K (1979) A sensitivity analysis of the Penman-Montieth actual evapotranspiration estimates. Journal of Hydrology, 44, 169-190

2) Calder I R, Hall R L, Harding R J and Wright I R (1984) The use of a wet surface weighing lysimeter system in rainfall interception studies of Heather (Calluna vulgaris). J. Climate and Appl. Meteorology, 23, 461-473

3) Gash J H C (1979) An analytical model of rainfall interception. Quart. J. Roy. Met. Soc., 105, 43-55

4) Gash J H C and Stewart J B (1975) The average surface resistance of a pine forest derived from Bowen ratio measurements. Boundary Layer Meteorology, 8, 453-464

5) Gimmingham C H (1972) Ecology of Heathlands. London: Chapman & Hall

6) Jarvis G P (1976) The interpretation of the variations in leaf water potential and stomatal conductance found in canopies in the field. Phil. Trans. R. Soc. Lond., B273, 593-610

7) McNaughton K G and Jarvis P G (1983) Predicting effects of vegetation change on transpiration and evaporation. In T T Kozlowski (ed) Water Deficits and Plant Growth, Vol 7, 1-47. Academic Press, New York

8) Miranda A C, Jarvis P G and Grace J (1984) Transpiration and evaporation from heather moorland. Boundary Layer Meteorology, 28, 227-243

9) Monteith J (1965) Evaporation and Environment. In: Symp. Soc. Exp. Biol., 19, 206-234

10) Pitman J I and Pitman R M (1983) Studies of the soil water regime of a lowland podzol, West Heath, Sussex. SeeSoil, 1, 24-41

11) Pitman J I and Pitman R M (1985) Factors affecting the stomatal conductance of bracken in open habitats. In preparation.

12) Roberts G (1981) The processing of hydrological data. Inst. Hydrol. Rept.. 70. IOH, Wallingford, Oxon

13) Roberts J, Pymar C, Wallace J S and Pitman R M (1980) Seasonal changes in leaf area, stomatal and canopy conductance and transpiration from bracken below a forest canopy. J. Appl. Ecol., 17, 409-422

14) Roberts J, Wallace J S and Pitman R M (1984) Factors effecting stomatal conductance of bracken below a forest canopy. J. Appl. Ecol., 21, 643-655

271

15) Russell G (1980)   Crop evaporation, surface resistance and soil water status. Agric. Meteorology, 21, 213-226

16) Rutter A J (1975) The Hydrological cycle of Vegetation. In: J L Monteith (ed) Vegetation and the Atmosphere, London, Academic Press

17) Scholander P, Hammel H T, Bradstream E D and Hammingsen E A (1965) Sap pressure in vascular plants. Science, 148, 339

18) Shuttleworth W J, Gash J H C, Lloyd C R, Moore C J and Roberts J (1984)   Eddy correlation measurements of energy partition for Amazonian forest. Quart. J. R. Met. Soc., 110, 1143-1162

19) Stewart J B (1983) A discussion of the relationships between the principle forms of the combination equation for estimating crop evaporation. Agric. Met., 30, 111-127

20) Strangeways I C (1972)   Automatic weather stations for network operations. Weather, 27, 403-408

21) Taylor J A (1985)   The bracken problem: a local hazard and a global issue. (This volume)

22) Thom A S (1972)   Momentum, mass and heat exchange of vegetation. Quart. J. R. Met. Soc., 98, 124-134

23) Wallace J S, Batchelor C H and Hodnett M G (1981)   Crop evaporation and surface conductance calculated using soil moisture data from central India. Agric. Meteorology, 25, 83-96

24) Wallace J S, Roberts J and Roberts A M (1982) Evaporation from heather moorland in North Yorkshire, England. In: Proc. Symp. Hydrol. Res. Basins, Bern, 397-405

25) Watt A S (1976) The ecological status of Bracken. Bot. J. Linn. Soc., 73, 1-36

26) Watt W R, Neilson R E and Jarvis P G (1976) Photosynthesis in Sitka spruce (Picea sitchensis) VII. Measurements of stomatal conductance of CO_2 uptake in a forest canopy. J. Appl. Ecology, 13, 623-638

Water balance studies in moorland bracken with reference to the changes following bracken clearance

J G Lockwood, D K Lyall, A T McDonald, P S Naden and R T Smith

INTRODUCTION

In many British upland areas, bracken (<u>Pteridium aquilinum</u>) is regarded as a weed and is being cleared locally by the use of herbicides. The progressive sequence of changes following herbicide application, from bracken to grassland or mixed heath through the transitional period of limited vegetation cover, is one which is accompanied by substantial hydrological changes. The aim of this paper is to present the preliminary results of a numerical hydrometeorological model which highlights the sorts of changes which might be expected.

The conventional opinion is that clearing vegetation decreases evapotranspiration loss and increases soil moisture and runoff. This view is based on observations in high rainfall areas where there is a large rainfall interception loss from coniferous trees as compared with grass, under windy conditions in winter. Bracken only exists above ground in the warm summer months, and there is growing theoretical evidence that under these conditions changing vegetation type may have very unexpected hydrological consequences. The possiblity that at higher temperatures, decreases in dry vegetation roughness may actually increase the evapotranspiration loss has been considered by Dickinson[1] and Rowntree[2]. Briefly, the mechanism is as follows. For a given meteorological input, there is a critical value of bulk surface resistance above which decreases in the aerodynamic resistance cause the Bowen ratio to increase (ie. evaporation decreases or sensible heat flux increases). For example, on a typical summer day at our moorland field site (net radiation 500 W/m^2, specific humidity deficit about 7 g/kg, temperature about 20°C) this mechanism is very evident. For very low or zero bulk surface resistances (wet surface), evaporation rates increase rapidly with decreasing values of the water vapour aerodynamic resistance. At bulk surface resistances above 100 s/m, the reverse situation is observed and evaporation rates decrease with decreasing values of water vapour aerodynamic resistance. Between bulk surface resistances of about 50 and 100 s/m, the water vapour aerodynamic resistance has only a small influence on evaporation rates. The bulk surface resistances are all within the range of values likely to be observed in summer. Also, under high energy input conditions, while the rainfall interception loss may be large, the differences in amount between different vegetation types may be small[3]. Some evidence of both these physical mechanisms is found in our preliminary analysis of the 1984 data, and suggests that the consequences of bracken clearance will depend largely on the meteorological input and the nature of the alternative crop.

THE HYDROMETEOROLOGICAL MODEL

As yet models to simulate the hydrology of moorland bracken have not been fully developed. The model presented here is based upon a series of submodels operating within the general framework of the Meteorological Office MORECS model[4]. The basic outline includes a Penman-Monteith equation with stomatal resistance calculated from the empirical equations of Roberts et al[5] derived for forest bracken and a Rutter type interception model[6]. The model also simulates the growth and decay of the bracken canopy with time. The hydrological components of the model are described briefly.

The Penman-Monteith equation

$$LJ = \frac{\Delta R_N + \rho C_p \delta e / r_a}{\Delta + \gamma (1 + r_s / r_a)} \qquad (1)$$

where J is the transpiration loss ($kg/m^2 s$)
L is the latent heat of vapourization (J/kg)
Δ is the slope of the saturated vapour pressure versus temperature curve (mb/degree C)
R_N is the net radiation (W/m^2)
δe is the vapour pressure deficit (mb)
ρ is the density of air (kg/m^3)
C_p is the specific heat of air (J/kg)
γ is the psychrometric constant
r_s is the bulk surface resistance (s/m)
r_a is the water vapour aerodynamic resistance (s/m)

assumes that the canopy may be considered to be a single evapotranspiring surface at a height of (z_o + d) metres where z_o is an aerodynamic roughness parameter and d is the zero-plane displacement. Values of r_a may be approximated by

$$r_a = [\ln(2/z_o)]^2 / (k^2 u) \qquad (2)$$

where z_o is of the order of 0.1h (m)
h is vegetation height (m)
u is wind speed at a height of 2 metres above zero

plane displacement (m/s)

k is von Karman's constant

There are good reasons to think that this equation may not apply in the case of upland bracken[4,7,8] and further field data are required in order to confirm the appropriateness of its use here.

When the canopy is dry, transpiration plus litter evaporation is given by equation (1) with the bulk canopy resistance, r_s, calculated from

$$1/r_s = (1-A)/r_{sc} + A/r_{ss} \qquad (3)$$

where r_{sc} is the crop surface resistance (s/m)

r_{ss} is the bare soil or litter surface resistance (s/m)

$A = f^{LAI}$ where $f = 0.7$ and LAI is leaf area index

The crop surface resistance for bracken is derived, after correction for LAI, using the relationships suggested by Roberts et al[5] for woodland bracken in which the reciprocal of resistance, bracken stomatal conductance, is given by

$$g_s = F_1 F_2 F_3 \qquad (4)$$

where $F_1 = P_1 Q/(P_2+Q) \qquad (5)$

$$F_2 = 1 - P_3 D \qquad (6)$$

$$F_3 = 1 - \exp[-P_4(\theta_s - P_5)] \qquad (7)$$

where g_s is the bracken stomatal conductance (mm/s)

Q is the solar radiation (W/m^2)

D is the atmospheric specific humidity deficit (g/kg)

θ_s is the soil moisture volume fraction in the upper 0.5 m of the soil

P_1 to P_5 are empirical constants

Equations (4) to (7) were not developed for moorland bracken and future work must assess the validity of these equations in the moorland context.

As regards bracken interception, a model has been used in which the proportion of rainfall intercepted by bracken is estimated from

$$p = 1 - 0.8^{LAI} \qquad (8)$$

and the total interception is given by

$$I = Rp \qquad (9)$$

where R is rainfall (mm)

The canopy is regarded as having an equilibrium surface storage capacity, S, which is charged by rainfall and discharged by evaporation and drainage. Preliminary work on moorland bracken suggests that this storage capacity may be approximated by

$$S = 0.5 \, LAI \tag{10}$$

where S is surface storage capacity (mm)

Following Rutter et al[6], when the amount of water on the canopy equals or exceeds this storage capacity, the evaporation rate from the vegetation canopy is given by equation (1) with r_s set to zero. When the amount of water on the canopy is less than the storage capacity, the evaporation rate is given by

$$E = IC/S \tag{11}$$

where I is potential evaporation rate given by equation (1)
    with r_s set to zero (mm)
C is amount of water on the canopy (mm)

The rate of drainage from the canopy is given by

$$D = D_s \exp [b(C-S)] \tag{12}$$

where D_s is the drainage rate from the canopy when storage is
    at capacity (typically 0.002 mm/min)
b is a constant

The final hydrological component of the model is a soil moisture store. The one used here is that based on Lockwood et al[9] and Lockwood[10] in which the water available for evaporation and transpiration is held in two reservoirs, X and Y, which at any time may contain reserves of x and y mm water respectively. All water in X is freely available, while that in Y becomes increasingly difficult to extract as the water content decreases. Water is drawn from the soil until X is completely exhausted and only replenishes Y when X is filled. X and Y can be regarded as conceptual stores and do not necessarily represent discrete soil layers. The soil moisture control on stomatal conductance in equation (7) is calculated using the sum of x and y. Bare soil or litter surface resistances are taken to be 100 s/m when store X contains moisture and, in other cases, calculated as in MORECS (4) using

$$r_{ss} = 100 \, [3.5 \, (1 - y/y_{max}) + \exp(0.2(y_{max}/y - 1))] \tag{13}$$

where y_{max} is soil moisture storage capacity of Y (mm)

This completes a description of the model used in the calculations presented here. Although, as pointed out, some of the relationships are not specifically designed for upland bracken, their use is thought to be adequate in this preliminary discussion paper.

MODEL CALIBRATION

In order to calibrate the numerical model presented above, the hydrology of an extensive area of moorland bracken near Pateley Bridge, North Yorkshire, has been monitored since September 1983. The site lies at an altitude of 250 m OD and is covered by Glacial Drift overlying Millstone Grits. The resulting podzolic soils are mostly ill-differentiated and of very variable depth. The texture is predominantly sand. Surface layers of litter and decomposing bracken debris are for the most part at least 20 cm thick.

The instrumentation of the site consists of a Didcot type automatic weather station modified to include a soil heat flux plate and an albedo meter. Two 12m by 0.105 m troughs feeding into tipping bucket raingauges measure the throughfall below the bracken canopy, while two similar troughs collect seepage below the bracken litter. An area 10 m by 20 m surrounding the troughs is fenced to prevent

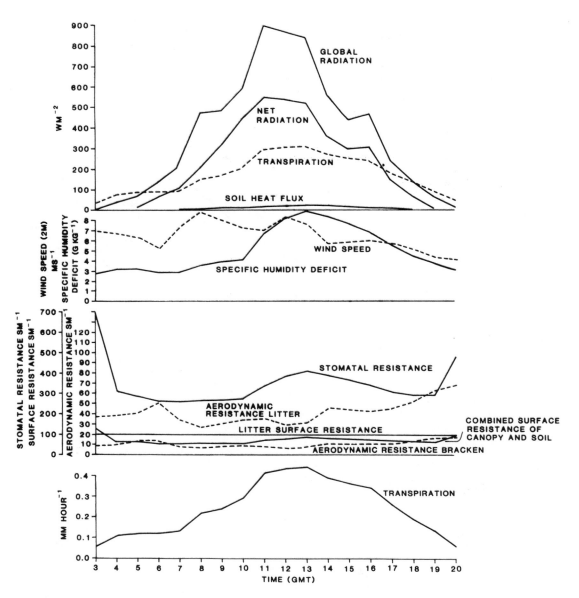

Figure 1 Hydrometeorological parameters during a typical sunny day in summer. All values are measured except transpiration and the resistances which are model predictions. The soil is moist, bracken leaf area index 5, bracken height 0.94m. Values are for the following hour. Transpiration includes litter evaporation. Soil heat flux is measured below the litter layer.

grazing and trampling. Automatic weather station and rainfall interception readings are taken at 5 minute intervals, while the seepage measurements are taken over two hourly periods. Soil moisture is monitored weekly at a number of sites using an Institute of Hydrology Neutron Probe.

Figure 1 shows the application of the model to a typical bright day in high summer. Soil moisture is assumed to be adequate and not limiting litter evaporation or plant transpiration. Input data are provided in the two upper graphs while outputs from the model as applied to a fully developed bracken canopy are given in the two lower graphs. Looking at the resistance values it is clear that the bulk canopy resistance of bracken is similar to other short green crops whereas its aerodynamic resistance is comparatively low due to its greater height. The highest transpiration losses (including litter moisture loss) occur around mid-day but are considerably less than the net radiation, and appear to be less than those expected from a short green crop such as grass. Values of aerodynamic resistance for bare litter are shown as a comparison. The soil heat flux, measured just below the litter layer, is small and downwards.

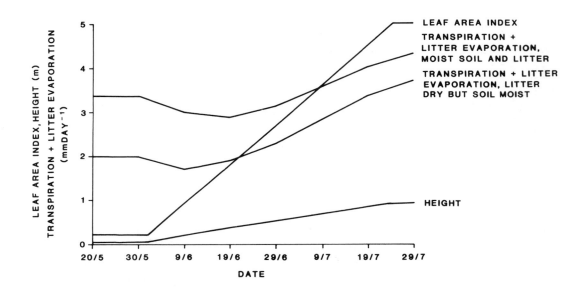

Figure 2 Variation in bracken model predictions as the bracken canopy develops.

Figure 2, constructed from model runs using the same meteorological input as given in figure 1, shows something of the effects of bracken growth on evaporation losses. Combined transpiration and litter evaporation show an initial decrease as the young bracken grows. When the leaf area index exceeds about 2, total evaporation loss rates increase as the canopy develops. A comparison of the curves for dry and moist litter suggests that evaporation rates from litter are relatively high and that the combined daily evapotranspiration loss for a fully developed bracken canopy with moist soil may exceed 4 mm. Figure 2 is interesting in that it does suggest that under certain meteorological inputs the total evaporative loss from sparse bracken could be less than that from bare litter

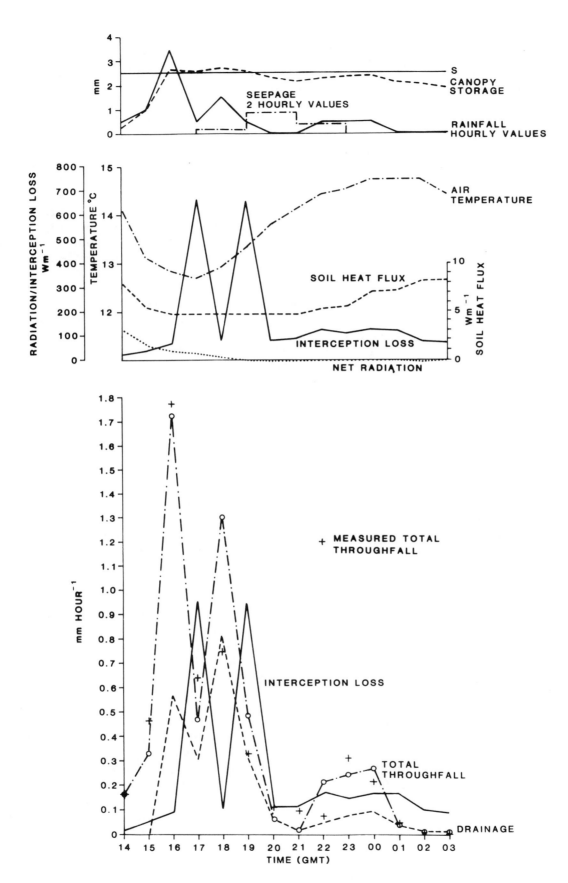

Figure 3

covered ground. This is due to the interaction of the bulk surface and aerodynamic resistances referred to in the introduction.

Under wet conditions, interception loss becomes extremely important. The application of the model to a wet canopy is shown in figure 3 - for the storm of 27 July 1984. The figure shows measured and predicted values of rainfall interception, the values being for the following hour. Conditions were dry prior to 1400 GMT. Thereafter, measured rainfall and seepage below the litter layer are given in the top graph as is the canopy storage capacity, S, and the predicted canopy storage level. Other measured meteorological conditions are given in the second graph as is the calculated interception loss in energy terms. The fact that interception losses are considerably higher than the net radiation values highlights the existence of strong sensible heat advection and this may be reflected in the air temperature curve at 2m. The importance of this is further reinforced by the fact that the soil heat flux, just below the litter layer, is down into the ground throughout the storm. In the third graph of figure 3, measured throughfall values (represented by crosses) are compared with the calculated values of total throughfall ie. free throughfall plus canopy drainage (dot-dashed line), canopy drainage (pecked line) and interception loss (solid line). These suggest reasonable agreement between the model and collected data. As an indication of the overall importance of interception loss in the water balance of a broken canopy, it may be noted that, of the 9.0 mm rain which fell during the storm, only 4.98 mm reached the litter layer and only 1.38 mm was recorded as seepage below the litter layer.

POTENTIAL APPLICATION OF THE MODEL TO BRACKEN CLEARANCE

This section discusses the application of the model outlined above to the bracken site over the months May to October 1984 and compares soil moisture variation under bracken with that under a nearby pilot plot sprayed with asulam in July 1983.

In addition to the site instrumentation discussed above, leaf area index was measured weekly on samples taken from two 0.5 m^2 randomly-chosen plots using an integrating TV camera. The measurements show a large amount of scatter reflecting the high spatial variability of the canopy. The top two graphs of figure 4 show the general pattern of leaf area index and green leaf area index per frond respectively.

Average values of weekly soil moisture deficit measured using a neutron probe are shown in the third graph both for bracken and for the cleared plot (under bracken litter). The values apply to the top 50 cm of the soil profile which is considered to contain the bulk of the bracken roots. Between the start of the growing season and the peak of bracken development at the end of July, about 70% of the soil moisture loss down to a depth of 150 cm was in the top 50 cm of the profile. Compared to the assumed available soil moisture capacity of upland soils of about 50 mm[4,9], the soil moisture deficits reported here under bracken are high for upland areas but low compared to many agricultural crops.

Measured rainfall (up to late August), throughfall below the bracken canopy and seepage below the litter are shown in the fourth

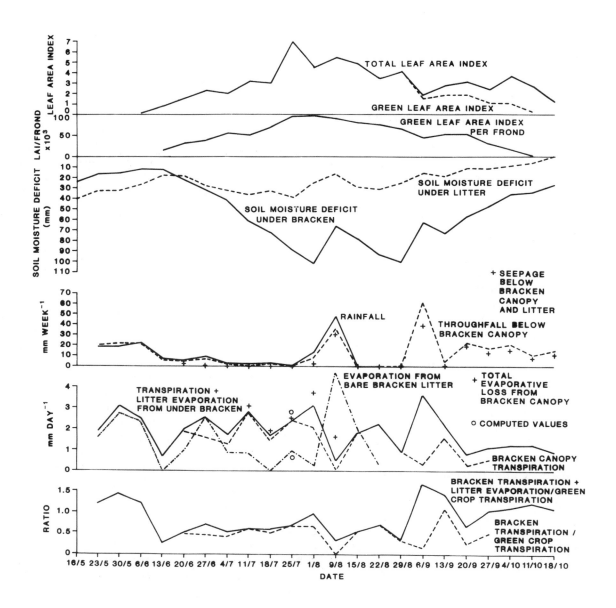

Figure 4   Hydrometeorological observations for a moorland bracken site during summer 1984. Values are for the previous week. Computed values refer to model predictions for week ending 25 July.

graph of figure 4. Assuming that soil drainage in summer is small, rough estimates, based on a simple water balance, have been made of the bracken canopy transpiration, the bracken canopy transpiration plus litter evaporation from under the bracken, and the evaporation from the cleared plot. These are shown in the fifth graph of figure 4. They compare reasonably well with the preliminary model calculations available of bracken transpiration plus canopy litter evaporation, and bare litter evaporation, for the week of 18-25th July and confirm the difference in the transpiration and evaporative losses from bracken and bare litter under dry summer conditions.

Before the bracken canopy is partly developed the evaporative losses from both the bracken covered and cleared plots are similar.

However, during the dry conditions of the early summer, evaporation from the cleared plot is low compared with that from the bracken because of the very high bulk surface resistance of the dry litter. This explains the relatively low soil moisture deficits observed under the cleared plot in summer. The reaction of the cleared plot to the intense rainfall during the week prior to the 9th August, however, is interesting. In the case of the bracken covered plot, most of the rain is used to recharge the soil moisture, and the total evaporation and transpiration losses remain small. In contrast to this, the evaporation from the wet litter is high and soil moisture recharge is limited. Under summer conditions, often with strong sensible heat advection, interception losses from bracken can be large. Total evaporation losses (transpiration + litter evaporation + interception loss) for bracken are shown by crosses in the fifth graph of figure 4. It is seen that during wet weeks the contribution of interception loss to total evaporative loss is significant. A detailed example of a rain storm was examined earlier.

As preliminary evidence of the likely effect on the hydrology of replacing bracken by an alternative green crop, the ratios of bracken transpiration and transpiration plus litter evaporation to the calculated transpiration rates from a standard fully developed short green crop with a moist soil are given in the final graph of figure 4. Values of the ratio bracken transpiration plus litter evaporation to standard crop transpiration are generally greater than unity at the beginning and end of the growing season. The surface resistances of wet bracken litter are low (or zero), as in the case of wet canopies, and model calculations suggest that these high evaporative losses can be explained by the evaporation from wet litter after rainfall. During the growing season, however, the transpiration from bracken is less than that expected from a "standard green crop" which suggests that the interaction of the two resistances of the bracken canopy and the high soil moisture deficits are limiting bracken transpiration. Up to 1 August there is no evidence that variations in soil moisture deficits are causing significant variations in the ratio of bracken transpiration to standard crop transpiration. However, in late August, when the bracken is no longer actively growing, large soil moisture deficits do appear to be strongly influencing transpiration loss. There is no clear evidence that the dieback in September is due to frost damage. Dieback in September is one possible mechanism for decreasing transpiration loss by reducing very high values of leaf area index and, therefore, increasing surface resistance.

CONCLUSIONS

This paper has presented some preliminary results relating to the likely effects of bracken clearance on the hydrology of upland areas during the summer months. In particular, it is clear that interception losses are high from both bracken and exposed wet litter. It is also clear that the evaporation losses from a dense bracken cover are far greater than for a cleared litter-covered plot, except during rainfall events. The picture with respect to other replacement crops is more complicated, with transpiration losses slightly lower in the case of bracken compared to a "standard crop" during the growing season of June to August. However, further research is required in order to apply the numerical model outlined here more specifically to a moorland environment and realistic alternative vegetation types.

ACKNOWLEDGEMENTS

The authors acknowledge financial support from the University of Leeds Research Fund and also financial support and the loan of instruments from the Natural Environment Research Council. They also thank the many members of staff at the Institute of Hydrology, Wallingford, and the technicians of the School of Geography who have given generously of their time to help in this study. Sincere thanks are also due to Mr Tom Guy, Keeper of Dallow Gill Estate.

REFERENCES

1) Dickinson R E (1980) Effects of tropical deforestation on climate. From Blowing in the wind: deforestation and long-range implications, No 14, Studies in Third World Societies, Department of Anthropology. College of William and Mary , Williamsburg, Va, 411-441

2) Rowntree P R (1984) Review of general circulation models as a basis for predicting the effects of vegetation change on climate. Met O, 20 Technical Note 11/225, Bracknell: Meteorological office

3) Lockwood J G and Sellers P J (1982) Comparison of interception loss from tropical and temperate vegetation canopies. Journal of Applied Meteorology 21, 1405-1412

4) Thompson N, Barrie I A and Ayles M (1981) The Meteorological Office rainfall and evaporation calculation system: MORECS (July. 1981). Hydrological Memorandum 45, Bracknell: Meteorological Office

5) Roberts J, Wallace J S and Pitman R M (1984) Factors affecting stomatal conductance of bracken below a forest canopy. Journal of Applied Ecology 21, 643-655

6) Rutter A J, Kershaw K A, Robins P C and Morton A J (1971) A predictive model of rainfall interception in forests. 1. Derivation of the model from observations in a plantation of Corsican Pine. Agricultural Meteorology 9, 367-384

7) Hancock N H, Sellers P J and Crowther J M (1983) Evaporation from a partially wet forest canopy. Annales Geophysicae, 1, 31-146

8) Thom A S and Oliver H R (1977) On Penman's equation for estimating regional evaporation. Quarterly Journal of the Royal Meteorological Society 103, 29-46

9) Lockwood J G and Venkatasawmy K (1975) Evapotranspiration and soil moisture in upland grass catchments in the eastern Pennines. Journal of Hydrology 26, 79-94

10) Lockwood J G (1979) Causes of Climate. London: Edward Arnold

283

The ecology of bracken-feeding insects:
Background for a biological control programme

J H Lawton, M MacGarvin and P A Heads

INTRODUCTION

Few will need reminding that bracken, Pteridium aquilinum (L.) Kuhn, is both one of the world's most widespread plants[1] and, where it occurs, one of the most abundant. What is rather less well known is that there are also a large number of insects that feed upon it, up to 40 in Britain alone[2]. This paper and its companion[3] ask, first, what is it that stops native herbivores from exploiting more effectively the vast amounts of food before them; and secondly, would introduced species fare any better, and hence act as effective biological control agents for bracken? The present paper concentrates on the first of these questions.

WHAT CONTROLS THE ABUNDANCE OF NATIVE HERBIVORES?

Basic population data

Of the 40 or so species of insect recorded that feed on bracken in Britain, there is a 'core group' of 27 species that regularly exploit the above-ground parts of the plant[2]. They feed in a variety of ways[2,3]. Some are externally-feeding caterpillars, such as the lepidopteran Petrophora chlorosata and various species of sawflies. There are sap-feeding species, including the bugs Ditropis pteridis and Monalocoris filicis. Others feed internally, either mining or galling the fronds, of which flies in the genera Dasineura and Chirosia are the commonest. The 27 core species are divided roughly equally between those that feed on bracken alone, those that feed on bracken and other ferns, and those that are broadly polyphagous[4].

For most of these species, a mean population size of five insects per frond would be very abundant indeed, and many never even approach these levels[2,4,5]. Although most of the native herbivores on bracken are rare compared to the biomass of their host plant, their

285

populations are relatively stable. The insects on bracken at Skipwith Common, North Yorkshire, have now been studied for 13 years. During this period, each of the species has fluctuated in abundance from year to year, but only within certain bounds (Figs. 1,2), with the result that the overall community structure - which species are commonest and which are rarest - is also fairly consistent[4,6].

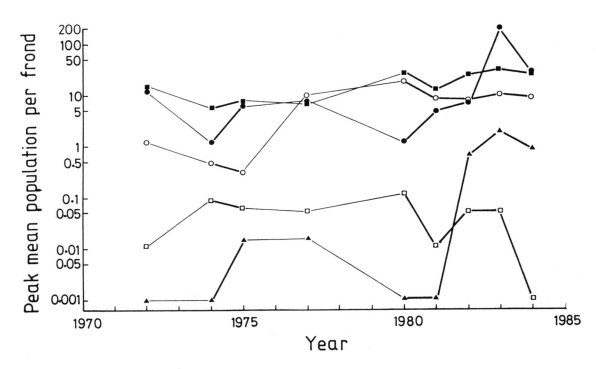

Fig.1   Peak abundance per frond of representative larval feeding stages of herbivorous insects on bracken at Skipwith between 1972 and 1984.   The species shown are ● - *Ditropis pteridis* (Hemiptera), ■ - *Dasineura filicina* (Diptera), ○ - *Chirosia histricina*, □ - *C. albifrons*, ▲ - *Phytoliriomyza hilarella*. (Samples separated by more than one year are joined by a thin line).

The important point is that these species do not just happen to be relatively constant in abundance: some factor or factors usually keeps populations of native, bracken-feeding insects in check, and prevents them from exploiting the apparent, vast surplus of food about them. If we can find out what is responsible, we will also be well on the way to knowing whether the same fate awaits any new species that might be introduced as a biological control agent. There are three possible sources of density-dependent mortality, capable of regulating populations of bracken herbivores at low levels of abundance[6,7]. The first is that bracken may increase its chemical defences as increasing numbers of insects start to devour it. Secondly, the different species of herbivores may start to compete and interfere with one another although their numbers are still below those that do any significant damage to the bracken. Finally, enemies of the herbivores - broadly defined to include disease, predation and parasitism - may prevent their expansion.

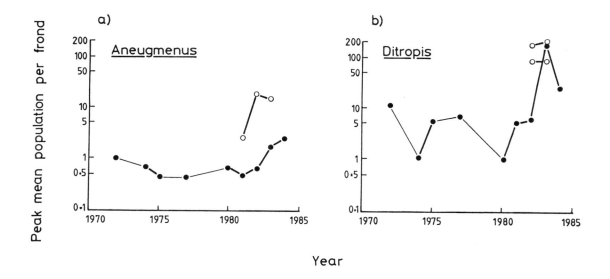

Fig.2 a) The peak abundance of a self-maintaining population of
Aneugmenus padi caterpillars (O) on an isolated bracken patch at the
University of York campus, compared to the peak population density of
all sawfly species (●) recorded at Skipwith between 1972 and 1984.
(b) The peak abundance of Ditropis on two plots of caged bracken on
the University of York campus (O), compared to the peak population
levels at Skipwith between 1972 and 1984 (●). Note that Ditropis was
unusually abundant at Skipwith in 1983.

The role of plant defences

Bracken has a large number of chemicals that make it
distasteful or fatal to non-adapted herbivores[8]. However, for
bracken-adapted herbivores, there is no obvious way that such
compounds can regulate insect populations. Recently, however, it has
been suggested that some plants not only have 'static' chemical
defences but also inducible defences, produced once a plant is under
attack. The subject is a controversial one,[6,9], but, if inducible
defences were present in bracken, and if they became more effective as
herbivore numbers increased, this could play a role in regulating
herbivore numbers. However, experiments carried out during 1984 (J H
Lawton and P A Heads, unpublished data), where different levels of
damage were experimentally created, showed no effect on the number of
herbivores that subsequently colonised the damaged fronds. It seems,
therefore, that chemical defences, of whatever type, can be ruled out
as factors primarily responsible for regulating populations of
bracken-feeding herbivores.

Competition between herbivores

Several lines of evidence suggest that interspecific
competition is extremely unlikely to play an important role in
maintaining insect-herbivore populations at low levels of
abundance[6].

The first comes from work on the relationship between the size of a bracken stand and the number of species found within it; fewer herbivore species find and colonise small patches of bracken[10]. This being so, if competition occurs between species, it means that once a species has found a small bracken patch it should show 'competitive release', and thrive in the absence of its competitors. However, exactly the opposite is true. Fronds in smaller patches not only have fewer species, but also fewer individuals of those species[10,11,12].

Secondly, if species compete, one would also expect the abundance of species on individual fronds to be negatively correlated with those of potentially competing species. Sensible comparisons (ie. where both species feed in a similar way and at the same time of year) are possible between seventeen pairs of species at Skipwith. None of these tests provided any evidence for interspecific competition[12].

Finally, we have carried out experiments in which we enhanced the population densities of two species of Chirosia (C. parvicornis and C. histricina) by caging ovipositing adults (unpublished data). Again, the data provide no evidence that this pair of closely related and ecologically similar species compete, even at enhanced densities.

The impact of natural enemies

Unlike the negative findings for plant defences and competition, the impact of natural enemies turns out to be considerably more interesting.

Sawflies: Common causes of death for sawfly caterpillars include fungal pathogens of Strongylogaster and ichnumonid parasitoids of Aneugmenus. Some of our most dramatic results came when we separated Aneugmenus padi from its enemies by introducing it to an isolated experimental bracken patch on the University campus at York. This species then reached population densities 10 times those of all sawflies at Skipwith (Fig.2a), and the bracken was completely defoliated. [Note that the bracken in this experiment originally came from Skipwith, and hence the outbreak of Aneugmenus is unlikely to be due to differences in the bracken.] This experiment demonstrates the effectiveness of natural enemies; it also confirms that plant defences and competition fail to confine Aneugmenus populations to low levels of abundance.

Ditropis bugs: Aneugmenus is not the only species whose numbers increase dramatically when introduced onto isolated bracken. Late instars of the delphacid bug Ditropis pteridis emerge from overwintering sites in the litter in large numbers at the start of the season but then rapidly decline in numbers. When this species was introduced onto caged bracken at the University of York, its numbers built up to levels well above those normally found at Skipwith (Fig 2b). Unlike the Aneugmenus populations discussed above, these populations are caged; hence several explanations, including confinement in cages, are possible for the outbreak. However, a recent experiment again points to natural enemies as the main cause of the rapid drop in numbers observed in the field soon after the spring

emergence.   The experiment involved a 100 m^2 area surrounded by a
0.75 m high polythene barrier, divided into six separate sub-plots
from which the Ditropis were unable to escape. To these we added
between 50 and 1,600 final instar nymphs. If some density-dependent
factor, such as predation, was involved, we would expect these
populations to converge rapidly, which indeed they did (Fig.3).
Although there are some puzzling features in this experiment that
remain to be explained, predation seems the most likely cause. We are
now planning more elaborate experiments to follow up this hypothesis
and to identify the important predator(s).

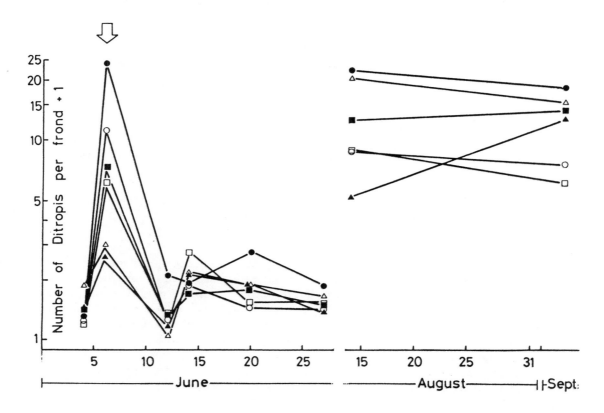

Fig.3   The effect of manipulating the population size of Ditropis
within six barrier plots. On 6 June 1984 (arrow) Ditropis were added
to the resident populations within each of the plots. The total
number added to each was: ● - 1,600; O - 800; ◼ - 400; ◻ - 200;
△ - 100; ▲ - 50.   The left hand side shows the subsequent
population level of Ditropis, per frond, within each plot during June;
the right hand side shows the size of the next generation of early
instar nymphs several months later. It rapidly became impossible to
distinguish those plots to which large numbers of Ditropis had been
added.

Ant predation: Ants as predators on bracken, have been studied in
detail[13-15,17].   They are often abundant, particularly early in the
season, when they are attracted by the extrafloral nectaries.
Experimentally-introduced insects are rapidly removed from bracken by
ants[13] although, in experiments so far published, ant predation has

had no effect on the population dynamics of British bracken-feeding herbivores[14]. Bracken insects apparently avoid ant predation in a variety of ways, for example by being distasteful, or by living relatively safely in galls and mines[15,16]. However, recent experiments have shown that these defences are not always effective against the very aggressive wood ant, <u>Formica lugubris</u>[17].

<u>Other predators and parasitoids</u>: Birds, titmice and warblers in particular, are often seen working their way through the bracken at Skipwith. However, when we placed bird exclusion cages over bracken we could detect no difference in the number of herbivores between these caged fronds and those in adjacent controls. Therefore, at low herbivore densities at least, there is no evidence for birds acting as important sources of mortality.

The final group of enemies, insect parasitoids, has already been mentioned for one species, Aneugmenus. We are now collecting data on temporal and spatial density-dependent mortality due to parasitism for several species, but it will take time before any firm conclusions can be drawn. However, it is already clear that parasitoids cause high levels of mortality in some species (the mining lepidopteran, <u>Paltodora cytisella</u>, for example) and that, as a general rule, they may be particularly important for endophagous species such as Paltadora and the Diptera.

CONCLUSIONS AND IMPLICATIONS
FOR INTRODUCED BIOLOGICAL CONTROL AGENTS

Drawing these data and arguments together, it seems that a powerful battery of natural enemies, disease, predators and parasitoids are largely responsible for keeping native herbivores within the bounds shown in Figures 1 and 2, preventing them from exploiting their food plant more vigorously. Perhaps this result was predictable because, in a review[6] of life-tables for insect herbivores on a wide range of plant species, regulatory effects attributable to natural enemies outnumbered those due to competition by a ratio of at least 2 to 1. In this context, at least, bracken is a very ordinary plant.

The implications of these conclusions for the possibility of biological control of bracken in Britain, using introduced insects[3], can be simply put. First, numbers of bracken-specific herbivores introduced from other parts of the world to Britain are unlikely to be limited either by plant defences, or by interspecific competition. Rather, relationships with natural enemies will be critical if introduced biological control agents are ever to become common enough to cause severe stress to the plant.

ACKNOWLEDGEMENTS

Work on the ecology of bracken-feeding insects has been generously supported by NERC. Work on biological control is supported by AFRC. Permission to work at Skipworth Common was given by the Yorkshire Wildlife Trust.

REFERENCES

1) Harper J L (1977) Population Biology of Plants. London: Academic Press

2) Lawton J H (1982) Vacant niches and unsaturated communities: a comparison of bracken herbivores at sites on two continents. J. Anim. Ecol., 51, 573-595

3) Lawton J H (1986) Biological control of bracken: plans and possibilities. (This volume)

4) Lawton J H (1984) Herbivore community organisation: general models and specific tests with phytophagous insects. In P W Price, C N Slobodchikoff and W S Gaud (eds). A New Ecology. Novel Approaches to Interactive Systems, 329-352. New York: Wiley

5) Caughley G and Lawton J H (1981) Plant-Herbivore Systems. In R May (ed). Theoretical Ecology, 132-166. Oxford: Blackwell Scientific Publications

6) Strong D R, Lawton J H and Southwood T R E (1984) Insects on Plants. Community Patterns and Mechanisms. Oxford: Blackwell Scientific Publications

7) Varley G C, Gradwell G R and Hassell M P (1973) Insect Population Ecology. An Analytical Approach. Oxford: Blackwell Scientific Publications

8) Jones C G (1983) Phytochemical variation, colonization, and insect communities: the case of bracken fern (Pteridium aquilinum) In R F Denno and M S McClure (eds). Variable Plants and Herbivores in Natural and Managed Systems, 513-558. New York: Academic Press

9) Fowler S V and Lawton J H (1985) Rapidly induced defenses and talking trees: The devil's advocate position. Am. Nat. (In press)

10) Rigby C and Lawton J H (1981) Species-area relationships of arthropods on host plants : herbivores on bracken. J. Biogeog., 8, 125-133

11) Lawton J H (1978) Host-plant influences on insect diversity: the effects of space and time. Symp. R. Ent. Soc. London, 9, 105-125

12) Lawton J H (1984) Non-competitive populations, non-convergent communities, and vacant niches: the herbivores of bracken. In D R Strong Jr, D Simberloff, L G Abele and A B Thistle (eds). Ecological Communities: Conceptual Issues and the Evidence, 67-101. Princeton: Princeton University Press

13) Lawton J H and Heads P A (1984) Bracken, ants and extrafloral nectaries. I. The components of the system. J. Anim. Ecol., 53, 995-1014

14) Heads P A and Lawton J H (1984) Bracken, ants and extrafloral

nectaries.   II.   The effect of ants on the insect herbivores of
bracken. J. Anim. Ecol., 53, 995-1014

15) Heads P A and Lawton J H (1985) Bracken, ants and extrafloral
nectaries.   III.   How insect herbivores avoid ant predation. Ecol.
Ent., 10, 29-42

16) Fowler S V and MacGarvin M (1985) The impact of the hairy wood
ant, Formica lugubris on the guild structure of herbivorous insects on
birch, Betula pubescens. J. Anim, Ecol, (in press)

17) Heads P A (in prep) Bracken, ants and extrafloral nectaries. IV.
The effect of wood ants, Formica lugubris Zett., on the insect
herbivores of bracken.

Polymorphism of Cyanogenesis in British populations of bracken (Pteridium aquilinum L. Kuhn)

P R Hadfield and A F Dyer

INTRODUCTION

Cyanogenesis is the release of hydrogen cyanide (HCN) gas by living organisms. A large number of plants[1] and a small number of arthropods[2] are cyanogenic. Cyanogenic plants release HCN by the enzymic hydrolysis of a cyanogenic glycoside or, rarely, a cyanogenic lipid[2] following tissue damage[3]. It has been suggested that cyanogenic glycosides in plants are stored nitrogenous waste, intermediates in amino acid metabolism, or a source of HCN to deter herbivores[4].

Cyanogenesis has been extensively studied in several angiosperm species[1]. It has been shown that Lotus corniculatus and Trifolium repens are polymorphic for cyanogenesis[5,6] and that this polymorphism is genetically controlled.[7]

Bracken, Pteridium aquilinum, is an important weed of marginal agricultural land in several parts of the world. It produces many toxic substances which are known to harm livestock which eat the fronds or rhizomes[8]. It is also cyanogenic, releasing HCN from the glycoside prunasin[8] (Fig 1). It has been shown to be polymorphic for cyanogenesis in north east USA[9], Papua-New Guinea[10], New Caledonia (P Hadfield, unpublished results) and at two sites in England[11,12]. However, there has been no detailed study of polymorphism. This paper reports on the distribution of the polymorphism in Britain and on the quantities of HCN released. The work reported here is part of a larger investigation into the basis and the ecology of cyanogenesis in bracken.

EXPERIMENTAL TECHNIQUE

At each of nine locations throughout Britain, large, vigorous stands of bracken at sites in open and, where possible, nearby coastal

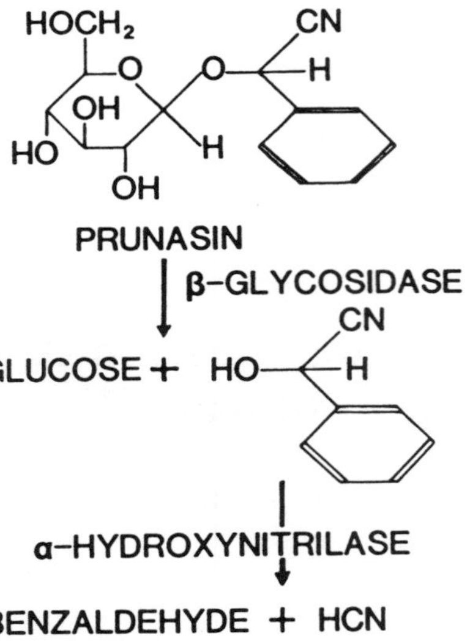

Figure 1   The HCN - release pathway in bracken.

and woodland habitats (Figure 2) were selected and an 18 x 18 m grid was marked out.   From this grid, 50 fronds were sampled at 2 m intervals on equally spaced transects (100 at locations 4 and 5).

Figure 2   The distribution of locations and sites sampled: ▲ coastal habitats (c); ■ open heathland habitats (o); ● woodland habitats (w).   The Grid References are as follows: 1c, SH637813; 1o, SH872605; 1w, SH808578; 2c, SX828372; 2o, SX745900; 2w, SX744897; 3c, TM475623; 3o, TL755805; 3w, 765815; 4o, SE658377; 4w, SE655376; 5c, NT445779; 5o, NT191643; 6c NX892548; 6o, NX882608; 6w, NX948678; 7c, NM816298; 7o, NM912274; 7w, NM892272; 8c, NC682632; 8o, NC710582; 8w, NC711579; 9o, NZ779679; 9w, NN778977.

Frond material was tested for cyanogenesis between late June and early August, using the sodium picrate test[5] for HCN, adapted for use as a quantitative as well as a qualitative test[5,13]. Whatman No 1 filter paper was cut into strips (35 x 7 mm) and soaked in saturated sodium picrate solution. These 'picrate papers' were bright yellow when fresh, but turned orange to dark brown in the presence of HCN. The colour obtained after 24 hours was calibrated with calculated amounts of HCN released from KCN solutions of known concentration following acidification with H_2SO_4. The calibration was reproducible and achieved results similar to other published accounts[5,13]. The continuum of colours was split up into seven classes, each with a colour standard matched against reference colours[14] (Table 1).

From each frond sampled, the terminal 4 cm of the lowermost pinna was removed and placed in a 50 x 12 mm glass tube. Two drops of toluene (c 0.07 ml) were added and the frond material lightly crushed. A freshly prepared picrate paper was placed in the mouth of the tube and secured by a plastic stopper which sealed the tube. After 24 hours, the colour class of each picrate paper was recorded. The data gave the number of cyanogenic fronds in each site sample and an estimate of HCN released by each frond tip. The mean estimate of HCN released by a frond tip was calculated for each site.

TABLE 1   The results of the calibration of the sodium picrate paper test for HCN and a comparison with the results of Jones[5] and Boersma et al[13]. The range of colours produced in the calibration was arbitrarily divided into seven classes (0-6) and a standard assessed against the RHS Standard Colour Chart[14]. The estimate of HCN required to produce the standard colour in each class was calculated from the regression line of -log[HCN] against the colour class

Colour Class	0	1	2	3	4	5	6
Colour Standard	4A	20A	22A	167A	170B	166C	174B
HCN Equiv (μg)	0-1	>1-<3	>3-7.5	>7.5-16	>16-30	>30-75	>75
HNC Est (μg)	0	2.08	4.56	10.00	21.98	48.19	105.68
Jones (μg)	-	0.4	1.7	2.7	3.57	13.9	27.7
Boersma et al (μg)	<1	1	2	5	10	20	50

The mean fresh weight of frond tips for each site was obtained by weighing a further 10 pinna tips. The height of each frond sampled, the frond density in selected one metre squares and the depth of the frond-bearing rhizomes were measured. The slope, aspect and altitude of each site were recorded. Soil samples were collected, soil pH being measured in the field and the remaining soil retained for laboratory analysis of potassium, phosphorus, magnesium and nitrogen. Climatic variables were estimated for each site using published equations[16]. The results were analysed using 'Genstat' computer programs for analysis of variance and correlation[17].

RESULTS

Each sample of fronds contained from 0 to 100% cyanogenic fronds while polymorphic stands were shown to occur throughout Britain. The mean HCN released from cyanogenic fronds at different sites varied from 15.8 to 402.5 μg/g fresh weight (Table 2).

TABLE 2 The percentage of cyanogenic fronds in each sample and the mean estimated amount of HCN released by cyanogenic pinna tips at each site

Location and site	Date of sample	Percentage of cyanogenic fronds	Estimated amount of HCN released μg/g fresh weight
1c	20.6	2	133.6
1o	21.6	100	277.3
1w	22.6	10	59.8
2c	27.6	58	44.1
2o	26.6	18	24.5
2w	25.6	96	116.5
3c	1.7	4	50.2
3o	29.6	98	143.0
3w	30.6	100	402.5
4o	3.7	18	33.7
4w	4.7	100	335.4
5c	16.7	38	53.0
5o	14.7	17	32.0
6c	23.7	0	0
6o	21.7	0	0
6w	22.7	2	103.6
7c	27.7	0	0
7o	25.7	60	39.4
7w	26.7	30	70.2
8c	30.7	6	16.0
8o	1.8	16	15.8
8w	31.7	0	0
9o	3.8	66	32.4
9w	4.8	38	47.0

The results were subjected to a blocked analysis of variance, with the locations as blocks and the three habitat types as treatments. The percentage data were first transformed using an angular transformation to render the data suitable for analysis[19].

Neither locations nor habitats have any significant effect on the percentage of cyanogenic fronds or the amount of HCN released. However, if the open site at location 1 is excluded, there is an effect of habitat on the estimated amount of HCN released by cyanogenic fronds (Table 3). This site is anomalous, the cyanogenic fronds on it releasing almost twice as much HCN as those from any other open site. The associated flora was composed of woodland species and the site was adjacent to a wood. It may therefore be a recently cleared woodland site, which would justify its exclusion from the analysis.

To analyse the relationship between the physical, biotic and climatic variables recorded, regression and correlation analyses were used. There was no correlation between any of the variables recorded and the transformed percentage of cyanogenic fronds at each site. There was, however, a significant correlation for fronds from woodland sites, between the estimates of HCN released and both the annual rainfall and the mean daily air temperature at 09.00. These results will be reported in greater detail in a later paper.

TABLE 3   Analysis of variance of the estimated amount of HCN released, μg/g fresh weight, and habitat (excluding the open site at location 1)

Source of variation	DF	SS	SS%	MS	F	
Locations	8	102702	45.17	12838	1.847	NS
Habitats	2	57050	25.09	28525	4.104	*
Residual	12	83403	36.68	6950		
Total	14	140453	61.78	10032		
Grand Total	22	243155	106.95			

NS   Not Significant   * $P \leq 0.05$

DISCUSSION

The relationship between the habitat type and the estimate of the amount of HCN released (excluding the open site at location 1) is of interest. The analyses showed that this was mainly due to the high levels of HCN released at woodland sites, there being no statistical difference between coastal and open sites. Similar results have been found by Cooper-Driver et al[11], although only qualitative results were published. This effect of woodland could be due to several factors, which would affect bracken either directly or indirectly. Shading is likely to have a direct effect on bracken, by altering carbon assimilation, mineral nutrition, and the water relations of the plant. These could influence either short term (eg frond morphology) or long term (eg development of the rhizome system; storage of nutrients in the rhizome) characteristics. The effect of trees on the soil and soil biota may indirectly effect the mineral nutrition and development of bracken. Such long-term effects may account for the anomalous results from the open site at location 1.

Theoretical arguments suggest that because of the altered carbon: nitrogen ratio, shade-grown plants have relatively greater quantities of proteins and thus have a greater nutritional value than non-shaded plants. Such plants may therefore be preferentially grazed by herbivores. However, the increased availability of nitrogen will lead similarly to a greater production of other nitrogeneous compounds, including a large number of secondary plant compounds. If these chemicals have a deterrent effect, the effect of preferential grazing would be countered; indeed, greater relative levels of secondary plant compounds might make the shade-grown plants less palatable than those grown in the open. Support for these ideas has been shown for undergrowth in a forest in USA[19], where shaded plants had higher nutritional quality but also higher levels of secondary compounds when compared to non-shaded plants.

Cooper-Driver et al[11] report anecdotal evidence from Richmond Park, England, that suggests that acyanogenic bracken is preferentially grazed by deer. This suggests that HCN in bracken may function as a deterrent to mammalian herbivores. There is no evidence that cyanogenesis in bracken has a deterrent effect on insect herbivores in northern England[12], north east USA[9], or Papua-New Guinea[10]; however, locusts have been shown to preferentially graze acyanogenic bracken in laboratory experiments[20].

The estimated mean amount of HCN (15.8 - 402.5 μg/g fresh weight) released from cyanogenic pinna tips is similar to that recorded by previous workers using different methods. Moon and Raafat[21] quote Greshoff as measuring 0.056% HCN (weight for fresh weight), or 560 μg/g, released from bracken, and they found 41.8 mg/100g dry weight (approximately 83.6 μg/g fresh weight) released from fronds harvested over a large area on an open hillside, without differentiating between cyanogenic and acyanogenic fronds. Schreiner[9] reported 42 μg/g fresh weight released from young cyanogenic fronds from an unspecified habitat in USA.

The mean estimated amount of HCN released from pinna tips at all sites in this study was 101.52 μg/g fresh weight. It can be calculated that if similar amounts are produced throughout the fronds, adult cattle would have to eat between 24 and 150 whole fronds before there was a fatal toxic effect. This suggests that if HCN released by bracken does act as a deterrent to mammalian herbivores, it does so with a qualitative rather than a quantitative effect[22]. The amount of HCN released from bracken will therefore rarely be lethal to cattle on its own account. It may nevertheless be a contributory factor in the aetiology of bracken-related disorders.

CONCLUSIONS

Bracken has been found to be polymorphic for cyanogenesis at sites throughout Britain. At some sites, samples of 50 or 100 fronds were wholly cyanogenic or wholly acyanogenic, but most contained both cyanogenic and acyanogenic fronds. The estimated amounts of HCN

298

released from cyanogenic pinna tips varied between 15.8 and 402.5 μg/g fresh weight. Bracken growing in woodland sites released significantly more HCN than bracken growing in most coastal or open sites. There was no relationship between the percentage of cyanogenic fronds sampled and the habitat type.

ACKNOWLEDGEMENTS

This work was undertaken whilst one of us (P H) was in receipt of a research studentship award from NERC. We would like to thank Professor D M Henderson, Regius Keeper of the Royal Botanic Garden, Edinburgh, for making available laboratory space where some of this work was performed, and Dr C N Page for his help and encouragement. We are most grateful to the numerous landowners and estates for permission to work on their property, and to those University Departments and Colleges who provided facilities close to the study sites.

REFERENCES

1) Hegnauer R (1977) Cyanogenic compounds as systematic markers in the Tracheophyta. In: K Kubitzki (ed). Flowering plants: evolution and classification of higher categories, 191-220. Supplement 1, Plant Systematics and Evolution, Vol. 127

2) Duffy S S (1982) Cyanide and arthropods. In: B Vennesland, E E Conn, C J Knowles, J Westley and F Wissing (eds). Cyanide in biology, 385-414. New York and London: Academic Press

3) Hesel W (1982) The enzymatic hydrolysis of cyanogenic glycosides. In: B Vennesland, E E Conn, C J Knowles, J Westley and F Wissing (eds). Cyanide in biology, 217-232. New York and London: Academic Press

4) Jones D A (1972) Cyanogenic glycosides and their function. In: J B Harbourne (ed) Phytochemical Ecology, 103-124. New York and London: Academic Press

5) Jones D A (1966) On the polymorphism of cyanogenesis in Lotus corniculatus. I: Selection by animals. Can. J. Genet. Cytol., 8, 556-567

6) Daday H (1965) Gene frequencies in wild populations of Trifolium repens. IV: The mechanism of natural selection. Heredity, 20, 355-365

7) Hughes M A (1982) The genetic control of plant cyanogenesis. In: B Vennesland, E E Conn, C J Knowles, J Westley and F Wissing (eds) Cyanide in Biology, 495-508. New York and London: Academic Press

8) Cooper-Driver G (1976) The chemotaxonomy and phytochemical ecology of bracken. Bot. J. Linn. Soc., 73, 35-46

9) Schreiner E (1980) Cyanogenesis and the herbivorous insects of bracken fern. Unpubl. PhD thesis, Cornell University

10) Kirk A A (1982) The insects associated with the bracken fern (Pteridium aquilinum (L.) Kuhn) in Papua New Guinea and their possible use in biological control. Acta Oecol. Appl., 3, 343-359

11) Cooper-Driver G, Finch S, Swain T and Bernays E (1977) Seasonal variation in secondary plant compounds in relation to the palatability of bracken. Biochem. Syst. Ecol., 5, 177-183

12) Lawton J H (1976) The structure of the arthropod community in bracken. Bot. J. Linn. Soc., 73, 187-216

13) Boersma P, Kakes P and Schram A W (1983) Linamarase and β-glucosidase activity in natural populations of Trifolium repens. Acta Bot. Neerl., 32, 39-47

14) Anon (1966) Colour chart. London: Royal Horticultural Society

15) White E J and Smith R I (1982) Climatological maps. London: NERC

16) Alvey N, Galway N and Lane P (1982) An Introduction to Genstat. New York and London: Academic Press

17) Sokal R S and Rohlf F G (1969) Biometry. San Francisco: W H Freeman

18) Rhoades D F (1983) Herbivore population dyanamics and plant chemistry. In: Denno R F and McClure M S (eds): Variable plants and herbivores in natural and managed Systems. New York and London: Academic Press

19) Blair R M, Alcaniz R and Harrell A (1983) Shade intensity influences on the nutrient quality and digestibility of southern deer browse leaves. J. Range Management, 36, 257-264

20) Bernays E A (1977) Cyanogenic glycosides in plants and their relevance in protection from insect attack. WRPS Bulletin, 3: 123-128

21) Moon F E and Rafaat M A (1951) Some biochemical aspects of bracken 'poisoning' in the ruminant animal. II - the significance of the cyanogenetic principle of bracken. J. Sci. Food Agric., 2, 327-336

22) Feeny P P (1975) Plant apparency and chemical defense. Recent Advances in Phytochemistry, 10, 1-54

Pteridium herediae: A dangerous diploid bracken?

E Sheffield, P G Wolf, C H Haufler and J M S Jubrael

INTRODUCTION

A vast body of data exists concerning the success of bracken as a weed, and much ongoing research concerns its control or utilisation. Far less is known of the evaluation and taxonomic status of bracken; indeed even its identity as a single species has often been questioned. This paper reports preliminary results of an ongoing study which seeks to improve our understanding of the genetics and evolutionary history of bracken. These aspects of the basic biology of bracken are highly pertinent to the selection of control methods as well as to our general knowledge of the plant.

A comprehensive taxonomic analysis of bracken is rendered difficult not only by its worldwide distribution but also by its extreme plasticity of form. The appearance of the plant is significantly influenced by factors including age, lighting, humidity and soil type[1]. Extreme morphological and geographical variability has prompted widely variable accounts of the number of species and/or subspecies and/or varieties attributable to Pteridium, although many authorities currently agree that the nomenclature established by Tryon[2] provides the best foundation upon which to build (see 1 and 3 for reviews). A study of chemical composition[4] supports the contention that Pteridium is a monotypic genus, with a single species, Pteridium aquilinum. Accepting Tryon's scheme, the bracken in Great Britain is P.aquilinum subsp. aquilinum var. aquilinum. This plant is generally accepted to have 104 chromosomes in the sporophyte after a study by Manton[5], and this, until recently was considered to be the diploid (2n) number, gametophytes being n (haploid chromosome number) = 52. There are several lines of investigation, however, indicating that this may not be the case.

Löve and Kjellqvist[6] reported a plant of Pteridium from Spain which had only 52 chromosomes in roots of the sporophyte, making the lowest chromosome number "known" (x for any taxon) 26 (being the number presumed in gametophytes, although neither spores or gametophytes were collected). Pictorial material of both the chromosome squash and the plant are lacking, although Löve and Kjellqvist considered it morphologically, cytologically and geographically distinct from P.aquilinum and suggested P.herediae as a suitable name[6]. They further suggested that the base number (x) was 13, (citing their own work and that of Molesworth Allen[7], although the latter made no mention of base number), and that P.aquilinum should be considered octoploid, P.herediae tetraploid. Further evidence, in the form of fragmentation of sperm nuclei[8], and electrophoresis of homozygous sporophytes[9] of P.aquilinum support the contention that it cannot be considered to be a straightforward diploid or be x = 52. The work reported here has a bearing both upon the classification of P.herediae as a separate species and upon the diploid nature of P.aquilinum.

MATERIALS AND METHODS

Collections of soil, living rhizomes and spores were made in the Manchester area of Great Britain, the Wageningen area of Holland and in the Formentor region of Majorca. The pH of each soil sample was tested. The rhizomes were planted out in pots and beds of the University of Manchester Experimental Grounds. Fronds were removed at intervals and spores collected or the DNA extracted. Full experimental details of the latter will appear elsewhere but were essentially as follows. The material was chopped into a Waring blender with extraction buffer, blended at high speed, filtered through muslin, centrifuged at 10,500 rpm and washed in washing buffer. Protein was enzymically removed, and the DNA banded in a CsC1 gradient. The DNA band was removed and digested with restriction enzymes (endonucleases) Bam H1 or Eco R1.

Spores were surface-sterilised and cultured on artificial medium to produce gametophytes according to established methods[10]. The resultant gametophytes were analysed micro-densitometrically, to ascertain the density and the area of Feulgen-positive material in each nucleus. Micro-densitometry was performed on gametophytes which were fixed in 3:1 absolute alcohol/glacial acetic acid overnight, hydrolysed in N HC1 at 60°C for 30 mins, rinsed, placed in Feulgen stain[11] (Shiffs' reagent) for 30 mins, and washed in tap water. The gametophytes were mounted in distilled water on slides and photometric measurements were made with a Vickers M86 Scanning Microdensitometer. Three measurements of optical densities and area of stain were taken from each of ten nuclei in the meristematic region of each gametophyte. Chromosome squashes were made according to established methods.

Population samples of Pteridium from 58 locations across the United States, Costa Rica, Mexico, Holland, England, Spain and Majorca provided material for the electrophoretic analysis. Both sporophytic samples and gametophytes raised from spore collections were tested. Electrophoretic analysis of haploid gametophyte progeny arrays facilitated interpretation of the number of genes coding each enzyme. Established electrophoretic protocols[12] were employed.

RESULTS

The pH values of soil samples taken from nine collecting sites in Majorca were 6.50, 6.80, 6.85, 7.20, 7.25, 7.30, 7.30, 7.35 and 7.50. The Manchester soil sample pH was 5.10, that of Wageningen, 4.95.

DNA extraction yielded DNA from both Majorca and Manchester bracken, digestion with <u>Bam</u> H1 yielded many fragments, that with <u>Eco</u> R1, very few.

Microdensitometry proved difficult as the density of "staining" in the Feulgen reaction was very low using established schedules. Use of long incubation times did, however, reveal that the mean optical density of nuclei in gametophytes from Majorca and Manchester was not significantly different (Majorca material = 40.01, that for Manchester material = 39.83 in arbitrary units).

Chromosome counts proved problematical for similar reasons, but did yield consistent counts of 104 for sporophytes from Manchester (Fig.1), 52 for the gametophytes. Counts of Majorcan material were more variable. Occasionally, sporophytic roots yielded counts of low numbers but more often were nearer to 104 and the gametophytes sampled were all found to be 52 (Fig.2).

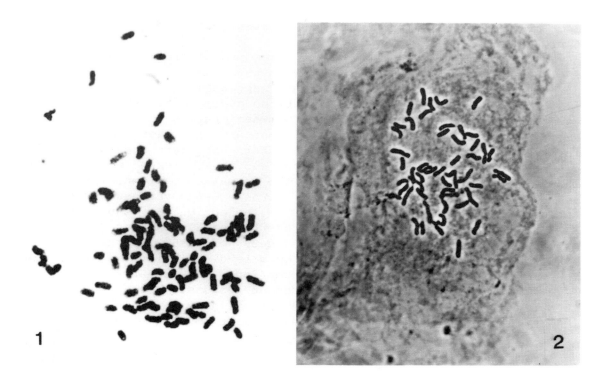

Figure 1. Chromosome squash of Manchester bracken root tip. At least 100 chromosomes are clearly present (104 could be identified by varying the focus during microscopic examination).

Figure 2. Chromosome squash of Majorcan bracken gametophyte cell, 52 chromosomes are clearly distinguishable.

Electrophoretic analysis showed that P.herediae is not enzymatically distinct from P.aquilinum. Both taxa expressed the same number of loci for all enzymes surveyed. Fifteen enzyme systems yielded consistently clear and interpretable banding patterns. Nine of these were coded by a single locus, five enzymes were coded by 2 loci and one by 4 loci. In heterozygous plants which expressed more than one band at a particular locus, the bands segregated in an approximately 1:1 ratio in the gametophyte progeny (Fig. 3C).

DISCUSSION

The number of coding genes, and consequently the number of different forms (isozymes) of an enzyme, have been correlated with ploidy level. Gottlieb[13] has shown that diploids express fewer isozymes and thus have fewer coding genes than do polyploids. Consider the simple case of a monomeric enzyme coded by a single genetic locus. If heterozygous at this locus, a diploid plant will express a maximum of two bands representing the two allelic forms of the gene, and these "allozymes" will segregate among the progeny (Fig. 3A). A tetraploid, on the other hand, will have two loci which may code for two isozymes of this enzyme, and these will not segregate (Fig.3B). Such "fixed heterozygote" banding patterns may be used to demonstrate that an organism has extra genes which may have been derived through polyploidy.

Isozyme expression in Pteridium provides no evidence of gene duplication through polyploidy. When there is more than one isozyme for an enzyme, and both are heterozygous, the isozymes segregate independently. This indicates that the coding genes are not linked, nor is there any recombination between them. Pteridium exhibits simple,diploid, genetic recombination patterns and there is no need to invoke the complex genetic model that has been hypothesised for polyploid ferns[14]. Although some enzymes expressed more than one isozyme, this can be attributed to the normal compartmentalization of the different isozymes into the cytosol and various organelles (chloroplasts, mitochondria etc.)[13]. Based on the assumption that P.herediae is a relict diploid, it has been presumed that P.aquilinum is a tetraploid. Our chromosome counts of n=52 for Majorcan and Spanish material and our discovery of only diploid isozyme expression in P.aquilinum suggest that both assumptions are untenable.

In the context of the present volume, perhaps the most important finding is that plants resembling P.herediae (sensu Löve and Kjellqvist) do exist as an ecotype if nothing else. The soils from which plants were collected in Majorca had pH's ranging from 6.5 to 7.5; those in which bracken abounds in Great Britain are more acidic (4.6 - 6.8)[1]. The report of Löve and Kjellqvist[6] stated that P.herediae dominated the forest floor and lime-rich soils in Spain. This is not at first alarming, but Molesworth Allen[7] suggests that similar plants are invading limestone outcrops in Malaya which is perhaps more sinister. It seems likely that P.herediae (sensu Löve and Kjellqvist) can be equated with P.aquilinum var. gintlii[15,16,17] and Pteris herediae[6,18] found in Portugal, Yugoslavia and Spain. The restriction of bracken in Great Britain to acidic soils is thus not a reliable delimitation; P.herediae (sensu Löve and Kjellqvist) may be capable of invading more alkaline areas.

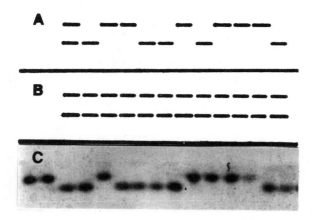

Figure 3.   Idealized and actual banding patterns of a monomeric enzyme.

A,B: Diagrammatic representation. A: Heterozygous diploid sporophyte followed

by haploid gametophytic progeny. Note the segregation of the allozymes.

B: A tetraploid sporophyte exhibiting no segregation among the progeny.

C: Photograph of the actual banding pattern observed for shikimate

dehydrogenase (a monomeric enzyme) from P. aquilinum showing segregation

among gametophytic progeny from a heterozygous sporophyte.

        Our inability to demonstrate that the plants collected from
Majorca are P.herediae (sensu Löve and Kjellqvist) on morphological or
cytological grounds can be attributed to several factors. The first
is that the phenotypic variation of P.aquilinum is so extreme that
separation of the plants we collected into different taxa (and perhaps
those of Löve and Kjellqvist?) is unmerited. The second is that
exhaustive chromosome counts have yet to be obtained. This is partly
attributable to the difficulty of staining Pteridium chromatin. The
endonuclease Bam H1 cuts DNA between adjacent G/Gs, ie. between
pyrimidines; Eco R1 cuts it at G/A junctions ie. between purines and
pyrimidines.   The good fragmentation with Bam H1 and the poor
fragmentation with Eco R1 may indicate that the DNA obtained in the
present study was high in pyrimidines. Since the Feulgen reaction
depends upon the selective hydrolysis of purines by mild acid
treatment (leaving aldehyde groups on the deoxyribose sugar moieties
exposed; the resulting apurinic acid can then react with Schiffs'
reagent, which recolours in the presence of aldehydes) the
difficulties of chromatin and chromosome staining may reflect the low
level of purines. Although longer staining times must be employed, it
does seem that Majorcan and British bracken have similar numbers of
chromosomes.   Counts of less than 104 in sporophytes obtained
occasionally in the present study may have resulted from broken cells
and are not considered important in the light of the counts of 104,
and consistent counts of 52 in gametophytes. It is possible, therefore,

that bracken in Majorca is not n = 26, and further collections of material from Spain are clearly essential before this apparent difference from P.herediae (sensu Löve and Kjellqvist) can be fully explained. If material from Spain can be shown to be n = 26 it is clearly a likely candidate for parenthood of P.aquilinum on the electrophoretic evidence obtained. The question of whether P.aquilinum was derived by fusion of unreduced gametes (in which case some n = 39 plants would be expected[19]) or by apospory, which is easily induced in this genus[20,21] will then have to be resolved. Collection and electrophoretic analysis of material from Spain is therefore planned; this, and extension of the studies reported here should shortly cast light on the evolution and taxonomy of the Pteridium genus.

ACKNOWLEDGEMENTS

Our thanks are due to The North Atlantic Treaty Organisation, The Research Fund of Kansas University, The Royal Society and the Iraqi Government for financial support, to Denise Jackson and Peter Sullivan for the microdensitometry, to Michael D Windham for help with gametophyte chromosome squashes and to David Moore for his advice and help.

REFERENCES

1) Page C N (1976) The taxonomy and phytogeography of bracken - a review. Bot. J. Linn. Soc., 73, 1-34

2) Tryon R M (1941) A revision of the genus Pteridium. Rhodora, 43, 1-31, 37-67

3) Fletcher W W and Kirkwood R C (1979) The bracken fern (Pteridium aquilinum L. Kuhn); its biology and control. In A F Dyer (ed) The experimental biology of ferns, pp 591-636. London and New York, Academic Press

4) Cooper-Driver G (1976) Chemotaxonomy and phytochemical ecology of bracken. Bot. J. Linn. Soc., 73, 35-46

5) Manton I (1950) Problems of cytology and evolution in the Pteridophyta. pp 122-125. Cambridge University Press

6) Löve A and Kjellqvist E (1972) Cytotaxonomy of Spanish plants 1. Introduction. Pteridophyta and Gymnospermae. Lagascalia, 2, 23-35

7) Molesworth Allen B (1968) Pteridium aquilinum on limestone. Brit. Fern Gaz. 10, 34-36

8) Wakeford R J and Bell P R (1980) Fragmentation of condensed chromatin in nuclei of a plant sperm, Pteridium aquilinum (L.) Kuhn. Gam. Res. 3, 291-298

9) Chapman R H, Klekowski E J and Selander R K (1979) Homoeologous

heterozygosity and recombination in the fern <u>Pteridium aquilinum</u>. <u>Science</u>, 204, 1207-1209

10) Sheffield E and Bastin J H (1978) Simple culture methods for fern prothalli. <u>Sch</u>. <u>Sci</u>. <u>Rev</u>., 60, 286-289

11) Jensen W A (1962) <u>Botanical Histochemistry</u> pp 96 San Francisco and London, Freeman

12) Soltis D E, Haufler C H, Darrow D C and Gastony G J (1983) Starch gel electrophoresis of ferns; a compilation of grinding buffers, gel and electrode buffers, and staining schedules. <u>Am</u>. <u>Fern</u>. <u>J</u>. 73, 9-27

13) Gottlieb L D (1982) Conservation and duplication of isozymes in plants. <u>Science</u> 216: 373-380

14) Klekowski E J and H G Baker (1966) Evolutionary significance of polyploidy in the pteridophyta. <u>Science</u> 153: 305-307

15) Rohlena J (1942) Conspectus florae Montenegrinae, <u>Preslia</u>, 20-1, 506

16) Vukicevic E (1970) Pteridophyta. <u>Flora S R Srbije</u>, 1, 59-121

17) Pinto da Silva A R (1970) A flora e a vegetacao das areas ultrabasicas do nordeste transmontano. Subsidos para o sen estudo <u>Agron</u>. <u>Lusit</u>, 30, 175-361

18) Colmeiro M (1867) <u>Enumeracion de las criptogamas de España y Portugal</u>. 1. Madrid.

19) de Wet J M J (1980) Origins of polyploidy, in W H Lewis (ed), <u>Polyploidy: biological relevance</u> pp 3-16 New York, Plenum Press

20) Sheffield E and Bell P R (1981) Experimental studies of apospory in ferns. <u>Ann</u>. <u>Bot</u>. 47, 187-195

21) Sheffield E (1984) Apospory in the fern <u>Pteridium aquilinum</u> (L.) Kuhn, I. Low temperature scanning electron microscopy. <u>Cytobios</u> 39, 171-176.

Polymorphisms in DNA of Pteridium aquilinum

J M S Jubrael, E Sheffield and D Moore

POLYMORPHISM: AN INTRODUCTION

Any investigation of evolutionary biology or population genetics must involve consideration of natural variation. Biological variation ranges from differences in the form of growth which are observable with the naked eye, to differences at the molecular level which require sophisticated techniques for detection.

Morphological variants - differences in the outwardly visible structure - often depend both on the genetics of an organism and on its response to the environment, so their fundamental basis may be obscured. Nevertheless, the genetic nature of morphological variations (or 'polymorphisms') in some organisms is known, an often-quoted example being melanism in the Peppered Moth, Biston betularia which has provided a classic example of natural selection based on genetic variation.

Bracken is notoriously variable in form but few, if any, of the observed variations have been traced to inherent differences in the plants. In this investigation we are seeking to examine variation at the molecular level in the genetic material (DNA) itself in the belief that if we can catalogue sufficient 'DNA polymorphisms' we will have the basic material needed for classical genetic studies and can later relate them to differences in morphology and/or physiology of Pteridium.

TECHNIQUE

DNA can be fragmented in a reproducible way by digestion with restriction enzymes. These are enzymes which cleave DNA at specific sites, depending upon the exact coding sequence of the DNA at those sites. The DNA from any one clone or variety of bracken will generate the same set of fragments whenever it is digested by a particular restriction enzyme. This is because the nature of the organism is determined by its DNA coding sequence and any given coding sequence will have a characteristic number and distribution of sites at which the enzyme can cleave the molecule. As with any other organism, though, different clones or varieties of bracken will be different because of variations (polymorphisms) in their DNA sequences. These are not large differences - but the sort of sequence difference which makes one strain grow more sturdily than another, or have differently branched fronds, etc. The sorts of differences which occur are: (1) deletion of a length of DNA; (2) insertion of a length of DNA; and/or (3) a simple change in a base sequence. Any one of these can remove or introduce a restriction enzyme digestion site and consequently change the type and number of fragments produced when the DNA is reacted with the enzyme. Potentially, therefore, the morphological polymorphisms which are so often observed in bracken are accompanied by subtle changes in the DNA which are detectable as a change in the 'restriction pattern'.

The restriction pattern can be observed by separating the fragments according to size, by electrophoresis. In this technique, fragments are caused to move in a slab of gel by applying an electrical field at low voltage for several hours. As DNA has a negative charge, restricted fragments will migrate to the positive end. The rate of migration is proportional to molecular size so the smaller the fragments the faster (and further) they move (Figs 1 & 2).

Particular fragments can be identified by 'Southern blotting'. This is based on transferring the DNA fragments onto a nitrocellulose sheet after electrophoresis. DNA binds permanently to the nitrocellulose so the 'blot' can be manipulated easily. The most significant type of manipulation is to 'probe' the blot with a ^{32}P-labelled DNA fragment which is available in pure form. Although the genomic (bracken) DNA is stuck to the nitrocellulose it can still hybridise to the probe if they have complementary regions. When this happens the radioactivity is localised and can be detected using autoradiography with X-ray films. Sequences complementary to the probe will be positioned on the blot according to their electrophoretic behaviour - which depends largely on the size of fragment complementary to the probe. DNA from different strains or clones may have the same probe-complementary region but occurring in DNA fragments of different size owing to their different restriction site arrangements. When this happens we have identified what are known as Restriction Fragment Length Polymorphisms (RFLP).

The preparation of probes involves preparation of gene libraries. In our work we have prepared a partial genomic library of bracken as follows: bracken DNA was isolated and purified, then digessted to the correct size for insertion into the cloning vector using restriction enzyme Sau 3A. The purified DNA of the cloning vector (a variant of the bacteriophage lambda) was prepared by digesting with Bam HI and Eco RI in order to remove the middle fragment. The next step was to join (ligate) bracken DNA with the vector DNA. This recombinant DNA was packaged in vitro to make infective virus particles, then introduced into the host bacteria. Using a selective strain of the host, only recombinant viruses will grow and form plaques (Fig 3). Each plaque is a 'clone' - a localised virus population derived from a single virus particle out of our original in vitro-packaged preparation. A number of these plaques were randomly selected and grown on a large scale. DNA was then extracted to become the probes.

310

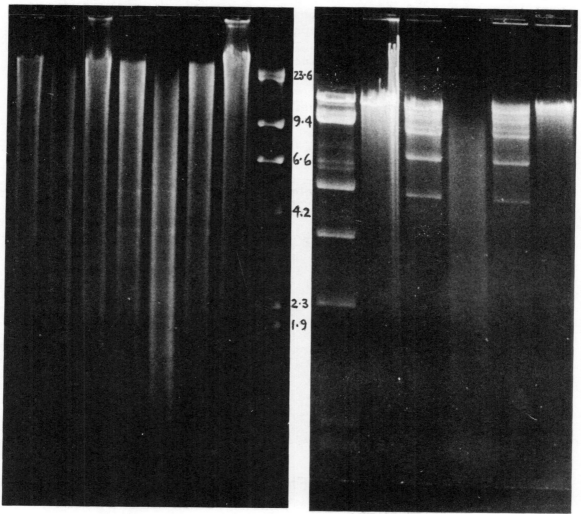

Fig. 1

Fig.2

Figs. 1 and 2. Agarose-gel electrophoresis of bracken DNA and its ligation to a cloning vector. Fig. 1 shows samples of bracken DNA purified from lyophilised fronds collected in different localities and digested with the restriction enzyme Bam H1; lane A = collection from Derby, B = Spain, C = Cumbria, D = Edinburgh, E = Cambridge, F = Manchester; lane G shows a sample of undigested DNA from the Manchester collection and lane H contains 'marker' DNA fragments of known molecular weight - as shown in Kb (10^3 nucleotide bases) to the right of the figure. Fig. 2 depicts joining of bracken DNA fragments to the genome of a cloning vector. Lane A = molecular weight markers, lane B = intact vector DNA, lane C = vector DNA digested with restriction enzymes Bam H1 and Eco R1 (note

the appearance of a series of discrete bands of
vector fragments), lane D = <u>Sau</u> 3A-digested bracken
DNA (appears as a smear because it consists of a
large and diverse population of DNA fragments of
differing size), lanes E and F are the products of
two ligation (= joining) reactions containing
mixtures of vector and bracken DNA (note the
disappearance of the vector fragment bands and
bracken smear as large, artificially recombinant,
DNA molecules have been created in the ligation
reaction).

Fig.3

Fig. 3. A petri dish showing the outcome of
cultivation of viruses prepared from one of the
ligations shown in Fig. 2. Each 'white dot' is a
bacteriophage plaque - essentially the sites of
epidemic viral infections which have destroyed the
bacterial layer which makes the rest of the petri
dish look turbid. Each plaque originates from
infection of one bacterial cell with a single virus
and since these bacteria are immune to infection by
the intact cloning vector, each plaque represents a
clone arising by infection with a recombinant virus
carrying a fragement of Pteridium DNA.

APPLICATIONS

Each one of these selected clones represents a fern DNA
fragment which we can prepare in pure form in quantity because it is
now part of a virus genome. For the time being it doesn't matter what
sort of genetic information the cloned fragment contains; the

312

important point is that it is a Pteridium DNA molecule. Thus we can use it as a probe in the manner described above to detect RFLPs. In this way we will build up a collection of probes which identify particular RFLPs in DNA from different geographical races of the plant. That collection will be one of molecularly-defined genetic markers which can be used in a variety of ways.

They can be employed as genetic markers in classical crosses to establish gene segregation patterns, linkage relationships, etc. Linkage studies can also be used to associate particular RFLPs with morphological or other characters which are of interest. Indeed, with luck and perseverance, one could anticipate carrying the analysis to the point where the DNA fragment containing a particular character of interest is identified. This approach has been highly developed in human clinical genetics where polymorphic DNA markers adjacent to genes causing genetic diseases serve as markers of those diseases which are identifiable even in utero, and often long before disease symptoms occur.

Advances in the clinical area have been spectacular. There are, of course, many clinical geneticists and a great deal of interest in the development of diagnostic tools. It will, however, be a long time before we can do the same sorts of thing with bracken. In principle, though, there is no difficulty in anticipating being able to define those regions of the genetic material which control characters of particular interest; and having defined them, they are then open to manipulation.

Protoplasts from pteridium Gametophytes

S M Attree and E Sheffield

INTRODUCTION

Protoplasts have been the subject of considerable interest for some time. As early as 1892 Klercker[1] was isolating protoplasts by cutting plasmolysed cells enabling the living protoplast to float free of its walls. Recent developments include the use of protoplasts in the production of clones of commercially valuable plants, the study of infection and diseases,[2,3] and the study of plasma membranes[4] and wall formation[5]. Our interests lie principally with the latter applications but the potential value of bracken protoplasts to others interested in nurturing and perhaps even improving the plant[6] or in eradicating it by chemical[7,8] fungal or insect[9] means should not be underestimated. Many of the world's crop plants are sterile; the only way to produce more plants is by tissue culture techniques such as protoplast isolation and regeneration. More importantly, protoplast fusion can generate hybrids from dissimilar, self-sterile or incompatible species[10]. Bracken protoplasts could therefore be used to overcome the possible incompatibility system[11] or even fused with a non toxin-producing fern. The latter, although a distant possibility at present, could generate plants with the aggressive and highly competitive strategies of bracken and the economic value of the edible fern Matteuccia struthiopteris[12], as fusion products are well known to have some, but not all, of the characteristics of parent plants in varying proportions such as the "pomatoes" and "topatoes" (see 10 for review).

Another exciting use of protoplasts is for genetic manipulations, such as in transformation studies. It has been shown that protoplasts take up foreign material such as organelles or DNA[13,14] and that new genetic information can be expressed[15]. The possibility exists therefore, that bracken could be permanently changed. Such changes might include the silencing of genes coding for toxins (yielding a harmless form of the plant), the inclusion of genes rendering the plants highly susceptible to insect attack, disease or herbicides (yielding a readily eradicable plant), or even the inclusion of useful genes (yielding a plant which produced something

315

of commercial value other than its own biomass).

Although protoplast fusion and transformation studies are well established for flowering (especially crop) plants[10], they will remain inaccessible to pteridologists until satisfactory yields of healthy protoplasts can be generated from ferns. The achievement of this aim is central to the present contribution.

The familiar bracken plant is the sporophyte generation, and protoplasts have been successfully isolated from such tissue[16]. Such plants are not as amenable to the sterile culture needed for protoplast studies as the less well known gametophyte generation and have double the genetic information (being perhaps tetraploid ?[17]) rendering them less suitable for genetic manipulations. Recent work has therefore concentrated upon gametophytic tissue[18,19] and the problems associated with protoplast release. One reason why fern protoplasts have been neglected to date is that the majority of workers isolating fern protoplasts have had little success in finding enzyme cocktails capable of effecting release by digestion of the cell walls[20]. This is not the case for bryophytes. Moss protonemal walls are almost completely digested after enzyme incubation periods of just a few hours[21] and one might expect pteridophyte gametophytes to be similar in this respect. This is not the case using similar enzymes, and this paper outlines some of the reasons why, and offers some experimentation to rectify the problem.

MATERIALS AND METHODS

Gametophytes of _Pteridium aquilinum_ were cultured and protoplasts isolated according to established methods[18]. The enzymes tested were untreated or desalted Driselase (Sigma) Macerozyme R-10 and Cellulase R-10 (Yakult Pharmaceutical Industry Co Ltd) and hemicellulase (Sigma). Enzyme desalting was carried out by chromatography on Sephadex G50 (Pharmacia Fine Chemicals Ltd) following methods similar to Slabas and co-workers[22]. 2 g of enzyme in 10 ml of 0.07 M phosphate buffer (pH 5.9) was centrifuged at 4000 rpm in a MSE Centaur centrifuge for 20 min and was then fractionated on a 20 x 2.5 cm column equilibrated with the same buffer. Peaks were resolved at 280 nm. Fractions containing protein were detected by the Folin-Lowry assay (BDH) and were pooled. Each enzyme was then filter sterilized and stored at 4°C until required.

Protoplast viability determination followed the method of Widholm[23]. Cell walls were stained using Calcofluor White (CW) at a concentration of 0.1%. For protoplast culture, protoplasts were cultured on filter paper supports as described by Partanen[24]. The supports were layered onto the same medium used to support gametophyte cultures, with the addition of 8% mannitol and 6 g/l sucrose. Cultures were placed in the dark at 20°C.

Freeze-dried material was prepared for scanning electron microscopy (SEM) following established methods[19]. For transmission electron microscopy (TEM) gametophytes were processed according to the methods of Sheffield and Bell[25]. Ultrathin sections were mounted on copper grids, stained in lead citrate and uranyl acetate and examined in an AEI 6B transmission electron microscope (Kratos, Manchester, UK).

RESULTS

Experimentation using different unpurified commercial enzyme preparations, alone or as mixtures, together with variations in concentration did not result in high protoplast yields. SEM of prothalli after enzyme incubation showed much undigested gametophyte tissue (Fig.1).

Elution of Driselase through the chromatography column resolved two peaks of an absorbance of 280 nm. The first peak eluent when assayed contained all the protein. This desalted enzyme released up to 100-fold fewer protoplasts than untreated Driselase. Elution of hemicellulase also resolved two peaks at 280 nm. Both peaks were found to contain protein and the fractions were therefore combined. Various concentrations of this mixture in combination with desalted 2% Cellulase R-10 released ten-fold fewer protoplasts than Cellulase R-10 alone, as did desalted Macerozyme R-10. A ten-fold increase in protoplast yield was generally achieved using desalted Cellulase R-10 alone, compared with unpurified, (10^5 - 10^6 protoplasts per gram of fresh culture) when used at a concentration equivalent to 2% unpurified enzyme. Further, protoplast release and viability was found to be greatest at this concentration. Viability of protoplasts released using non-purified enzyme ranged from 60-80%. This was increased to 80-90% or higher, once purified. Storage of this enzyme at 4°C for up to two months had no noticeable effect on enzyme activity. Folin-Lowry estimation of total protein present in purified Cellulase R-10 preparation was 2-5% of the original dry weight.

Entire gametophytes stained with CW showed only weak fluorescence of all cells other than rhizoids, although cut or damaged cells showed intense cell wall fluorescence (Fig.2). After culture for 24-48 hours, protoplasts could be observed to be fluorescing using CW (Fig.3).

During preparation for TEM, the penetration of osmium was found to be greatest in cells around rhizoids and in cells nearest to cut edges (Fig.4). TEM of gametophytes showed that they were bounded by substantial cell walls. A thin but distinct layer could be seen external to the cell wall (Figs.5,6).

DISCUSSION

Desalted Cellulase R-10 gave better protoplast yield and viability than non-purified enzyme. This enzyme contains a pectinase[22], therefore no further pectinase need be added. The estimated 2-5% protein in crude enzyme cannot consist solely of desalted cellulase and pectinase as other cellular proteins must be present. Complete digestion of gametophyte walls did not take place and yields of protoplasts were variable. This variability probably resulted from variation in gametophyte age, a factor found to affect protoplast release in both Pteridium[26] and Lygodium[27]. The best yields are obtained from gametophyte cultures greater than 6 weeks old[27,28].

It seems that the impermeable nature of outer gametophyte walls is shared by many fern species. A thin outer component in Onoclea cell walls was found to prevent the binding of CW[20]. Here, fluorescence occurred, as with Pteridium, when cells were damaged. External walls of Polypodium gametophytes have also been shown to be

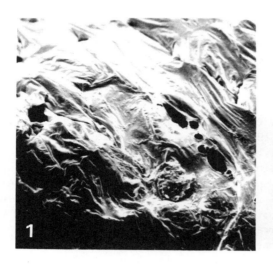
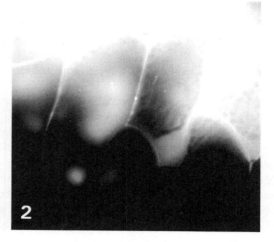

Fig.1. Appearance of Pteridium gametophyte in the scanning electron microscope after 3h incubation in unpurified 2% Cellulase R-10 Macerozyme R-10. Much undigested tissue remains. x 425.

Fig.2. Calcofluor White fluorescence of Pteridium gametophyte walls. Weak fluorescence takes place (bottom) except where cells have been damaged (top), here intense cell wall fluorescence occurs. x 300.

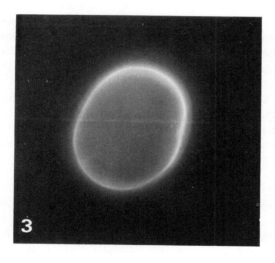
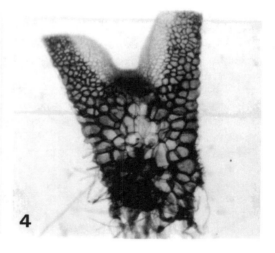

Fig.3. Calcofluor White fluorescence of a newly regenerated cell wall around a Pteridium protoplast after 48h culture. x 500.

Fig.4. Penetration of osmium tetroxide into gametophyte cells along the line of the cut edge, not through the surfaces. x 35.

impermeable to a range of stains[28]. Stain enters cells via rhizoids and passes from cell to cell via plasmodesmata.

An external waxy cuticle has been reported in gametophytes of the fern Adiantum capillus-veneris[29]. Although chemical characterisation has not yet been carried out it seems likely that the thin layer external to Pteridium walls is also cuticular in nature.

318

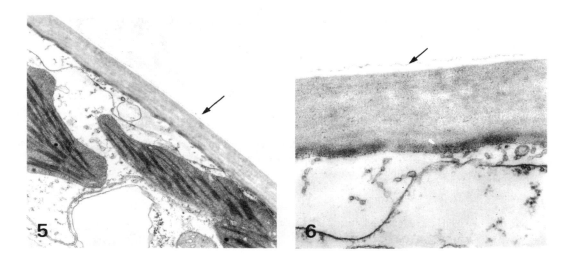

Fig.5.   Transmission electron micrograph of Pteridium gametophyte cell
wall.   A thin electron opaque line, considered to be a cuticular
layer, is visible (arrow). x 19,200.

Fig.6.   As above. x 37,500.

The limiting pore size of Onoclea prothallial cell walls has been
measured[30].   Pore size was found to be between 2.9 - 3.5 ħm, far less
than that of angiosperms[31].   The pore size of Pteridium walls has
not been measured but it seems likely that the electron opacity of the
cell wall, especially towards the innermost surface, reflects a small
pore size and thus limited penetrability.   The impenetrable nature of
outermost walls is evidenced by the restriction of osmium fixative,
which enters fragments of gametophytes only via rhizoids or cut
surfaces.   The strong fluorescence of newly regenerated walls around
protoplasts indicates that such cells have not as yet produced
impermeable wall layers or cuticle.
      From our work and from the literature it appears that the outer
walls of fern gametophytes are highly impermeable. Whether this is
due primarily to a cuticular layer or to densely packed wall material
is unclear and may vary between different fern species, but this
impermeability clearly accounts for the low yields of protoplasts
obtained to date. The superficial abrasion or slicing of gametophytes
can therefore be expected to enhance yields and thus pave the way for
the more ambitious studies outlined earlier.

ACKNOWLEDGEMENTS

      We gratefully acknowledge the financial support of SERC.
Thanks are also due to Ms S Laird for the specimen shown in Fig.4.

REFERENCES

1) Klercker J (1982)   Eine Methode zur isolierung lebender
protoplasten. Ofvers Vetensk Akad. Forh. Stokh. 49, 463-475

2) Cocking E C (1966) An electron microscope study of the initial stages of infection of isolated tomato fruit protoplasts by tobacco mosaic virus. Planta. 68, 206-214

3) Cocking E C and Ponjar E (1969) An electron microscopic study of the infection of isolated tomato fruit protoplasts by tobacco mosaic virus. J. Gen. Virol. 4, 305-312

4) Burgess J, Watts J W, Fleming E N and King J M (1973) Plasmalemma fine structure in isolated tobacco mesophyll protoplasts. Planta 110, 291-301

5) Pojnar E, Willison J H M and Cocking E C (1967) Cell wall regeneration by isolated tomato fruit protoplasts. Protoplasma 64, 460-479

6) Callagham T V, Lawson G W, Scott R and Mainwaring A M (1986) Bracken as a resource. (This volume)

7) Robinson R C (1986) Practical herbicide use for bracken control (This volume)

8) Burge M N, Irvine J A and McElwee M (1986) Fungal pathogens on bracken. (This volume)

9) Lawton J H, McGarvin M and Heads P A (1986) The ecology of bracken-feeding insects. (This volume)

10) Shepherd J F, Bidney D, Barsby T and Kemble R (1983) Genetic transfer in plants through interspecific protoplast fusion. Science, 219, 638-688

11) Wilkie D (1956) Incompatibility in bracken. Heredity, 10, 247-256

12) Von Aderkas P (1984) Economic history of the ostrich fern, Matteuccia struthiopteris, the edible fiddlehead. Econ. Bot. 38, 14-23

13) Carlson P S (1972) Towards a parasexual cycle in higher plants. Colloques Internationaux CNRS. No. 212. Protoplastes et fusion de cellules somatiques vegetales. 497-506

14) Krens F A, Molendijk L, Wullems G J and Schilperoort R A (1982) In vitro transformation of plant protoplasts with Ti-plasmid DNA. Nature, 296, 72-74

15) Rochaix J D and Van Dillewijn J (1982) Transformation of the green alga Chlamydomonas reinhardtii with yeast DNA. Nature, 296, 70-72

16) Sheffield E (1978) The establishment of the gametophyte phase in the life cyle of a fern. PhD thesis. University College, London

17) Sheffield E, Wolf P G, Haufler C H and Jubrael J M S (1986)

Pteridium herediae: a dangerous diploid bracken? This volume

18) Attree S M and Sheffield E (1984) Scanning electron microscopy of protoplasts isolated from gametophytes of the fern Pteridium - 1 Preparative methods. Micron Microsc. Acta, 15, 181-186

19) Attree S M and Sheffield (1985) Plasmolysis of Pteridium protoplasts: a study using light and scanning electron microscopy. Planta. (In press)

20) Huckaby C S, Bassel A R and Miller (1982) Isolation of rhizoid and prothallial protoplasts from gametophytes of the fern, Onoclea sensibilis. Plant Sci. Lett. 25, 203-208

21) Grimsley N H, Ashton N W and Love D J (1977) The production of somatic hybrids by protoplast fusion in the moss Physcomitrella patens. Molec. Gen. Genet. 154, 97-100

22) Slabas A R, Powell A J and Lloyd C W (1980) An improved procedure for the isolation and purification of protoplasts from carrot suspension culture. Planta, 147, 283-286

23) Widholm J M (1972) The use of fluorescein diacetate and phenosafranine for determining viability of cultured plant cells. Stain Technol. 6, 169-194

24) Partanen C R (1980) Filter paper as a support and carrier for plant protoplast cultures. In Vitro, 17, 77-80

25) Sheffield E and Bell P R (1981) Cessation of vascular activity correlated with aposporous development in Pteridium aquilinum (L.) Kuhn. New Phytol. 88, 533-538

26) Attree S M and Sheffield E (1985) Isolation and regeneration of Pteridium protoplasts. Proc. Roy. Soc. (Edin.). (In press)

27) Maeda M and Ito M (1981) Isolation of protoplasts from fern prothallia and their regeneration to gametophytes. Bot. Mag. Tokyo. 94, 35-40

28) Smith D L (1972) Staining and osmotic properties of young gametophytes of Polypodium vulgare L. and their bearing on rhizoid function. Protoplasma 74, 465-479

29) Wada M and Staehelin L A (1981) Freeze-fracture on the plasma membrane, the cell wall and the growing protonemata of Adiantum capillus-veneris. Planta, 151, 462-468

30) Miller J H (1980) Differences in the apparent permeability of spore walls and prothallial cell walls in Onoclea sensibilis. Am. Fern J. 70

31) Carpita N, Sabularse D, Montezinos D and Delmer D P (1979) Determination of the pore size of cell walls of living plant cells. Science, 205, 1144-1147

Bracken Control

Current policies on the reclamation of bracken land with particular reference to Northern England

J Johnson

INTRODUCTION

Details of the approximate area of bracken in Northern England are not available but the estimated rate of encroachment on the North York Moors of 1% per annum could be extrapolated to the rest of the area (Taylor, pers comm). A localised survey of 24 farms in 1972 (ADAS, unpublished), in a problem bracken area in Yorks/Lancs region, indicated that bracken was present on 13% of the total area of grassland and two-fifths of this area was classified as deep litter bracken. Ticks were seen as a major problem on half of the farms surveyed. The area of bracken on a farm bears little relationship to its effect, for even small areas of bracken can cause problems in managing the surrounding grassland. It is against this background that MAFF has been supporting bracken control in the form of financial assistance[1,2,3], advice, research and development[4] and published literature[5] for farmers.

GRANT AID FOR BRACKEN CONTROL

There is a long tradition of Government financial assistance for bracken control in the UK - the 1947 Agriculture Act provided grants for bracken control. Currently, two grant schemes are available as follows:

(i) The Agricultural and Horticultural Development Scheme (AHDS), which puts into effect EEC Directive 72/159 on farm modernisation and generally allows for higher rates of grant where farmers set out development plans for their businesses over a number of years. This scheme closes to new entrants on 1 October 1985.

(ii) The Agricultural and Horticultural Grant Scheme (AHGS) is the national scheme for farmers not wishing to formulate development plans. Claims under this scheme must be received by 31 December 1985, but special arrangements will be made to extend the closing date for bracken eradication where a programme of work cannot be completed in time.

These schemes cannot both be held at the same time. Table 1 shows data for the percentage rate of grant currently available on each scheme.

TABLE 1 Bracken control - current percentage rate of grant

	Standard	Less Favoured Areas
AHGS	Nil	30%
AHDS	32.5%	50%

Eligible work would include cutting, crushing or other acknowledged mechanical treatment carried out over a period of several years (normally not less than three). This method has been superseded by chemical spraying, eg. with asulam, provided that it is included in an overall treatment which includes follow-up methods to promote the growth of grass, to inhibit regrowth of bracken and to achieve a durable improvement of a capital nature. It is important that farmers should consult the necessary explanatory leaflets[1,2,3].

Liming, fertilisers and perhaps reseeding are not always feasible in difficult terrain, and conditions for grant were relaxed in 1980 and now depend on evidence that the work has achieved a lasting improvement in the grazing value of the land, which will be maintained with normal husbandry. Controlled spring grazing could be sufficient to inhibit regrowth. Alternatively, a follow-up spray to control any re-growing fronds is likely to be sufficient to attract grant but suffers the disadvantage of at least one year's delay in payment after the initial spray. Although not essential under AHGS, farmers wishing to claim grant on bracken spraying should consult with their local ADAS officers so that sites of highest potential and ease of after-care management are identified for treatment.

Environmental constraints

Farmers using chemicals for bracken control are urged to comply with manufacturers instructions, taking special care not to pollute ponds or water courses, either with chemical or its containers, and, in water catchment areas, ensuring that the Water Authority has no objection before treatment. In operating the two Grant Schemes the Ministry has regard to the environment and requires a farmer who proposes to claim grant or any capital investment to firstly consult the National Park Authority, if the investment is to be carried out on land within a National Park, or the Nature Conservancy Council for work to be carried out on land within or immediately adjacent to a Site of Special Scientific Interest or National Nature Reserve.

Trends in bracken control under grant

Statistics for the area sprayed for bracken control with the aid of grants cannot be readily extracted for England, but there is little reason to believe that the trend in recent years is any different from that in Scotland[6]. Here, it reached a peak of 8000 hectares in 1952 but declined to 200 hectares by 1970. The introduction of asulam in 1972 gave an immediate increase to 3500 hectares in 1974 but this had declined to around 1200-1400 hectares by the early 1980s.

Statistics are, however, available for the amount of grant paid. The total paid in 1984 for the Northern England MAFF Divisions (Newcastle, Carlisle, Beverley, Northallerton, Preston) is shown in Table 2.

TABLE 2 Grant paid for bracken control in 1984 in Northern England

Scheme	AHGS	AHDS	FHDS	Total
Grant paid	£20,734	£2,117	£11,010	£33,861

(Source MAFF, London)

The figure quoted for grant paid for bracken control constitutes only a tiny percentage of the grant paid on land improvement nationally.

Assuming no further cost over and above the cost of spraying (say £85/ha) and a grant rate of 50%, the above figure would cover some 800 hectares in total. The actual figure of area sprayed under grant is likely to be less than this, since some follow-up treatment is normally practiced. Where grant is claimed for bracken control it is usually on land that has deteriorated from grassland in the past.

Contacts with landowners, Public Bodies and spraying contractors suggest that in Lancashire alone, at least a further 250 hectares were sprayed in 1984 without grant aid. In addition, other bodies may run their own grant aid schemes. The North York Moors National Park Authority has given a 50% grant for spraying open moorland for visual amenity purposes (around 320 hectares sprayed last year), although this will not be repeated in 1985.

In the agricultural context, doubts have been expressed on the economics of bracken control in terms of dry matter response of native grasses after spraying[7], although a full reseed based on ryegrass/clover would allow a higher yield potential[8]. The continued interest in bracken control could be for three other reasons:-

(i) farmers are prepared to control bracken to improve ease of sheep gathering, reduce bracken poisoning and reduce tick levels.

(ii) landowners wish to limit bracken encroachment onto heather moorland in order to maintain grouse bags.

(iii) conservationists consider that bracken is not as attractive visually or environmentally as the plants it replaces.

In any event, the elimination of dense, deep-litter bracken results in very slow regeneration of indigenous vegetation, and runs the risk of invasion by other plants such as foxgloves. Examples are available of sites sprayed five years ago, and followed up by hand roguing or spot treatment to eliminate bracken completely, which are only now being recolonised to any extent. There is likely to be a big increase in bracken sprayed if a cheaper chemical becomes available, and the consequences of spraying large areas with only slow regrowth

327

potential must be appreciated.

Other support measures

In addition to the grants referred to specifically for bracken control, guidance premiums are payable under AHDS for approved plans which concentrate on the breeding or keeping of cattle or sheep for meat production. These are based on size of farm up to a limit of around £6000 per agricultural business. Since the traditional hills and uplands are designated 'Less Favoured Areas', Hill Land Compensatory Allowances are payable on breeding cows and breeding ewes, and form a vital part of the income of hill farmers. In the last few years, the European Community's annual suckler cow and ewe premiums, which are payable throughout the livestock sector, have provided further support. This heavy level of support is necessary not only to maintain incomes but also indirectly to assist in the maintenance of grazing pressure to prevent bracken from further encroachment.

ADAS BRACKEN CONTROL STUDIES IN NORTHERN ENGLAND

Studies on chemical control of bracken in ADAS Yorks/Lancs region have recently been reviewed[5]. During 1969-71 the National Agricultural Advisory Service (now the Agricultural Development and Advisory Service) investigated the use of dicamba, MCPA, asulam and aminotriazole at a range of rates and timings for bracken control. Applications of dicamba at 3.3 kg ai/ha were effective, and could be applied when the bracken was dormant and the terrain more easily visible, but dicamba proved too expensive for agricultural use. Asulam applied at 4.4 kg ai/ha during the full frond stage was found to be the most cost-effective chemical rate. In 1973, various rates of asulam and glyphosate were compared when applied at full frond emergence, and both achieved over 90% control (2.2 and 4.5 kg ai/ha of glyphosate and 3.4 and 4.4 kg ai/ha asulam). Glyphosate, however, cost 3 to 4 times more than asulam at that time for the rates quoted and, both for this reason and the fact that glyphosate was more damaging to grass and heather, no further development work was undertaken with this product.

More recently, ADAS, in cooperation with The Weed Research Organisation, has worked with sulfonyl urea materials in the hope of developing a cheaper, but as equally effective a chemical as asulam, and with fewer deleterious effects on grasses. Preliminary results suggest that a commercial mixture of chlorsulfuron and metsulfuron methyl is showing promise[9].

The cost of herbicides exerts an overriding influence on whether they are used or not. Dicamba cost £32/ha in 1970 and was considered too expensive when compared with asulam which cost around £20/ha, when approved in 1972, at a rate of 4.4 kg ai/ha. Currently, that cost is over £70/ha. Sulfonyl ureas are cheap. If the 100g of product chlorsulfuron and metsulfuron-methyl proves successful the current cost would be around £14/ha. It is hardly surprising that there is considerable interest in the progress of sulfonyl urea herbicides for bracken control.

The effect of lack of follow-up treatment after spraying for bracken control has been admirably demonstrated by recent work in ADAS Northern Region[10]. Broad conclusions following a single spray would be as follows:

(i) The degree of initial control determines the speed of return to full ground cover of bracken. (Table 3)

(ii) Where there is no undergrowth of grass, heather or bilberry, the bare ground allows sheep to congregate and can cause surface erosion so that little vegetation develops.

(iii) Heather areas colonised by bracken regenerate only slowly, and seedlings tend to be pulled out by sheep, with established plants being over-grazed by sheep and unable to produce seed.

(iv) Stands with an undergrowth of bilberry and grass may not be recolonised by bracken, as the plants are extremely competitive and regenerating fronds can often be damaged by trampling.

TABLE 3   Number of fronds (in 100 m^2) following one spray

Site	Spray Date	1975	1977	1979	1981
A	1974	2	3	113	129
B	1974	226	2171	6371	(5000)*

*   approximate estimation   Source: ADAS[10]

ADAS Staff have been encouraged to coordinate activities in moorland management. Mention has been made elsewhere of the ADAS/North York Moors National Park Study (see R Brown and D Barber, herein) to assess the effects of large-scale bracken control on sheep and grouse production, conservation and amenity[8].

For a number of years, ADAS has been monitoring the effects of a serial dipping programme on tick levels in the Trough of Bowland in Lancashire, where bracken is a serious pest and where surveys have indicated lamb deaths due to ticks were over 10%. The cooperation of 20 farmers, with a total of 10,000 ewes, was secured and tick levels on dipped and undipped sheep were monitored. In some cases the landlords contributed to the extra cost of dip. Tick numbers have been reduced to only 20% of their starting level, and lamb losses are now comparable to those on farms where ticks are not a problem. The overall health and performance of flocks have also improved, and grouse bags have increased dramatically over the trial period. Similar programmes are being initiated in other areas. While bracken spraying does not form part of the tick programme the improved profitability of sheep and grouse enterprises may in the longer term allow for diversion of more funds towards bracken control.

FUTURE SUPPORT FOR BRACKEN CONTROL

A Consultation Paper on the implementation of the new EC Structures Directive (Council Regulations 797/85) has reiterated "the continuing development of agriculture in the Community ... at the same

329

time ensuring permanent conservation of agriculture's natural resources." Included among a range of items on which national or EC grant may be paid is "Burning heather or grass or making muirburn or regeneration of heather by cutting or reseeding; bracken control by surface treatment only (ie. by spraying)."

In July 1985 the Minister of Agriculture confirmed that bracken control will continue to be grant-aided, but, unfortunately, along with other items, the level of grant will be lower than in the past. This continuing, if modest, support for bracken control should be welcome to both agriculturalists and conservationists alike.

ACKNOWLEDGEMENTS

The author wishes to thank ADAS advisors in the Northern, Midlands and Western Regions, farmers, landowners and other Public Bodies, especially the North West Water Authority and the North York Moors National Park, for their detailed help and advice.

REFERENCES

1) MAFF (1985) Agriculture and Horticulture Grant Scheme (AHGS) Explanatory leaflet for Investment Grants (AHS 2)

2) MAFF (1984) Agriculture and Horticulture Development Scheme (AHDS) Explanatory leaflet for Grants under Approved Development Plans (AHS 5)

3) MAFF (1981) Guide to Reseeding and Regeneration of Grassland (AHS 26)

4) MAFF (1983) Leaflet 190 Bracken and its control. HMSO

5) Flint C E and Lea H V (1985) Chemical control of bracken (Pteridium aquilinum) - a review of some Agricultural Development and Advisory Service field experiments BGS/BCPC Symposium, Nottingham 1984 (in press)

6) Mackay J T (1984) Paper presented at May and Baker Conference, April 1984

7) Newbould P (1984) The economics of hill farming and the benefits of bracken clearance. Paper presented at Galway, October 1984

8) Barber D D (1986) Bracken on the North York Moors - the agricultural problem. Paper at Bracken 85, (this volume)

9) Oswald A K and Richardson W G (1986) The control of bracken by sulfonyl-urea herbicides. Paper at Bracken 85, (this volume)

10) ADAS (1985) Recovery rate of bracken after spraying with asulam under conditions of uncontrolled grazing without other improvement (in press)

11) MAFF (1985) Consultation Paper on implementation of new EC Structures Regulations

Practical herbicide use for bracken control

R C Robinson

INTRODUCTION

Bracken deserves a better epithet than 'weed'. It is a plant worthy of respect since it offers a substantial challenge to any technique yet devised for its control. Not only is bracken naturally tenacious but it continues to survive eradication programmes not planned to an effective standard.

Where cultivation is restricted, herbicides represent the most efficient means available for tackling bracken. Nevertheless, herbicides are frequently misused owing to a lack of available advice on clearance strategy, difficulties of product application, and insufficient attention to the requirements of subsequent after-care. Such problems are usually compounded by the limited returns from development of grazing land, particularly in hill areas.

The following discussion attempts to highlight better ways to approach bracken eradication programmes with herbicide sprays in the UK, based on experience with asulam[1]. 'Ag-bracken' situations are considered, where maximum levels of control are required, rather than forestry situations where control levels may be relaxed somewhat for tree-releasing work.

HERBICIDE USE AND BRACKEN CLEARANCE STRATEGY

The nature of the response of bracken and underlying sward to herbicide treatment determines the style of clearance strategy, site management, and how spraying must fit into the scheme of land reclamation[2]. Before embarking upon an eradication programme, the cost of materials and the labour requirements of all the necessary inputs must be fully appraised. The initial spraying operation is but one of these inputs, although vital to the success of the scheme. The major programme input will be the degree of after-care required in the

331

years following spraying. This comprises three important aspects.

Firstly, aftercare should allow for annual treatments to discourage frond regrowth over a period of approximately five years after the initial spray treatment. In some cases less supervision is required, while inputs will depend on the efficacy of the initial treatment. Secondly, a change must be made in the pattern of land-use which led to the infestation in the first place. This could involve greater stocking rates, fencing, reseeding, or other changes. Thirdly, after-care must deal with the weed species which inevitably invade after bracken removal.

The costs of such after-care are large, and dictate the scale and timetable of the clearance programme that can be afforded. Sometimes bracken has been sprayed on a scale without regard to after-care commitment and this has led to failure of long-term clearance. Where resources are limited, a piecemeal approach[3] to the operation can be strongly recommended where the annual attention required by the programme is compatible with the effort that can be spared.

The scale of the clearance to be undertaken and the type of bracken encountered will determine the type of application equipment to be used for the initial treatment. Full understanding of the equipment and its characteristics will not only help to assess the input required for the treatment but will also lead to improved usage and a better degree of kill, which will minimise after-care requirements to control regrowth. In all respects, herbicide application must be orientated towards achieving maximum herbicide activity, and this must include correct timing and the advised use of additives. Besides initial treatment, herbicide may also be used as a form of after-care measure where further application requirements may need to be considered.

The practical use of a herbicide in bracken is thus an integral part of eradication where the clearance programme both depends on, and dictates how the spraying is to be done. The following sections illustrate these considerations although space precludes a fully comprehensive discussion.

MAXIMUM HERBICIDE EFFICACY TO MINIMISE AFTER-CARE REQUIREMENTS

A 98% control, an effective value for most herbicide uses, of an initial frond density of $50/m^2$ will permit a regrowth of one frond/m^2 after treatment. Such recrudescence looks bad and is likely to cause complaints if the user has failed to realise the density of the initial infestation. Further, the remaining growth will burgeon and render the control useless within a five-year period unless after-care is carried out.

This pattern of regrowth is similar over a range of sites (Fig.1). It may thus be appreciated that herbicide efficacy should be pushed to its maximum in all cases; even fractions of a percentage having a measurable consequence on the after-care required. This places importance on both the method and timing of herbicide application.

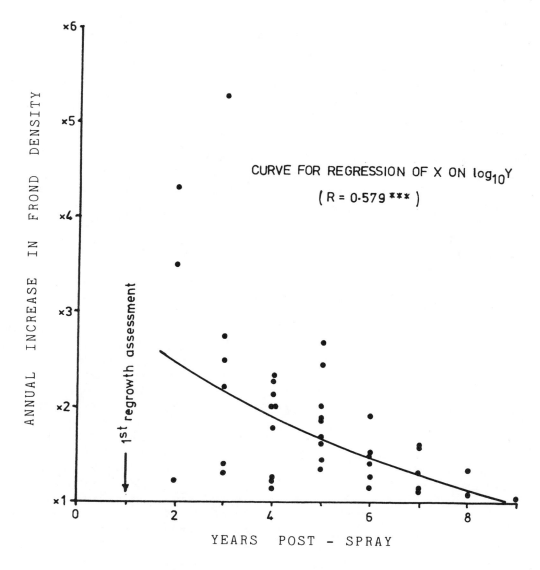

Figure 1   Rates of frond regrowth on 9 sites (calculated from data of Schofield and Davies[5])

APPLICATION METHOD

Bracken frequently occupies rough ground which can make application awkward and where relatively greater effort is required to ensure correct delivery of the herbicide dose on-target.   The following comments complement details already given for the application of asulam[4].

Aerial spraying is the easiest means of treating large areas but the standard of application depends largely on the skill of the pilot hired for the job (see Davies, herein). Adjustments of the helicopter to reduce vortices and evaporation, or to encourage spray deposition, can achieve only so much. Observance of a half-overlap method of swathing, accurate marking, slope correction, use of minimum height and correct flying speed are all subject to human error, especially in the difficult environs of hill-land, not to mention the interpretation of weather in respect of rainfall and local meteorological phenomena. Aerial spraying is rarely as meticulous or as predictable as ground-based methods, and any errors made are compounded by the scale of operation. Aerial treatment should be planned only where facilities for after-care are adequate to deal with extensive missed-strips and large partially-dosed areas that can sometimes occur. The possibility of aerial resprays of missed areas should be included in contracts with aerial operators.

But despite some of the problems of aerial application the method does generally leave the treated stand undamaged. Stem breakage in course of access, leading to incomplete herbicide translocation, is a problem to be faced in all ground-based methods, especially those which are motorized. Use of vehicle-mounted sprayers in bracken is not advised except on sites well surveyed before fronds have obscured the land surface. In general, hill-farms do not accrue the same expertise in calibration, operation and maintainance of sprayers as their arable counterparts, which sometimes leads to difficulty. Competent operators can, however, achieve good bracken control with vehicle-driven sprayers on flatter patches of bracken land.

Portable appliances provide a ready means of treating bracken for the widest spectrum of land-users, but little practical guidance is generally available for their use. Hand-spraying accords well with the piecemeal concept of bracken clearance on smaller areas, whilst it is also the principle means of applying herbicide to control frond regrowth in after-care situations. Spraying of fronds can be divided into 'overall treatment' or 'spot treatment', depending on frond density. Choice of portable application equipment is dictated not only by the stature of the fronds but also by the area to be treated. The suitability of a range of applicators for each of these situations is suggested in Figure 2. Treatment of bracken using portable equipment tends to be very physical, dirty and fatiguing. Many bracken sites have limited vehicular access and are without a supply of water for use as a spray carrier. All materials and equipment, including marker canes, usually need to be carried some distance before starting work, and any application method that makes the task easier is therefore welcome.

For overall-spraying work, only spinning-disc equipment appears to be suitable for all types of application (Figure 2). It is lightweight, quiet and may be shut-off easily when the user inevitably becomes entangled with fronds. One hand may generally be left free to deal with obstacles whilst the operator's full attention can be given to the ground ahead. Chemical may be applied in low volume without the need for water, treating one hectare in approximately 2.5 hours, even in tall stands. Drift-spraying with machines such as the Micron Ulva can be highly successful but sometimes leaves partially-dosed areas due to wind speed variation. A portable boom system producing a heavier spray (eg. using Herbi discs) can avoid this and produce more acceptable results. As yet, this system of treating bracken has not been commercially developed except as vehicle-mounted equipment such as the Mogi or Ulvaforest.

Hand-operated, knapsack sprayers involve hard work and require large volumes of water. At the slow walking speeds (0.5 m/sec) necessary on rough land, volume rates can rarely be applied below 110 L/ha, even using flooding nozzles at 1 metre spacing on a boom.

STAND AND TREATMENT STRATEGY	STATURE OF BRACKEN FRONDS	AREA OF INFESTATION TO BE TREATED	APPLIANCES AVAILABLE											
			ROPEWICKS	MICRON ULVA	2-MAN HERBI-BOOM	OTHER HERBI-DISC SYSTEMS	MANUAL KNAPSACK + BOOM	MANUAL KNAPSACK + LANCE	MOTORISED KNAPSACK + BOOM	MOTORISED KNAPSACK + LANCE	DRENCH GUNS/SPOT GUNS	AEROSOLS AND OTHER DISPENSERS	MOTORISED KNAPSACK MISTBLOWERS	AIR-ASSISTED ULV APPLICATORS
DENSE (OVERALL TREATMENT)	TALL	LARGE		✓	✓									
		SMALL		✓	✓									
	SHORT	LARGE		✓	✓	✓		✓						
		SMALL		✓	✓	✓	✓	✓						
SPARSE (SPOT TREATMENT)	TALL	LARGE								✓	?	?		
		SMALL						✓		✓	✓	✓	?	?
	SHORT	LARGE	✓							✓	?	?		
		SMALL	✓					✓		✓	✓	✓	?	?

Figure 2   Summary of the suitability of manual appliances for bracken control. Ticks denote suitable combinations.

        Motorised knapsacks   allow the operator a greater range before
fatigue and, when fitted with a lance, represent the only portable
method suitable for all types of spot-treatment work on bracken
(Figure 2).   Hand-operated spot-guns and aerosol dispensers can be
used to treat large areas but have yet to be adopted for widespread
use in the UK.   It is considered that useful spot-treatment can be
achieved using a single cone nozzle (0.2 L/min) delivering a 5 ml
squirt per frond. A fine spray, with little penetration and released
close to the frond, is necessary to avoid excessive wastage and
possible damage to underlying grasses or other desirable flora. It is
useful to mix a red foodstuffs dye (eg. Standacol Red 2G) with the
spray to distinguish treated fronds.   Spinning disc equipment is
generally not suitable for spot-treatment since swaths are too wide

and switch-on/off times are generally too slow and wasteful.

Air-assisted equipment has proved unsuccessful for overall spraying in a number of cases but the reasons are not clear. Nevertheless, this form of spraying can be useful for spot-treatment of bracken patches under trees, along walls and similar areas. Ropewick systems have an untested potential for large-scale spot-treatment, either mounted on all-terrain vehicles or for use by gangs of unskilled operators, and may yet provide a valid means of follow-up in instances of poor aerial spraying.

TIMING OF APPLICATION

Long-term control of bracken is obtained by preventing the generation of new fronds by the rhizome buds. Asulam is applied to the bracken frond and must be transported within the plant to these subterranean sites of action[6]. This process requires healthy plants with active basipetal translocation, conditions that prevail only in mature fronds for a limited period or 'window', making the timing of application critical.

The width of treatment window, as determined by the physiological age of the bracken, will vary according to region and climate[7]. Local variations can be important, such as between slopes of different aspect or sites at different altitudes and these are rarely considered in spraying operations[8]. In practice, it is much easier to recognise and avoid areas of sickly fronds where plants are damaged, droughted or otherwise likely to be suffering reduced translocation rates, and will not respond well to treatment. As a general rule, fronds to be treated, including regrowth, must be healthy and should possess three pairs of fully expanded pinnae. Dense, tall, vigorous stands will succumb much more readily than sparse, stunted growth on exposed or impoverished sites. In some poor stands, it may be best to defer herbicide treatment for a year or more to allow the stand to develop. After a previous treatment, fronds may also be small and lack vigour and, in such cases, where herbicide is to be used as a form of after-care, it may be better to delay re-treatment.

In some years, poor frond emergence can result from adverse weather conditions. In such cases, the rhizome bulk is not represented by the aerial frond density, and sufficient quantities of foliar-absorbed herbicide are therefore unlikely to reach all of the rhizome buds. The phenomenon of bud dormancy is not fully understood[9], but it is likely that live, crippled fronds on exposed sites inhibit subsequent growth[10] and could explain frequent poor control on such sites. Various pre-treatments to break dormancy (eg. early cutting) could offer a fresh approach to this problem but will alter the traditional timing of herbicide application.

When spraying large areas of bracken, it is rarely possible to make detailed surveys of the condition of the fronds. Attention to timing serves only to avoid the worst of adverse conditions that may result from a variety of causes. Correct timing should refer as much to identifying small patches ready for treatment within a single field as to initiating a spraying operation in a given region. For such reasons, small-scale, piecemeal clearances, where timing may be better observed, are most likely to lead to permanent bracken control.

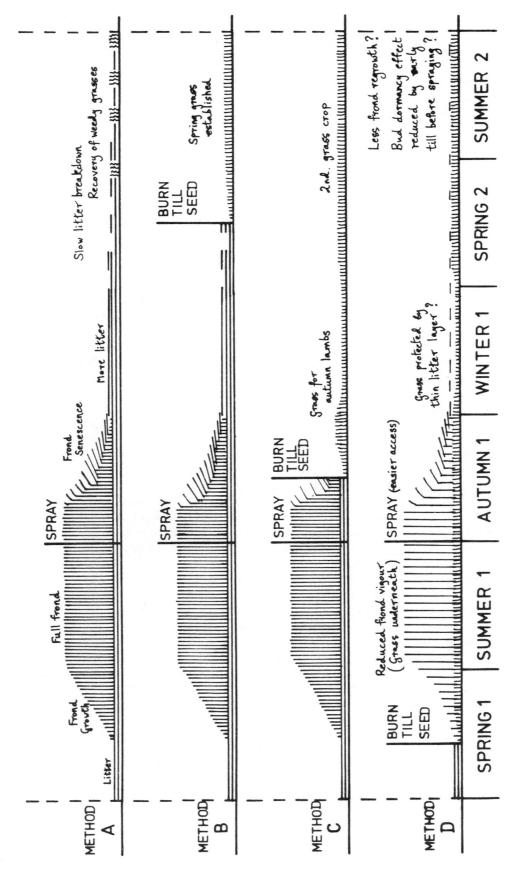

Figure 3 Four possible means of establishing grass after bracken

Because it is usually impossible to achieve perfect timing of application, spray additives become an attractive investment. Except in forestry, surfactants are added to asulam to increase both the rate and total quantity of foliar absorption and translocation as an insurance against adverse conditions[11]. This benefit counteracts the effects of sickly, poorly-translocating fronds; of rainwashing and loss of dose; or of low dosage levels applied in error through poor application.

HERBICIDE USE AND AFTER-CARE

Whilst a single-spray treatment may be insufficient to eradicate bracken[12], on some sites the repeated use of herbicide alone may be an equally frustrating form of after-care[13]. Increased exposure, rotavation, rolling, handpulling, slashing, and especially trampling by stock, can all be used as adjuncts to spraying, whilst residues of bracken litter will impose additional requirements on after-care. Overall, however, few determined efforts have been made to find suitable after-care strategies for the full range of existing land-use situations.

One example is sufficient to illustrate the need for further detailed investigations into the strategy of bracken clearance so that recommendations of efficient practice can be made to land-users. Figure 3 shows four alternative approaches to spraying bracken in an enclosure where a fast recovery of grass is required. The first, and conventional, alternative is the inefficient process normally adopted. Where burning and shallow rotavation is feasable to encourage breakdown of trash, followed by reseeding, the three other systems will produce grass more quickly, but little work to investigate these alternatives for sward production has yet been carried out[14].

Each site has its own special requirements for after-care (follow-up treatment) but general principles will be defined by the intended land use. Grouse-moor requires different after-care to 'in-bye' land whilst nature-conservation areas may not permit the same treatments as are appropriate on common-land. Different regional policies exist over grant-aiding bracken clearance and the nature of follow-up required, which can also lead to confusion. Bracken clearance can be considered an environmentally more acceptable and cost-effective means of increasing useful land area than either marshland drainage or woodland felling. Nevertheless, little practical advice, in terms of alternative approaches for farmers in different physical and financial situations, is as yet available to encourage better, more fully integrated strategies of bracken clearance. The latter would enable much more efficient use to be made of applied herbicide.

REFERENCES

1) Williams G H (1980) Bracken Control: A review of progress, 1974-1979. R & D Publication No 12, West of Scotland Agric. College, Ayr

2) Martin D J and Sparke C J (1982) Field trials in S W Scotland. Bracken in Scotland. Proc. Royal Soc. Edinburgh, 81B, 117-123

3) Smith R T (1977) Bracken in Britain III: Towards alternative strategies of bracken control with the use of herbicide. Working Paper 191, School of Geography, University of Leeds

4) Robinson R C (1984) Systems of bracken control using asulam. Aspects of Applied Biology, 5, 321-332

5) Schofield J B M and Davies T H (1982) Bracken control by asulam spraying. MAFF/ADAS N Region report RD/LMC/01. (CRU 02385)

6) Veerasekaran P, Kirkwood R C and Fletcher W W (1978) Studies on the mode of action of asulam in bracken III. Long-term control of field bracken. Weed Res., 18, 315-319

7) Scragg E B, McKelvie A D and Kilgour D W (1974) Further work on the control of bracken in the North of Scotland. Proc. 12th Brit. Weed Cont. Conf., 761-769

8) Taylor J A and Platt A (1985) Research Investigation into bracken encroachment rates and reclamation strategies in West-Central Wales. Research Report, Geography Dept. University College, Aberystwyth

9) Kirkwood R C, Veerasekaran P and Fletcher W W (1982) Studies on the mode of action of asulam in bracken. Bracken in Scotland: Proc. Royal Soc. Edinburgh,81B, 85-96

10) Watt A S (1964) Some factors affecting bracken in Breckland. J. Ecol. 52, 63-77

11) Horsnail G B and Robinson R C (1984) Further developments in the use of asulam for the control of bracken. Proc. Crop Protection in Northern Britain, Dundee University, 315-320

12) Martin D J (1974) Weed control in grassland. Weed control in the Northern Environment: BCPC Monograph 9, 40-47

13) Williams G H (1980) Follow-up treatments for control of Pteridium aquilinum. Proc. Brit. Crop Prot. Conf. - Weeds, 423-428

14) Williams G H and Fraser G (1979) The effect of asulam, frond cutting and ground mineral phosphate on the yields of swards dominated by bracken. Grass and Forage Science, 34, 95-100

The rhizome as a target site for the control of bracken using foliage-applied herbicides

R C Kirkwood and L Archibald

INTRODUCTION

The problem of bracken control hinges around the difficulty of killing the underground rhizome system with its frond buds and rhizome apices which vegetatively propagate the plant. The rhizome acts as a carbohydrate store which is used as an energy source. Once the fronds have fully expanded they become autotrophic and export surplus carbohydrates to replenish the depleted resources of the rhizome system. Thus the developing fronds initially act as regions of sugar utilisation ('sinks'), progressively becoming regions of sugar production ('sources')[1]; during this latter phase the photosynthates are exported to the developing rhizome and frond buds which act as sinks.

This suggests that foliage-applied, translocated herbicides should be applied to fully expanded fronds in order that efficient translocation of the herbicide can occur. Asulam (4-aminophenyl sulphonyl carbamate) and glyphosate (N-(phosphono-methyl) glycine) are foliage-applied phloem-translocated compounds which control bracken by inhibiting the development of frond buds and rhizome apices. Glyphosate however, is not normally recommended for the control of bracken in grassland since it is liable to cause damage to the underlying grass sward[2,3]. Glyphosate is active in reducing the weight of storage and frond-bearing rhizomes and their carbohydrate content[4,5], while the number of dormant buds and their viability are markedly reduced[5]. In Australia, work carried out with <u>Pteridium aquilinum</u> sub sp. <u>caudatum</u> var. <u>esculentum</u> showed that glyphosate affected chloroplast structure, starch synthesis and breakdown in the rhizome and disruption of the rhizome apices allowing infection by microorganisms[6]. It seems likely that, as in other species, glyphosate inhibits the aromatic amino acid biosynthetic pathway, preventing the formation of phenylalanine and tyrosine[7].

The rhizome is also the target site for asulam[8,9,10]. Application of asulam to the fronds is followed by basipetal protein syntheses are inhibited; there is evidence also that in

341

susceptible species folic acid synthesis is inhibited[11]. If asulam is applied outside the recommended time or dose rate, there is a possibility of frond regeneration occurring. This could be due to inadequate concentrations of herbicide being absorbed and translocated into the rhizome buds; alternatively a proportion of the rhizome buds may be dormant and fail to act as sinks for photosynthates and associated herbicide. There are indications that both factors may operate. When formulated with an appropriate surfactant, asulam can penetrate the cuticle and absorption into the frond tissues is increased, yet only a relatively low proportion of the absorbed dose may be basipetally translocated[9]. This may be due to fixation or conjugation of a portion of the absorbed dose in the tissues of the treated frond, possibly to cell proteins or polysaccharides. Furthermore, the existence of dormant yet potentially viable buds is well established; presumably these fail to accumulate ^{14}C-labelled sugars or ^{14}C-asulam and remain potentially viable.

A series of experiments has been carried out using an explant system to examine absorption/translocation characteristics of asulam under varying conditions of sink activity. Previously such a system has been used to examine the source-sink movements of a variety of ^{14}C-labelled herbicides in leaves of broad bean (Vicia faba)[12].

EXPERIMENTAL TECHNIQUE

The last pair of pinnae were removed from the fronds of bracken grown in the greenhouse. After excision of the basal pinnules the stems were placed in sealed vials containing 7ml of distilled water. ^{14}C-asulam (specific activity 46.22 μ Ci/mg) was applied to the second pair of pinnules using a Hamilton microsyringe (4 x 2 μ l droplets; 0.08 Ci/pinna). The treated explants were placed in a growth cabinet for 48 h (20°C $\pm$ 0.5°C; RH 70% $\pm$ 5%; light for 14 h in 24 h).

At harvest, the pinnae were divided into three regions; the treated region, and the portions above and below. These assessments indicate the amount remaining in the treated region, acropetal and basipetal transport respectively. The treated regions were washed in 2 ml of distilled water (2 min) and dipped in 2 ml chloroform for 30s. 1 ml aliquots of the water and chloroform washes were incorporated in 5 ml of a xylene-based scintillation 'cocktail' (NE 266) and radioassayed using a Packard Liquid Scintillation Spectrometer (Model 300C). The tissues of the three regions were dried overnight at 50°C, wrapped in Whatman No 1 filter paper, pelletised and combusted in a Packard Sample Oxidiser (Model B306). The $^{14}CO_2$ formed was trapped in 8 ml 'Carbosorb' and 10 ml 'Permafluor'. Each region was radio-assayed as before. Previous studies with ^{14}C-asulam have indicated that no degradation of the labelled compound occurred[8] and it is presumed that the distribution of ^{14}C is indicative of the herbicide molecule. Analysis of variance was carried out on the data and where relevant Duncan's Multiple Range Test[13]. A number of experiments were devised in order to evaluate the factors which may restrict translocation of herbicide into the 'sink'.

RESULTS AND DISCUSSION

In order to determine if asulam or Agral (0.01%) had an adverse effect on the translocation mechanism, pretreatments of these materials were applied to the 'source' region in advance of the ^{14}C-asulam treatment. The results (not presented) suggest that formulation of ^{14}C-asulam with 0.01% Agral and 10,000 ppm asulam has no deleterious effect on uptake and movement and also that a relationship exists between these two processes.

The effect of age of pinnae on the efficiency of uptake/translocation again demonstrated the relationship between these factors (Table 1). Treatment of pinnae removed from immature fronds resulted in relatively high translocation of ^{14}C-asulam to the 'sink' region, presumably indicating that the frond tips were acting as net importers of photosynthates. Conversely in the intermediate and mature frond pinnae the diminishing translocation to the 'sink' and relatively high translocation to the 'region below' and the vial reflect the change in physiology of assimilate movement in the mature 'fully exporting' tissue. These changes in pattern coincide with the results obtained following treatment of fronds of different age[8].

TABLE 1 Effect of pinnae age on uptake and translocation of ^{14}C-asulam

Age	Immature		Intermediate		Mature	
	Frond A	Frond B	Frond A	Frond B	Frond A	Frond B
Region						
H_2O Wash	5.2	3.2	7.4	15.2	13.3	15.1
$CHCl_3$ Wash	0.9	1.9	2.2	1.3	1.5	4.4
Region Above	18.9	31.4	18.9	9.7	12.9	14.2
Treated Region	15.7	14.9	10.5	9.9	1.2	14.2
Region Below	7.1	6.6	1.7	3.6	11.5	11.2
Vial	5.5	1.5	14.4	20.8	14.5	11.4
% Recovered	53.4	59.4	55.3	60.5	75.7	70.7
% Absorbed	47.2	54.2	45.4	44.1	60.9	65.7
	(88.4)*	(91.2)	(82.1)	(72.9)	(80.4)	(92.9)
% Translocated	31.6	39.4	34.9	34.1	48.8	51.5
	(59.2)*	(66.3)	(63.1)	(56.4)	(64.5)	(72.8)
	66.9#	72.7	76.9	77.3	80.1	78.4

* Figures in parenthesis corrected to 100% recovery.
\# % of absorbed. A and B are replicates.

Application of ^{14}C-asulam to the abaxial as compared to the adaxial surface resulted in much greater absorption (in light or dark) and translocation to the tissue above (sink region) (Table 2). The higher abaxial absorption may reflect differences in the physico-chemical nature of the cuticle wax and the presence of stomata on the lower surface. Presumably the increased translocation to the sink region which is associated with high absorption is a reflection of the enhanced concentration of herbicide molecules potentially available for transport. It is noteworthy, however, that the proportion of the absorbed dose translocated was actually lower than in the case of the adaxial treatment. It is possible that this is due to phytotoxic effects of this relatively high concentration of asulam within the frond tissue, or to binding of the herbicide to plant materials[14]. It may reflect 'over-loading' of the phloem system due to a surfeit of asulam molecules potentially capable of translocation.

TABLE 2 Effect of application to adaxial and abaxial surfaces under light and dark conditions on uptake and distribution of ^{14}C-asulam

| Treatment Region | ^{14}C-distribution (% of applied dose) | | | |
| | LIGHT | | DARK | |
	Adaxial	Abaxial	Adaxial	Abaxial
H_2O Wash	31.4	16.7	38.5	15.0
$CHCl_3$ Wash	0.7	2.4	3.7	4.7
Region Above	2.2	15.3	1.3	18.5
Treated Region	18.1	61.9	8.5	57.6
Region Below	3.9	2.9	11.1	2.2
Vial	14.9	9.2	17.2	5.9
% Recovered	71.4	108.2	80.2	104.6
% Absorbed	39.2	89.3	37.7	83.3
	(54.9)*	(82.5)	(47.0)	(79.6)
% Translocated	21.1	27.4	29.2	26.7
	(29.6)*	(25.3)	36.4)	(25.5)
	53.8#	30.7	77.4	32.0

The effect of applying benzyladenine (BA) to the adaxial surface of the second last pair of pinnules (4 x 2 μ 1), 20 min prior to herbicide application was also assessed (Table 3). Absorption and translocation were enhanced by BA, particularly where application was made to the abaxial surface. Increased translocation was largely due to the increased translocation of ^{14}C-asulam into the 'sink' region of the pinnae. Cytokinins such as BA can act as mobilising agents directing the movement of a number of substances to the treated area[15]. There is evidence also that treatment with kinetin augments the ratios of RNA or protein to DNA, indicating effects on protein synthesis[16].

TABLE 3 Effect of pre-treatment of pinnules above treated region with 50ppm BA (4 x 2 μ l droplets)

| Treatment Region | ^{14}C-distribution (% of applied dose) | | | |
| | ADAXIAL | | ABAXIAL | |
	No Sink	Sink (BA)	No Sink	Sink (BA)
H$_2$O Wash	21.0	27.5	14.9	7.8
CHCl$_3$ Wash	1.3	2.5	0.6	0.07
Region Above	13.0	28.1	29.6	50.1
Treated Region	11.4	6.0	40.8	33.1
Region Below	8.9	8.3	17.5	12.4
Vial	1.0	2.9	0.4	0.1
% Recovered	56.7	75.4	103.8	103.6
% Absorbed	34.4	45.3	88.3	95.7
	(60.7)*	(60.0)	(85.1)	(92.3)
% Translocated	23.0	39.4	47.5	62.6
	(40.1)*	(52.2)	(45.8)	(60.4)
	66.9#	87.0	53.8	65.4

Removal of the epicuticular waxes from the adaxial surface using cotton wool impregnated with chloroform, greatly increased absorption and translocation of ^{14}C-asulam, particularly when combined with BA application to the sink region (Table 4). It is evident that in the absence of 'sink' stimulation by BA, translocation to the 'sink-region' was greatly reduced, despite the apparently high level of absorption which occurred where the epicuticular waxes were removed. This indicates the importance of sink creation in phloem transport, and thereby, the absorption gradient into the frond. As noted previously, there was a positive correlation between absorption/ translocation and absorption/recovery. The latter may be due in part, to the observed loss of asulam from the plant surface probably through photochemical degradation.

TABLE 4   Effect of cuticle removal on uptake and distribution of ^{14}C-asulam

| Treatment | ^{14}C-distribution (% of applied dose) | | | |
| | CUTICLE INTACT | | CUTICLE REMOVED | |
Region	No Sink	Sink	No Sink	Sink
H$_2$O Wash	21.6	16.6	11.2	13.1
CHCl$_3$ Wash	1.8	0.9	0.5	0.2
Region Above	13.5	39.5	24.9	66.5
Treated Region	18.0	14.6	32.6	10.0
Region Below	12.8	8.2	18.2	13.2
Vial	1.3	3.2	6.5	3.9
% Recovered	68.9	82.9	93.9	106.9
% Absorbed	45.5	65.4	82.3	93.4
	(66.0)*	(78.9)	(87.6)	(87.4)
% Translocated	27.5	50.9	49.7	83.3
	(39.9)	(61.4)	(52.9)	(77.9)
	60.4#	77.8	60.3	89.1

Absorption and translocation of ^{14}C-asulam were enhanced by a range of concentrations (0-5%) of the surfactant Actipron (4 x 2 μ l), applied 55 min prior to herbicide treatment (Table 5). The optimum concentration appeared to be around 0.5 - 1.0% and the increased translocation was largely due to movement into the apical sinks. The importance of formulation of polar herbicides such as asulam with an appropriate surfactant concentration has been emphasised since the enhanced rate of absorption reduces the danger of wash-off by rain[17]. It is evident that surfactant-induced absorption leads to increased translocation, though the proportion of the absorbed dose translocated is slightly reduced. Absorption and translocation were markedly reduced by a surfactant concentration of 5%, probably due to phytotoxic effects at the absorption site.

In order to determine whether translocation to the sink was taking place in the xylem or phloem, heat treatment was applied to the petiole between the source and the sink. The inhibition of movement which resulted (data not presented) confirmed that translocation involved the phloem system[18]. The phloem cells are living while the xylem vessels are dead and transport within the latter is unaffected by heat treatment. The results suggest either that heat treatment was only partially effective, or that movement to the 'sink' may occur partially within the xylem. This requires further investigation.

TABLE 5   Effect of pre-treatment of pinnules with 0, 0.1 ,0.5, 1 and 5% Actipron on uptake and distribution of ^{14}C-asulam

Treatment	^{14}C-distribution (% of applied dose) Actipron Concentration				
Region	0%	0.1%	0.5%	1.0%	5.0%
H$_2$O Wash	31.5	27.4	27.6	27.8	13.3
CHCl$_3$ Wash	0.5	1.0	0.5	1.1	0.7
Region Above	18.3	9.7	26.6	21.3	22.8
Treated Region	4.0	9.9	5.9	19.2	9.9
Region Below	2.6	6.9	17.5	9.6	5.2
Vial	1.7	6.2	3.9	4.5	1.4
% Recovered	58.7	61.1	82.1	83.5	53.5
% Absorbed	26.7	42.7	54.0	54.6	39.5
	(45.5)*	(69.9)	(65.8)	(65.4)	(73.8)
% Translocated	22.6	32.8	45.1	35.4	29.6
	(38.5)*	(53.7)	(54.9)	(42.4)	(55.3)
	84.6#	76.8	83.5	64.8	74.9

In whole plants the translocation of ^{14}C-asulam follows a similar pattern of movement to that of assimilates[8]. In young fronds the ^{14}C accumulates in the apical regions of the treated frond (acropetal transport) while in older fronds, a greater proportion is translocated to the rhizome system (basipetal transport). In mature fronds, the ^{14}C-asulam is translocated basipetally. Clearly in these explant experiments, induction of sink activity by dark treatment or growth regulator application, re-establishes the condition which exists in immature fronds. The level of sugar demand in such immature tissues presumably reflects the relative levels of photosynthesis and respiration. Where photosynthetic activity is low, the energy requirements of dividing, elongating or differentiating cells must be met by sugars translocated from adjacent mature tissues. In the latter, gross photosynthetic production is sufficiently high to meet respiratory requirements and the net photosynthetic production is potentially available for translocation to other regions. The nature of the association, if any, between translocating molecules of sugars and herbicide is still a matter for conjecture. It is known, for example, that MCPA (4-methyl-2-chlorophenoxyacetic acid) or 2,4-D (2,4-dichlorophenoxyacetic acid) may conjugate with glucose forming glycosides or glucose esters but whether phloem translocation of these herbicides occurs in such form is uncertain.

CONCLUSION

The results of this study indicate that in the pinnae system, efficient acropetal translocation of asulam to the 'sinks' depends upon several factors including frond maturity, degree of cuticle waxiness, sink activity, surface of application and formulation of the herbicide. Also, the findings of similar experiments carried out on pot plants, are confirmed, indicating that in terms of 'source-sink' movement, the explant system is representative of the whole plant. The value of the explant system lies in its ability to replicate treatments with relatively uniform material, together with the conservation of growth cabinet space.

The activity of asulam and presumably other foliage-applied, translocated herbicides, depends upon a complex of inter-related factors. Of these, sink activity of the rhizome buds and apices at the time of treatment or subsequently is of critical importance.

REFERENCES

1) Whittle C M (1964) Translocation in Pteridium. Ann. Bot. 28, 331-338

2) Williams G H (1980) Bracken control: a review of progress, 1974-1979. West of Scotland Agricultural College, Research and Development Publication No 12., 55pp

3) Martin D J and Sparke, Carole J (1982) Field trials in south-west Scotland. Proc. Roy. Soc. Edin. 81B, 117-123

4) Williams G H and Foley A (1975) Effect of herbicides on bracken rhizome survival. Ann. Appl. Biol. 79, 109-111

5) Al-Jaff D M A, Cook G T, Stephen N H, Atchison T C and Duncan H J (1982). The effect of glyphosate on frond regeneration, bud development and survival, and storage rhizome starch content in bracken. Ann. Appl. Biol. 101, 323-329

6) Herrmann, Christine (1981) The effects of two herbicides on bracken (Pteridium esculentum Forst. f Cockayne) BSc Hons Thesis, Monash University, Australia

7) Jaworski E G (1972) Mode of action of N-phosphonomethylglycine: inhibition of aromatic amino acid biosynthesis. J. Agric. Fd. Chem., 20, 1195-1198

8) Veerasekaran P (1975) The mode of action of asulam in bracken. PhD Thesis, University of Strathclyde, Glasgow

9) Veerasekaran P, Kirkwood R C and Fletcher W W (1977a) Studies on the mode of action of asulam in bracken (Pteridium aquilinum L. Kuhn). I Absorption and translocation of ^{14}C-asulam. Weed Res., 17, 33-39

10) Veerasekaran P, Kirkwood R C and Fletcher W W (1977b) Studies on the mode of action of asulam in bracken (Pteridium aquilinum L. Kuhn).

348

II Biochemical activity in the rhizome buds. <u>Weed Res.</u>, 17, 85-92

11) Veerasekaran P, Kirkwood R C and Parnell E W (1981) Studies on
the mechanism of action of asulam in plants. Part I. Antagonistic
interaction of asulam and 4-aminobenzoic acid. <u>Pestic Sci.</u>, 12, 325-
329

12) Kirkwood R C (1979)   The uptake and translocation of foliar-
applied herbicides using the explant system. <u>Adv. Pest Sci.</u>, part 3:
410-415

13) Snedecor G W and Cochrane W G (1969) <u>Statistical methods</u>. 6th
Edition. Iowa State University Press, 593pp

14) Kirkwood R C and Hinshalwood, Anne (1985) Recent studies on the
biology of bracken and the mode of action of herbicides used in its
control.   <u>Proc. Int. Symposium Biology of Pteridophytes, Edinburgh
Sept. 1983.</u> (In press)

15) Mothes K and Engelbrecht L (1961)   Kinetin-induced directed
transport of substances in excised leaves in the dark.
<u>Phytochemistry</u>, 1, 58-62

16) Osborne, Daphne J (1962) <u>Pl. Physiol. Lancaster</u>, 37, 595-

17) Cook G T, Stephen N H and Duncan H J (1982) Fundamental studies
in bracken control - the use of additives to enhance herbicide uptake
and translocation. <u>Proc. Roy. Soc. Edin.</u>, 81B, 97-109

Lessons from fifteen years of bracken control with asulam

D Soper

PRODUCT DEVELOPMENT

In August 1970 we obtained the first long-term results of applying the grass herbicide asulam against bracken on hill-land. We were conditioned at that time by the short-term effects that had been achieved by chemicals such as 4-CPA, so with some scepticism I started further experiments before the end of that summer in order to decide the required dose. The rate of 4.5 kg of asulam per hectare (using the 40% aqueous concentrate) was established as a UK recommendation for agriculture in 1973, once we were permitted to sell, and has stood ever since.

Excellent control of hill bracken was achieved with the early trials[1] even with one aerial treatment. Although these results have never been bettered, (reduced rates : poorer, double : little improvement) the problem has been to ensure a high standard with large-scale aerial spraying once commercialisation took place. There was an understandable lack of pilot experience in operating in rugged terrain. Sites such as those with scattered scrub were tackled which were unsuitable for aerial treatment while heavy rainfall would sometimes negate an application.

A response to adding surfactant to asulam was first observed in 1970[2] but it was not until ten comparative trials were carried out in 1977/78 that benefit with aerial application was demonstrated on a sufficient scale[3]. The authors reported consistent improvement averaging at 4%, and a recommendation for adding a proprietary surfactant was accordingly made in 1980. In addition to surfactants ensuring more rapid uptake of asulam[4,5] it has now been shown that certain oils confer a degree of rainfastness and assist when spraying is not optimally timed (Table 1). In six, 1981 aerially-applied user trials the application of asulam with a branded oil gave control averaging at over 98%. So, rather than taking out an expensive 'Pluvius' policy which had been considered in earlier years, the best form of insurance proved to be adjuvants. The chronological development of asulam as a herbicide against bracken is shown in Table 2.

351

TABLE 1 Effect of adjuvants on the activity of asulam on bracken

% control of frond numbers 12 months after treatment

(A) Under dry or wet conditions at optimum timing (July/August).

Kg/ha	+ wetter	no wetter	
2.2	71	14	1 site
4.5	58	52	1969/70
9.0	88	58	(wet)
2.2	97.5	99.5	2 sites
3.4	98.5	98	1971/72
			(dry)
4.5	92	88	Mean of
	(80-98)	(73-95)	10 sites
			1977/78

(B) At sub-optimal doses with oils at 5.6 L/ha (1976/77)

Asulam kg/ha /oil	1.0 v. dry	2.0 wet	2.0 dry	3.0 v. dry
Actipron	71	60	80	94
Diesel*	65	40	75	94
Sifren	76	10	78	95
None	43	8	80	91

* plus Triton X-45 at 0.6 L/ha

Actipron is a registered trade mark of the British Petroleum Company plc. Sifren is a trade mark of Pepro. Triton X-45 is a trade mark of Rohm and Haas Co.

TABLE 2

1968	First trials. Cleared for commercial use against docks.
1972	Cleared for commercial use from ground and for limited use from the air.
1974	First usage year on Civil Aviation Authority list and as a Ministry of Agriculture Approved product from the air.
1980	First usage year with branded wetting agent from air and ground.
1980	Commercial clearance with branded mineral oil from the ground.
1983	Commercial clearance for aquatic use.
1984	Commercial clearance with branded mineral oil from the air.

ENVIRONMENTAL IMPACT

Water Catchment Areas

Hostility was encountered from Water Boards when large-scale aerial application of asulam was proposed. These Boards, (now amalgamated as Authorities) had - and still have - a legal obligation to supply potable water. They could debar the use of asulam in the areas under their jurisdiction, notwithstanding that clearance for hill-land application was already granted under the Pesticides Safety Precautions Scheme. We decided on three courses of action: firstly to discuss the matter with a major Water Supply Authority, secondly to organize odour tests in water with the co-operation of the Water Research Association, and thirdly to monitor the extent of any adventitious contamination in a hill-stream. It was accepted that because of the high dilution factor a risk hardly existed, but there was still concern about the chances of an aircraft crash and the oil pollution that might then result.

In hard and soft potable waters the detection of odour has been undertaken using the standard procedure for 'taint' tests.[6] The conclusions were that levels considerably in excess of the minute quantities envisaged entering a reservoir would be needed, for odour to be detected. In a monitoring study in Northumberland[7] the maximum adventitious spray contamination with asulam at the junction of two streams flowing through an aerially-sprayed site was 0.5 ppm, much lower than odour detection and fish toxicity levels. With this reassurance, the low toxicity to all animals as well as fish[8], and after the discovery of some activity on water-lily[9], procedures to obtain full aquatic clearance for asulam were instigated.

Conservation Areas

Other sources of opposition to large-scale bracken clearance in hill-land arose from conservation groups (eg. Dartmoor, Peak District) and from aerial application in high summer-populated areas (eg. Hindhead, parts of the Lake District). Noise of low-flying aircraft can frighten people and animals while grass inadvertently sprayed without bracken canopy can be damaged. Even if every precaution and correct procedure was followed to the letter, successful spraying means increased 'agricultural activity' of some kind and a change in the landscape: certainly a change of colour. Did the farmers concerned have a right to bring this about?

Following work by the Nature Conservancy Council[10] and the RSPB[11] showing that except for indigenous ferns and birch, little harm would come to other plants, small-scale treatment in nature reserves became acceptable. Treatment by shepherds to clear pathways for animals also became widely practised, particularly with the advent of lightweight application equipment. Even with large-scale treatment, conservation interests seem unlikely to be seriously threatened.

ASULAM AND FARM ECONOMICS

Efforts were made by May and Baker[12] and many agricultural advisors to try and promote large-scale clearance of bracken. The Hill Farming Research Organization[12] presented data showing post-treatment increases in dry matter herbage yield of 18 to 47%. Clearing a site with grass understorey brought about especially large benefits. The uptake of bracken spraying by hill farms over thirteen years has been slow but steady. There has been fluctuation in the amount of asulam sprayed, not because of difficult weather, but largely as a response to the cash available from livestock (mainly fat lamb) sales the previous year. Comparative increases in costs of spraying, and lamb prices, are shown in Table 3.

TABLE 3

Year	Asulox + Application £/ha	£ PER FINISHED Lamb
1973	32.50	7-12
1978	65.00	20-30
1985	106.00	32-40

Fear of bracken poisoning, unless non-native stock were to be introduced, has generally not been an inducement to spray. The latter has been helped by the various provisions for grant-aid, but coupling this with insistence on certain after-care measures has often been a disincentive. There was originally a wide variation of opinion on many possible management options, for example whether phosphate should be used, and whether treatment was desirable before spraying.[14] Also, would it not be better to make the optimum use of, or wait for the influx of, indigenous grasses such as Agrostis and Festuca, not needing lime, rather than re-seed with potentially higher-yielding species?

The herbicide manufacturer should obviously concentrate on application methods. A large number of techniques are available[15] and with all of these the need for early follow-up spraying must be avoided. So, what is the length of control that can be guaranteed from a good aerial application? Small plot trials indicate recovery from 4.4 or 8.8 kg/ha, as new frond buds differentiate, and the necessity for respraying after four years[16], while ingress of 1 to 2 metres per annum from plot margins has been observed.

Larger areas treated can either be achieving or failing their objectives after two to three years (Table 4), often in relation to farmer-motivation. Quick recovery may arise from 'shielded' spots, but rarely some problem areas fail to respond, perhaps suggesting a different bracken type. The norm is some limited recurrence of bracken after 4-6 years due to sparse, short frond-regrowth and invasion, although good persistence for 7 to 12 years is quite common. Not much late follow-up spraying is practised. Such treatment should now be coupled with continuous well-managed utilization by livestock of the reclaimed land.

TABLE 4 Long-term control of bracken with 4.5 kg Asulam/ha

(A)   Results based on July assessment

Sites	Months after treatment	Fronds per m^2 (untreated)	% control of frond numbers	Observations
Parton	24	45	99	Lower dose (3.36kg/ha) giving 96% control
Kirkcarswell	24	41	98	Additional sheep grazing provided
Alnwick	12	48	96	Missed strips – land eventually reclaimed by ploughing
	36	32	75	
Sundaywell	24	50	94	Change of owner – understocking

(B)   Farm C case study[13]

1973   – Aerial treatment of 120 ha.

1975-78   – Net livestock returns of approx. £10,000.

1975-85   – Nos: Per annum   Increase

            Ewes   635   + 80-100

            Cattle   300   + 60

1978   – Bracken re-growth started.

1984-85   – Re-growth causing concern.

ASULAM AND FORESTRY

Usage of asulam in timber-producing woodlands has been developed since 1971 in co-operation with the Forestry Commission. Because of the effects on incremental growth of young conifers, adjuvants (except pre-planting) are precluded. Dosage from 2-4 kg/ha depends on the desired period of freedom from bracken, while dead fronds need to be cut away from growing trees after spraying. Work study exercises have been undertaken and by contrast with agriculture, development has been straightforward.

CONCLUSIONS

At an early stage, May and Baker provided guidance to enable users of asulam to take care of the environment while the dose, timing, and persistence of asulam against bracken have all been proven. The greatest difficulty has been getting the spray on target. Aerial application is now much improved while better lightweight spraying equipment needs still to be developed.

The economic incentive to reclaim and maintain land free of bracken is unquestionly linked to the future of the livestock industry. More thought should be directed to pre-care, applying fertilizer for example in the early spring and monitoring from the year before spraying, thus graduating the change, rather than concentrating only on after-measures. The latter should not be mandatory for grant aid and at present there is over-emphasis on reseeding with costly grass species. Adequate mixed stocking as soon as practicable after spraying is of the greatest importance. Asulam in the bracken context must therefore be regarded as one of several management tools.

REFERENCES

1) Soper D (1972) Review of bracken control experiments with asulam. Proc. 11th Brit. Weed Control Conf., 24-31

2) Holroyd J, Parker C and Rowlands A (1970) Asulam for the control of bracken Pteridium aquilinum (L) Kuhn. Proc. 10th Brit. Weed Control Conf., 371-6

3) Horsnail G B and Robinson R C (1984) Further developments in the use of asulam for the control of bracken. Proc. Crop Protection in N. Britain, 315-320

4) Babiker A G T and Duncan H J (1974) Penetration of bracken fronds by asulam as influenced by the addition of surfactant to the spray solution and by pH. Weed Res., 14 375-7

5) Holroyd J and Thornton M E (1978) Factors influencing the control of bracken with asulam. Weed Res., 18 181-6

6) Arthey V D, Dakin J C, Ellis R and Esnor H L (1968) A proposed standard procedure for taint tests with agricultural chemicals. J.Fd.

Technol. 3 183-202

7) Ball R W E, Pink R B and Brockelsby C H (1974) Some environmental aspects of the use of asulam for bracken control in upland areas. Proc. 12th Brit. Weed Control Conf., 59-66

8) Heywood B J (1982) Bracken control by asulam. Proc. Royal Soc. Edinburgh 81(B) 111-6

9) Barrett P R F (1974) The susceptibility of Nuphar lutea to some foliage-applied herbicides. Proc. 4th International Symposium on Aquatic Weeds, (Vienna), 253-9

10) Horrill A D, Thomson A G and Dale J (1976) Effects of the herbicide asulam on non-target plant species and communities. Annual Report of Institute of Terrestrial Ecology, 63

11) Cadbury C J (1976) Botanical implications of bracken control. Bot. J. Linn. Soc. 73 285-294

12) Drummond J M and Soper D (1978) The long-term benefits of bracken removal with asulam on hill farms in N. Britain. Proc. Brit Crop Protection Conf. - Weeds, 317-324

13) Davies G F, Newbould P and Baillie G J (1979) The effect of controlling bracken on pasture production. Grass and Forage Science, 34, 163-171

14) Williams G and Fraser D (1979) The effects of asulam, frond cutting and ground mineral phosphate on the yields of swards dominated by bracken. Grass and Forage Science, 34, 95-100

15) Robinson R C (1985) Practical herbicide use for bracken control, (This volume)

16) Veerasekaran P, Kirkwood R C and Fletcher W W (1978) Studies on the mode of action of asulam in Bracken III. Long-term control of field bracken. Weed Res., 315-9

A comparison of the effects of cutting with those of the herbicide asulam on the control of bracken

J E Lowday

INTRODUCTION

Evidence from pollen records suggests that bracken was once a relatively minor component of the forest understorey[1]. However, under certain systems of land-use following forest clearance by man, it has spread vigorously, and now poses a major obstacle to grassland utilisation, re-establishment of trees, and wildlife conservation in many parts of its extensive worldwide range. These problems are aggravated by the toxic properties of bracken to domestic livestock[2,3,4], while possible threats to human health[5] require further investigation.

In the medieval period, bracken was considered to be an asset, and had several important uses in the rural economy as fuel, thatch, animal bedding and a source of potash for the glass and soap-making industries[6]. Indeed, in some areas, local by-laws were designed to prevent over-exploitation of this evidently valuable resource[7,8]. However, as these economic uses declined, and the problems that bracken posed for pasture and timber production became apparent, it began to be regarded as a weed.

Much research effort has been directed towards bracken control, and is summarised in earlier papers[9,10]. However, a successful method of control which can economically eradicate bracken from large areas has proved elusive and this is simply because bracken is so resilient to both mechanical and herbicidal control. The main reason for this is the large (15-20 t/ha) underground rhizome network which is made up of storage and frond-bearing rhizome. The larger fraction of the rhizome network (70-80% by weight) is storage rhizome, which contains large reserves of nutrients and energy. The remainder is frond-bearing rhizome, carrying a large number of buds which are capable of developing into mature fronds.

Cutting for bracken control

Where cutting is used to control bracken, timing is of fundamental importance. Cuts should be timed to cause maximum damage to the bracken system in relation to the seasonal partition of dry matter and nutrients between fronds and rhizomes[11,12,13]. A cut applied in mid-June to late July to sever fronds which have developed at the expense of a depletion of the rhizome reserves will remove resources from the system. However, it is essential that fronds are cut before late summer when basipetal translocation of assimilates will have started to replenish the rhizome reserves. Cutting generally needs to be repeated over several seasons because even when the standing crop of fronds is maximal, the majority of the dry matter of the system (60%) is underground[12]. Bracken fronds regenerate rapidly in response to cutting early in the summer[13] and frond regrowth after early cuts can be removed by subsequent cuts. Two or more cuts per year will deplete the resources of the bracken system more rapidly than single, annual cuts.

Herbicides for bracken control

The complex and extensive rhizome network, with numerous dormant buds, presents a difficult target for herbicides. Compounds tested in the 1950s and 1960s proved unsuccessful for long-term control of bracken because of their inability to move to the more distant branches of the rhizome network and accumulate in lethal amounts in the buds[14,15,16]. Currently, asulam is the most widely used herbicide for bracken control and its mode of action has been thoroughly described[17,18,19,20]. It is a phloem-mobile herbicide and is best applied at or near the time of full frond expansion, which also coincides with the flow of assimilates to the rhizome network. Asulam then accumulates in the frond buds and rhizome apices where it interferes with metabolic processes and protein synthesis, causing severe local damage to metabolically active sites.

This paper describes the contrasting effects of cutting and asulam on the frond-rhizome system of bracken over a seven-year period, and discusses the depletion of dry matter and bud resources in response to control treatments.

EXPERIMENTAL PROCEDURE

In early June 1978, a four-replicate, randomised block experiment investigating five control treatments compared with an untreated control (Table 1) was set up on an area of uniform, dense bracken at Weeting Heath National Nature Reserve, Norfolk, England (GR TL 757885). A thick layer of bracken litter (approximately 8 kg/m^2) covered the entire experimental area. Ground flora was very sparse or absent from all the plots throughout the course of the experiment.

The plots were cut using a mechanical scythe, with cut fronds left where they fell. The asulam was applied in the form of Asulox, using a motorised backpack sprayer, at the rate of 4.4 kg a.i./ha diluted to 400 litres/ha with water. In summer 1979, fronds on treatment 6 were spot-sprayed using the same equipment. No rain fell for at least 24 hours on both spraying dates.

360

TABLE 1   Description of experimental treatments

Treatment number	Cutting	Asulam
1	None	None
2	Once/year in late July from 1978 to 1983	None
3	Twice/year in mid-June and late July from 1978 to 1983	None
4	None	Once in August 1978
5	Once/year in late July from 1979 to 1983	Once in August 1978
6	None	Twice in August 1978 and 1979

From 1978 to 1984 the standing crop of bracken fronds was estimated annually in mid-July. On two occasions, April 1981 and April 1983, rhizomes growing within one 50 x 50 cm quadrat per plot were excavated to a depth of 79 cm. The rhizomes were then thoroughly washed, and after discarding dead or decaying material, were separated into storage and frond-bearing categories. The numbers of active and dormant frond buds were counted on the frond-bearing rhizomes; a bud was considered active if it was lightly coloured and swollen, in contrast to dormant buds which were smaller and covered by a dark brown protective scale.

RESULTS

Fronds (Table 2)

All treatments significantly reduced the standing crop of bracken fronds compared to untreated plots. Asulam caused the greatest initial reduction in standing crop of fronds, although on plots sprayed once (but not cut) and plots sprayed twice (treatments 4 and 6), there was an exponential increase in standing crop in subsequent years. Indeed, by July 1984, there was no significant difference in standing crop of fronds between those plots sprayed once in 1978 and untreated plots. Spraying twice (treatment 6) delayed frond regeration by one year compared with plots sprayed once. However, where fronds were cut once annually from 1979 onwards, following a single 1978 application of asulam (treatment 5), frond regrowth was restricted to below 10% of the standing crop of the untreated plots, although attaining 17% of the untreated value in 1984.

361

TABLE 2 The effects of bracken control treatments on the standing crop of fronds (g/m^2), mid-July 1978-1984 (n=4)

Treatment	1978	1979	1980	1981	1982	1983	1984
1 Untreated	414	638	472	574	809	715	620
2 Cut once/year	361	407	146	164	321	277	284
3 Cut twice/year	n/a	20	9.5	5.5	9.8	8.6	6.3
4 Asulam once	447	7.4	14.8	80.5	321	505	593
5 Asulam once then cut once/year	434	7.7	2.7	35.9	48.6	24.4	107
6 Asulam twice	329	9.7	1.4	22.7	79.3	308	382
LSD (P=0.05)	159	120	57	145	140	138	134

On plots cut once annually in late July (treatment 2), there was a 36% reduction in standing crop of fronds in July 1979, following a single cut in 1978. This reduction in standing crop was sustained between 1979 and 1980, but from 1980 to 1984 the standing crop of fronds was relatively stable, with reductions in standing crops of 54-71% being observed.

On plots cut twice annually (treatment 3), the standing crop of fronds was restricted to 1-3% of untreated values. However, direct comparisons are difficult to make because the fronds sampled in July represent the regrowth from the first of the two cuts applied in mid-June.

Rhizomes (Table 3)

In both April 1981 and April 1983, all bracken control treatments significantly reduced the total standing crop of rhizomes, and that of both the frond-bearing and storage fractions, compared to untreated plots. In both years, the largest reductions in rhizome standing crop were observed on plots cut twice per year (treatment 3). However, in contrast to the massive reduction in standing crop of fronds after spraying asulam, there was a much smaller reduction in the standing crop of rhizomes. But whereas the standing crop of fronds increased exponentially after spraying with asulam (in the absence of cutting), the standing crop of rhizomes continued to decline between April 1981 and April 1983. Amongst asulam-treated plots, in both 1981 and 1983, the lowest standing crop of rhizomes occurred on the plots cut annually from 1979 onwards (treatment 5).

After three single cuts (treatment 2), a 66% reduction in total rhizome compared to untreated plots was observed in April 1981; two further cuts in 1981 and 1982 reduced this value to a 75% reduction by April 1983. A similar pattern was observed on plots cut twice

362

TABLE 3   The effects of bracken control treatments on the amount of
          frond-bearing, storage and total rhizome in April 1981 and
          April 1983 (n=4)

Treatment	April 1981			April 1983		
	Frond-bearing	Storage	Total	Frond-bearing	Storage	Total
1 Untreated	259	1307	1566	205	1105	1310
2 Cut once/year	140	398	538	38	293	331
3 Cut twice/year	15	104	119	4	63	67
4 Asulam once	187	891	1078	35	546	581
5 Asulam once then cut once/year	109	655	764	1.1	125	126
6 Asulam twice	163	632	795	19	365	384
LSD (P=0.05)	44	286	304	55	184	182

annually (treatment 3) where, in April 1981, there was a 92% reduction
in total rhizome after 6 cuts, compared with a 95% reduction in 1983
after ten cuts. The first few cuts therefore reduce the standing crop
of the bracken relatively quickly, but the rate of depletion of the
bracken's resources slows down in response to further cuts.

Frond buds (Table 4)

     On untreated plots a total of 350-450 buds/m^2 was observed,
most of which (70-80%) were dormant. Substantial fluctuations in the
number of active buds were observed in April 1981 and 1983 (47 and
113/m^2 respectively), but in all years (1978 to 1984), there were
20-25 mature fronds/m^2 present on untreated plots. Factors
regulating the number of active buds, mature fronds and the fate of
active buds not developing into mature fronds, are poorly understood
and require further investigation.
     In both 1981 and 1983 all treatments significantly reduced the
numbers of dormant, active and total fronds on treated compared with
untreated plots, except in 1981 when there was no difference in
numbers of active buds on plots cut once/year compared to those
untreated.
     The largest reductions in populations of active, dormant and
total buds occurred on plots sprayed with asulam, but in the absence
of cutting (treatments 4 and 6), bud populations increased from 1981
to 1983. On all plots there were more dormant than active buds in
1981, but on all treated plots this was reversed in 1983, with active
buds being in the majority.

TABLE 4 The effects of bracken control treatments on the numbers of active, dormant and total frond buds on rhizomes sampled in April 1981 and April 1983 (n=4)

Treatment	April 1981			April 1983		
	Active	Dormant	Total	Active	Dormant	Total
1 Untreated	47	298	345	117	319	436
2 Cut once/year	63	164	227	72	51	123
3 Cut twice/year	11	24	35	38	13	51
4 Asulam once	5	14	19	61	30	91
5 Asulam once then cut once/year	7	9	16	10	4	14
6 Asulam twice	6	11	17	33	18	51
LSD (P=0.05)	36	105	116	37	125	143

DISCUSSION

Untreated plots

In an undisturbed stand of bracken the supply of buds for maturation into fronds, and the production and seasonal partition of dry matter between fronds and rhizomes are all uninterrupted. In these conditions, bracken can maintain a dense, closed canopy on many sites over a long period of time[21], and exert strong dominance over other species. If long-term cyclical processes[22,23,24] and annual fluctuations in productivity are ignored, then we can assume that a steady state or equilibrium exists in the bracken system. In this steady state there will be an adequate supply of frond buds to replace those which mature into fronds, together with croziers killed by late spring frosts and frond buds damaged or killed by severe winter frosts penetrating the litter layer and soil. Furthermore, in an equilibrium, the photosynthetic production from the fronds will offset the various natural losses of dry matter of the bracken system due to respiration and senescent fronds entering the litter pool.

Any bracken control treatment must interrupt this equilibrium condition, so it is clearly necessary to reduce the resources of frond buds, dry matter or both to a critical level in order to achieve this. The effects that experimental cutting and application of asulam had on these resources will now be discussed in more detail.

Cutting

Cutting reduces the dry matter resources of the bracken system by severing fronds which have developed at the expense of rhizome reserves and, as a consequence, prevents the replenishment of rhizome reserves by basipetal translocation of assimilates which normally occurs in late summer. Furthermore, the gross photosynthetic input may be substantially reduced on cut plots.

At the start of the cutting programme the first cuts applied to the dense stand of bracken removed substantial amounts of dry matter from the system; for example, the frist two cuts on plots cut once/year (treatment 2) removed 360 and 407 g/m^2 in 1978 and 1979 respectively. Moreover, respiration losses from the relatively large standing crop of the rhizome network may have further contributed to the overall losses of the system at this early stage. However, as the dry matter resources of the bracken system decline, two factors may interact to slow down the rate of loss of dry matter from the system. First, as the standing crop of fronds is reduced, the amount of dry matter that can potentially be removed from the system by cutting, also declines, and secondly, with a depleted rhizome system, the respiration losses may be reduced. Indeed, after the initial substantial reduction, broadly similar standing crops of fronds were observed in consecutive seasons, despite a single cut being applied annually in July. A similar pattern was observed on plots cut twice/year. We may speculate that under a constant cutting regime a new equilibrium, albeit at a much lower level, would be achieved.

Cutting a dense stand of bracken, where litter has accumulated, may also have a number of important but indirect effects on the bracken system. Cutting machinery will compact and fragment the litter layer, thus reducing its insulating properties which, in turn, modifies the microclimate above and around the rhizome network. The rhizomes may be exposed to more extreme temperatures; frost may penetrate deeper into the soil in winter, whereas the soil may warm up quicker in the spring. An increased incidence of frost damage to emergent fronds was observed on experimentally cut plots, where fronds emerged earlier, possibly in response to warmer soil temperatures[25].

Furthermore, dispersion of the litter layer by cutting machinery may allow opportunities for colonisation and establishment of other vegetation which, in turn, may compete with bracken. The relative importance of direct and indirect effects of cutting on reducing the resources of the bracken system is not known, but could vary widely in different seasons and sites.

Asulam

Asulam caused very severe but local damage to the frond buds and apices on the rhizome network, sealing them with black, necrotic, wart-like lesions. Apart from this local damage, the rhizome system remained largely intact although with a reduced standing crop. However, in subsequent seasons, new sections of frond-bearing rhizome developed on sections of storage rhizome occuring deep in the soil, possibly from buds which were dormant at the time of spraying. There may be at least two reasons why some buds receive a sublethal dose of herbicide. First, they may be dormant, and because of a low metabolic rate, do not attract enough sugars to receive a lethal dose of herbicide. Secondly, with a limited mobility of the herbicide within the rhizome network, buds on sections of the rhizome network remote from a herbicide source (a sprayed frond) may not receive a lethal dose.

Cutting prior to an application of asulam was shown to increase the effectiveness of the herbicide (Lowday, in prep.). Cutting causes a number of modificatins to a stand of bracken; it increases frond density and the number of active frond buds, but decreases the standing crop of the system and reduces canopy height. Any one, or a combination of these factors, could improve herbicide performance. Indeed, a combination of cutting (to deplete dry matter reserves) and a herbicide (to kill frond buds) appears to have complementary effects compared to either method used in isolation.

ACKNOWLEDGEMENTS

This work was commissioned by the Nature Conservancy Council as part of its programme of research into nature conservation. J D and R Cheesman, D Malins and G B Nevison gave valuable assistance on field work.

REFERENCES

1) Page C N (1982) The history and spread of bracken in Britain. Proc. R. Soc. Edinb., 81B, 3-10

2) Evans W C (1976) Bracken thiaminase-mediated neurotoxic syndromes. Bot. J. Linn. Soc., 73, 113-131

3) Evans I A (1976) Relationship between bracken and cancer. Bot. J. Linn. Soc., 73, 105-112

4) Jarret W F H (1982) Bracken and cancer. Proc. R. Soc. Edinb., 81B, 79-83

5) Evans I A, Prorok J H, Cole R C, Al-Salmani M H, Al-Samarrai A M H, Patel M C and Smith R M M (1982) The carcinogenic, mutagenic and teratogenic toxicity of bracken. Proc. R. Soc. Edinb., 81B, 65-77

6) Rymer L (1976) The history and ethnobotany of bracken. Bot. J. Linn. Soc., 73, 151-176

7) Davies-Shiel M (1972) A little-known late mediaeval industry, Part 1. The making of potash for soap in Lakeland. Trans. Cumberland, Westmorland Antiq. Archaeol. Soc., 62, 85-111

8) Mabey R (1980) The common ground: a place for nature in Britain's future? 166-167. London, Hutchinson

9) Braid K W (1959) Bracken: a review of the literature. Hurley, Commonwealth Agricultural Bureaux

10) Williams G H (1980) Bracken control: a review of progress, 1974-1979. Research and Development publication no 12. Auchincruive, West of Scotland Agricultural College

11) Hunter J G (1953) The composition of bracken; some major- and

trace-element constituents. J. Sci. Fd Agric., 4, 10-20

12) Williams G H and Foley A (1976) Seasonal variations in the carbohydrate content of bracken. Bot. J. Linn. Soc., 73, 87-94

13) Lowday J E, Marrs R H and Nevison G (1983) Some of the effects of cutting bracken (Pteridium aquilinum (L.) Kuhn) at different times during the summer. J. Environ. Manage., 17, 373-380

14) Conway E and Forrest J D (1961) The effects of 4-chlorophenoxy-acetic acid on the rhizome of Pteridium aquilinum (L.) Kuhn. Weed Res., 1, 114-130

15) Hodgson G L (1964) Chemical control of bracken. A progress report on research during years 1959-63. Oxford, Agricultural Research Council

16) Conway E (1959) The bracken problem. Outl. Agric., 2, 158-167

17) Veerasekaran P, Kirkwood R C and Fletcher W W (1976) The mode of action of asulam (methyl, 4-aminobenzenesulphonyl carbamate) in bracken. Bot. J. Linn. Soc., 73, 247-268

18) Veerasekaran P, Kirkwood R C and Fletcher W W (1977) Studies on the mode of action of asulam in bracken (Pteridium aquilinum (L.) Kuhn). I. Absorption and translocation of ^{14}C asulam. Weed Res., 17, 33-39

19) Veerasekaran P, Kirkwood R C and Fletcher W W (1977) Studies on the mode of action of asulam in bracken (Pteridium aquilinum) (L.) Kuhn). II. Biochemical activity in the rhizome buds. Weed Res., 17, 85-92

20) Veerasekaran P, Kirkwood R C and Fletcher W W (1978) Studies on the mode of action of asulam in bracken (Pteridium aquilinum (L.) Kuhn). III. Longterm control of field bracken. Weed Res., 18, 315-319

21) Oinonen E (1967) Sporal regeneration of bracken (Pteridium aquilinum (L.) Kuhn) in Finland in the light of its dimensions and the age of its clones. Acta For. Fenn., 83, 3-96

22) Watt A S (1945) Contributions to the ecology of bracken (Pteridium aquilinum). III. Frond types and make-up of the population. New Phytol., 44, 156-178

23) Watt A S (1947) Contributions to the ecology of bracken (Pteridium aquilinum). IV. The structure of the community. New Phytol., 46, 97-121

24) Marrs R H and Hicks M J (1986) Studies on the dynamics of bracken in Breckland. This volume

25) Lowday J E (1983) Frost damage to emerging fronds during bracken cutting experiments. Trans. Bot. Soc. Edinb., 44, 153-157

Bracken control and land management in the Moel Famau Country Park, Clwyd, North Wales

I W Brown and P Wathern

INTRODUCTION

The Moel Famau Country Park, covering an area of 861 hectares, is situated on the highest tract of the Clwydian Range in north-east Wales. The park extends along the crest, watershed and southwest-facing slopes overlooking the Vale of Clwyd for a length of 8.9 km. The topography is one of rolling hills, the highest point, 544 m O.D, being at Moel Famau, with subsidiary peaks at Moel Fenlli (511 m) and Moel Arthur (455 m). The lowest point is at about 221 m OD. The estate was formed from the amalgamation of the two adjoining Country Parks of Moel Famau and Moel Arthur, which were purchased by the former Counties of Denbighshire and Flintshire, respectively, before local government re-organisation in 1974. It is now owned and administered by Clwyd County Council. Thus, the park comprises two virtually self-contained sections which differ markedly with respect to land use. The Moel Famau section of the park, which extends for 740 hectares, is common land devoted to extensive sheep grazing. Over 145 hectares of this area were reclaimed for agriculture during the 1970s, which has produced a much more intensive grazing regime. The 121 hectares of the Moel Arthur section are not common and are let on an agricultural tenancy basis.

The park contains major Iron Age hillforts capping the main summits. In addition, it is an important wildlife reserve, a reflection of its diverse habitats which are also significant in determining the landscape value of the area. Many demands, particularly for recreation, are made upon the area. For example, the Offa's Dyke long-distance footpath runs along the length of the park. The nature and extent of recreational activity has been monitored in detail by various surveys undertaken by the County Council between 1973 and 1984. The figure of approximately 150,000 visitors in 1984 to the Moel Famau viewpoint indicates the intensity of recreational activity. By contrast, visits to Moel Arthur, about 20,000 visitors per annum, are much fewer.

PHYSICAL RESOURCES OF THE PARK

Although various papers have been written on the general geomorphology and geology of northeast Wales, virtually nothing pertaining to this area has been published. Relevant information on physical characteristics such as geology, geomorphology, soils, vegetation and drainage, therefore, has had to be generated by original research and survey.

The park is located on a broad, west-facing, fault-line scarp above the late Hercynian Vale of Clwyd fault, and all of the rocks found in situ are late Silurian, marine, clastic sediments (shales, mudstones, flags, sandstones and greywackes of Ludlovian age). They are obscured under a thick layer of glacial till, head and colluvium, and outcrops are almost entirely restricted to old quarry workings and short stream sections. Minor streams and nivation cirques have dissected the escarpment along a number of NE-SW-trending minor faults, with the result that prominent spurs jut out from the main mass into the Vale of Clwyd. Steeply sloping (15-25°) and very steeply sloping (25-35°) are the predominant slope categories of the park, with ESE-WNW providing the majority of aspects.

Soils of the podzolic major group, notably brown podzolic soils on the middle and lower slopes and ferric stagnopodzols, ironpan stagnopodzols and typical podzols on the higher slopes, are the most common, with occasional lithomorphic or terrestrial raw soils where the drift thins or is absent. Surface-water gleys are found in the stream valleys, and man-made soils are associated with the hillforts and summits of the area. Soil erosion, caused by the overgrazing of sheep, imprudent land reclamation and recreational activity is a problem[1].

Although the vegetation of the park is predominantly dry moorland and heath (Calluna vulgaris - Vaccinium myrtillus) and acid grassland (Agrostis tenuis - Festuca ovina), the long-maintained management regimes of (i) sheep grazing and (ii) heather and gorse burning have resulted in the development of a mosaic of vegetation types (Figure 1). Generally, moorland dominates the hilltops and plateaux, whilst grasslands clothe the spurs and the middle and lower slopes. Where the soil thins, the grassland is frequently infested with bracken (Pteridium aquilinum) and, locally, gorse (Ulex gallii and U. europaeus). Since 1974, uncontrolled burning, covering some 70 hectares, has left large areas of poor vegetation cover or bare ground. Flushes and wet valley bottoms support a distinctive vegetation, characterised by Sphagnum spp. and Juncus effusus.

BRACKEN INFESTATION

Bracken has invaded, to varying degrees of intensity, substantial areas of acid grassland. Approximately 210 hectares (28%) and 30 hectares (25%) of the Moel Famau and Moel Arthur sections respectively, are dominated by bracken. It also forms a component of some 188 hectares of mixed vegetation mosaics classified as heathland, acid grassland and wetland vegetation. These areas form an important buffer or transitional zone between infested lower slopes and pure stands of heather and bilberry above.

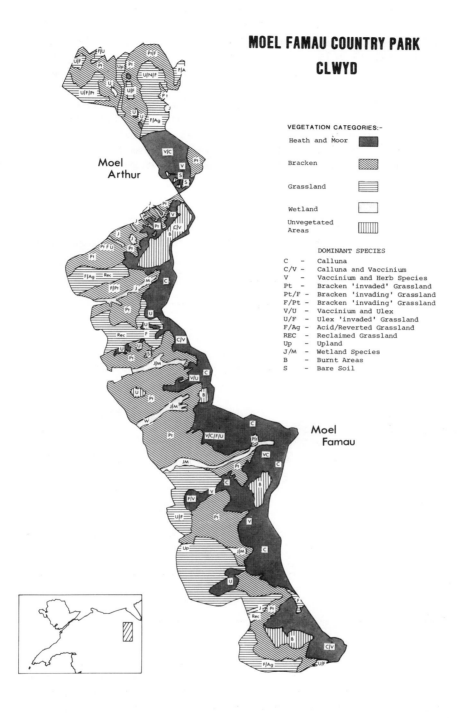

MOEL FAMAU COUNTRY PARK
CLWYD

VEGETATION CATEGORIES:-

Heath and Moor

Bracken

Grassland

Wetland

Unvegetated Areas

DOMINANT SPECIES

C - Calluna
C/V - Calluna and Vaccinium
V - Vaccinium and Herb Species
Pt - Bracken 'invaded' Grassland
Pt/F - Bracken 'invading' Grassland
F/Pt - Bracken 'invading' Grassland
V/U - Vaccinium and Ulex
U/F - Ulex 'invaded' Grassland
F/Ag - Acid/Reverted Grassland
REC - Reclaimed Grassland
Up - Upland
J/M - Wetland Species
B - Burnt Areas
S - Bare Soil

Moel Arthur

Moel Famau

Figure 1   Vegetation map of Moel Famau, 1984

Conditions in the park are especially favourable for bracken
growth. It inhabits a wide range of physiographic types, being
particularly associated with the comparatively deep (35 cm average)
and well drained brown podzolic soils of the Banc and Manod Series.
It achieves maximum development on sheltered, steep (15-25°)

371

SW-facing slopes and spurs below the pronounced, upper, convex margins which divide these slopes from the less steep (<15°), but more inhospitable, moorland plateau. Bracken is also found in profusion on very steeply sloping land (25-35°) at Moel Famau, but infests flatter land at Moel Arthur where it has invaded areas of gorse and acid grassland.

Land facet analysis of the park, based on physiographic factors (landform, soils and drainage) indicates the extent of areas vulnerable to possible bracken infestation (Table 1). This analysis suggests that up to 623 hectares, 72.4% of the total land area of the park, are vulnerable to bracken invasion where microclimatic factors allow.

TABLE 1   Areas vulnerable to bracken infestation: Moel Famau Country
Park (Ha)

Land facet/subfacet	Moel Famau	Moel Arthur	Total area	% of total area
Valley toe-slope (<15°)	56.9	11.0	67.9	7.9
Steeply sloping spurside (15-25°)	199.1	19.7	218.8	25.4
Very steeply sloping spur side (25-35°)	50.7	7.3	58.0	6.7
Spur plateau (3-15°)	49.1	12.6	61.7	7.2
Steeply sloping hillside (15-25°)	91.6	29.5	121.1	14.1
Very steeply sloping hillside (25-35°)	91.7	3.9	95.6	11.1
Total area vulnerable to infestation	539.1	84.0	623.1	72.4

The pattern of bracken distribution throughout the park is complex. In some situations it is invasive, but in other areas it appears to have reached a state of equilibrium. The overlap with heath and grassland communities is evident throughout the area, and clear boundaries are often difficult to define. Thus, detrended correspondence ordination and TWINSPAN analysis[2] clearly delimits two distinct groups of quadrats within the area. In the first group, bracken dominates whilst in the second it is absent. There is, however, an ill-defined transitional region into which numerous bracken-containing quadrats fall. Thus, bracken is intimately associated not only with acid grassland, but also with heather and bilberry where they occur at lower altitudes. In addition, it is found, locally, in wetter areas dominated by Juncus effusus and

<u>Molinia caerulea</u> where its advance is probably checked by high soil moisture. A regime of advance and retreat according to variations in local drainage probably occurs throughout the wet valley bottoms. The ordination also shows that climatic factors probably delineate the upper limit of bracken.

Large areas of the park have been burnt, in most cases accidentally, over the past ten years (Fig.1). In such burnt areas, where the physical conditions of climate, drainage and soil provide a suitable environment, bracken quickly invades. This has resulted in the continued loss of valuable heather at the margins of the moorland plateau throughout the park.

Changes in the distribution of bracken at Moel Arthur, determined from aerial photographs, are shown in Figure 2. Analysis of rates of invasion are difficult to determine because there is only partial coverage for 1948 and 1964. However, at Brynffynnon where direct comparisons can be made, bracken increased by 95% over the

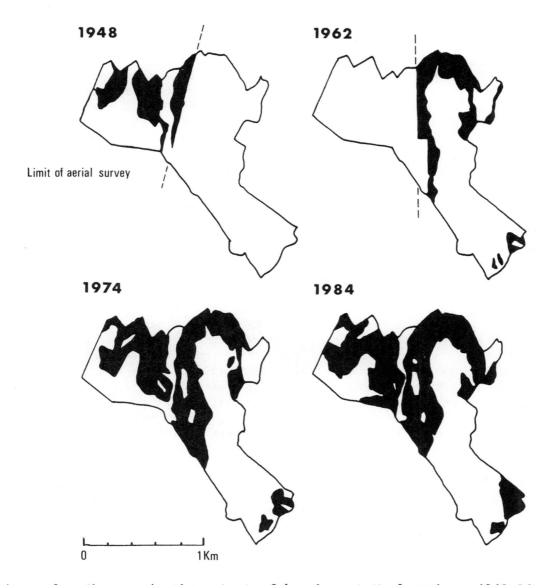

Figure 2   Changes in the extent of bracken at Moel Arthur, 1948-84

period 1948-84. This is an average encroachment rate of 2.6% per annum which is compatible with rates quoted by Taylor, herein, for other sites in Wales and elsewhere in Britain. Much of the increase has occurred since 1974. The situation at Moel Famau is further complicated by the extent of land reclamation. In this area, the rate of bracken advance is much slower, probably as environmental factors become limiting. Much of the advance occurred prior to 1974, further underlining the differences between the two areas.

LAND MANAGEMENT AND BRACKEN CONTROL

Bracken not only dominates much of the park at present, but also has the potential to invade nearly three-quarters of the total area. Consequently, land management cannot ignore the effects of bracken invasion on the main users of the area, namely recreation, wildlife and agriculture, as it may affect the whole future of the park. In the past when a more labour-intensive farming practice existed, bracken formed a significant part of the local agricultural economy. Its use for bedding, as thatch and as a source of potash is well documented[3], and it appears that this applied equally in the Clwydian Range. For example, an 1866 valuation of a farm in Llangynhafal parish, which now lies partly within the Country Park, mentions a 'quantity of bracken', presumably cut for litter.

Recently, changes in agricultural practice have favoured bracken. Various factors, such as the absence of intensive control, unwise burning, overgrazing and a general reduction in the number of cattle grazed over the winter period, have enabled bracken to spread over large areas.

The deleterious effect of bracken on the grazing potential of the land has encouraged the investigation of appropriate methods of grassland improvement. Early attempts involved a bracken crushing scheme using a serrated-edge cutter. Since 1973, however, some 145 hectares of formerly heavily-infested land in the Moel Famau section of the park have been enclosed and reclaimed for permanent pasture. This has involved a complete spraying, ploughing or rotavating and re-seeding regime, with lime and fertilizer applied.

In terms of recreation, the presence of bracken has both benefits and drawbacks. Although it restricts access, bracken makes a significant contribution to landscape quality (visual amenity). Despite the presence of much reclaimed land with its monotonous green colour, the Clwydian Range is still scenically attractive. Seasonal variations in the colour of a mosaic of different vegetation types is important in determining its landscape character, and, in this respect, bracken-dominated vegetation makes an important contribution. Thus, throughout the winter months, the dark colour of heather with the russet brown of bracken contrast with the vivid green of the lower slopes and fields of the Vale of Clwyd. Prior to the creation of the visually harsh field boundaries which characterise reclaimed areas, this altitudinal gradation displayed transition, resulting from the interaction of less intensive grazing regimes with physiographic and climatic factors.

The development of a strategy for the management of bracken, therefore, required the careful integration of agricultural, wildlife and scenic interests. Clwyd County Council, assisted by the

Department of Botany and Microbiology at the University College of Wales, Aberystwyth, is presently engaged in developing a vegetation management plan covering the park. Experimental treatments, involving both cutting and spraying, have been established to investigate suitable methods of bracken control on this site. In addition, an extensive area has been mown with a flail mower at intervals through the growing season, followed by harrowing in the autumn, to determine whether this approach is practicable on a large scale.

Marked differences in the physical characteristics and land tenure of Moel Famau and Moel Arthur require the development of alternative approaches. Taking current agricultural practice into account, it is envisaged that some 107 hectares of Moel Famau (14.5%) are suitable for bracken control on landscape and soil conservation grounds. On the other hand, 102 hectares (13.9%) are better retained as bracken, particularly on slopes viewed from the Offa's Dyke footpath. These proposals should be contrasted with the management policy for other vegetation types. Thus, 189 hectares (25.5%) of heather and bilberry will be conserved or restored. Similarly, 188 hectares of mixed vegetation, much of which contains bracken as an element, also requires management. Bracken will be controlled over some 10 hectares, whilst elsewhere its spread will be monitored and remedial measures adopted as necessary. It is hoped that agreement will be reached shortly with the Clwydian Range Graziers on a package of work covering these management proposals.

The tenure system at Moel Arthur demands an alternative approach. Over a part of this area (69 hectares), covering Brynffynnon and Penybryn Mountain, a draft management plan has been agreed between the County Council and its tenant (Figure 3). The plan, grant-aided by the Welsh Office Agriculture Department, will result in bracken control and pasture improvement over approximately 30 hectares. This will take three broad forms, depending upon the nature of each specific land parcel and its location. Firstly, some 18 hectares of relatively flat land will be cut twice each year in mid-June and at the end of July for a three-year period. This area will also receive applications of lime, triple superphosphate and compound fertilizer, and heavy harrow treatment to scarify the surface and to break up any remaining bracken litter. The second treatment has been designed for areas with a minimum of 70% grass sward on slopes <16°. Initially, 12 hectares will be sprayed with asulam in July, followed by grassland renovation. The grassland will be treated with lime and triple superphosphate in the first year, and heavy harrowing and compound fertilizer in the following year. Thirdly, areas of deep-litter bracken with virtually no grass will be reclaimed by spraying and reseeding. Over an area, again of approximately 12 hectares, asulam will be sprayed in July. In the second year, the area will be rotavated, reseeded and treated with triple superphosphate, and compound fertilizer. The exact nature of seed mixtures has yet to be decided but, because of the landscape and wildlife importance of the park, it is envisaged that a series of 'conservation mixes' will be adopted.

To complement the programme of bracken control, attempts will be made to re-create Calluna heath, using the technique developed by Gilbert and Wathern[4], since Meaden[5] has shown that this can be achieved on Moel Famau if sheep are excluded during the establishment period. Elsewhere, the creation of diverse, acid grassland will be

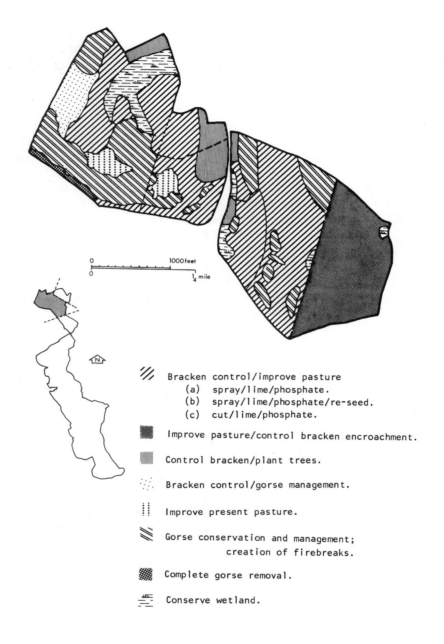

Figure 3   Vegetation management plan for Brynffynnon and Penybryn
Mountain

the objective.   It is important that these areas are not simply
converted to Lolium perenne swards.   In this way, a balance between
conservation and agricultural development will be achieved, retaining
the present diverse nature of the park.

ACKNOWLEDGEMENT

We would like to acknowledge the contribution of Kate Wyer to this study of bracken at Moel Famau.

REFERENCES

1) Baker C F, Morgan R P C, Brown I W, Hawkes D E and Ratcliffe J B (1979) 'Soil Erosion Survey of the Moel Famau Country Park.' National College of Agricultural Engineering, Occasional Paper No 7, Silsoe.

2) Wyer K (1985) The Vegetation of Moel Famau Country Park and its Management. Unpublished BSc thesis, University College of Wales, Aberystwyth

3) Rymer L (1976) The history and ethnobotany of bracken. Bot. J. Linn. Soc., 72, 151-176

4) Gilbert O L and Wathern P (1976) Towards the production of extensive Calluna swards. Landscape Design, 114, 35

5) Meaden D P (1984) The Restoration and Creation of Heather Moorland Vegetation. Unpublished PhD thesis, University of Liverpool

Bracken control in the Bulgarian uplands

N Fetvadjieva and P I Petrov

INTRODUCTION

The bracken fern, <u>Pteridium aquilinum</u>, is commonly to be seen in the upland and mountainous regions of Bulgaria. Mechanical control of the weed produces a lasting effect when, over a two-year period, the plant's aerial portion is cut or bruised on eight successive occasions. Between 1965 and 1981 tests have been conducted with some 15 herbicides, of which asulam, and to a lesser extent glyphosate, have been the most effective[3].

MATERIALS AND METHODS

In tests for herbicide effectiveness, four field experiments were carried out between 1981 and 1984 at the Institute in Troyan[1,2]. The first of these, testing 5 herbicides and 2 herbicide combinations, was conducted in late July 1981 and repeated in early August 1982. The second, in 1981, was an assessment of the relative effectiveness and persistence of asulam, applied at 4.8 kg/ha on June 15, before complete frond unfurlment, on July 15, 15 days after complete unfurlment, on August 15, 45 days after, and on September 25, 85 days after unfurlment. The third was an assessment of the rope-wick method of applying asulam or glyphosate, the former at 4.0 and 4.8 kg/ ha, the latter at 3.6 and 4.32 kg/ha. Herbicide to water ratios were 1:1, 1:2 and 1:4. The experiment was conducted in early August 1982 and repeated in late July 1983. The fourth, an assessment of the ultra-low-volume application of asulam at 4.8 kg/ha, was conducted in late July 1983 and repeated in late July 1984.

Preparations (a.i.) to be tested were asulox (40% asulam), roundup (36% glyphosate), tordon 22K (25% picloram), krenite (48% fosamine), velpar 90 WSP (90% hexazinone) and SYS 67 omnidel (90% dalapon). The block design utilized had 25 m^2 plots and 4 replicates. In the third experiment, the rope-wick treatment was carried out with Monsanto equipment adapted in Troyan to sloping local terrain[4]. In the fourth experiment, ultra-low-volume treatment was carried out with a Micron Ulva 8 sprayer.

The features of the experimental site were: altitude 500 m, grey forest soil with 2.7% humus, continental climate, average annual rainfall 746 mm, average annual temperature 9.9°C, vegetation consisting of grasses 60%, (Agrostis capillaris and Festuca fallax predominating) legumes 20%, and mixed fodder plants.

In all four experiments, herbicide effectiveness was assessed on day 330 and day 660 after treatment by counting the number of regenerated fronds. In the first experiment, rhizomes were recovered on day 90 after treatment from a depth of 40 cm, their length and weight (both at recovery and after air-drying) were determined, and the viability of dormant buds was assessed. In the first and second experiments, the effect of herbicide on the grass sward was assessed on day 60 after treatment, and again at ripeness the following year, and a year later. Asulam translocation into the fronds and rhizomes was assessed within 6, 12 and 24 hours after treatment, and then again on days 7, 15 and 30. Herbage samples were taken on days 15 and 30 after treatment. Soil samples from different layers were taken on days 1, 7, 15 and 30, and analysed for residual asulam. Asulam concentration in the fronds and rhizomes, as well as in the herbage, was determined by spectrophotometry[5,6], but with certain procedural alterations for better plant extract purification.

RESULTS AND DISCUSSION

First experiment

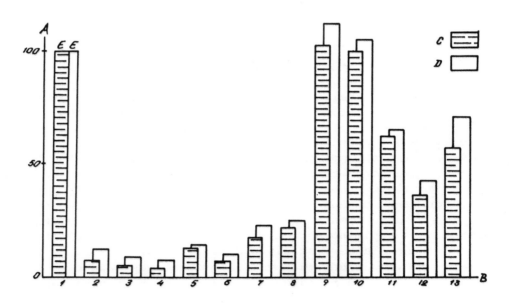

Fig.1. Frond regeneration in the 2nd and 3rd year after treatment. A. bracken canopy, %; B. Herbicides, a.i. in kg/ ha; C. On day 330; D. On day 660; E. 18 plants per m². 1. Controls; 2. Asulam 4.0 kg; 3. Asulam 4.8 kg; 4. Asulam 6.0 kg; 5. Glyphosate 3.6 kg; 6. Glyphosate 4.32 kg; 7. Asulam 3.2 kg + Dalapon 9.0 kg; 8. Glyphosate 2.88 kg + Dalapon

9.0 kg; 9. Hexazinone 2.7 kg; 10. Hexazinone 4.5
kg; 11. Picloram 1.5 kg; 12. Picloram 2.5 kg;
13. Fosamine 4.8 kg

As the first experiment data (Fig.1) show, asulam and
glyphosate destroy the aerial portion of the bracken fern. In the
first year after treatment, the plots were practically free of the
weed. In the second year, in the case of asulam the average frond
emergence came to 7%, 8% and 12% respectively of that in the controls,
and in the case of glyphosate, 10 and 15% respectively. At these
rates both herbicides reduced the length of newly-formed rhizomes by
62%, their weight at recovery by 56-58%, their air-dried weight by
72%, and the number of viable dormant buds by 80-88%. When mixed with
dapapon at 9.0 kg/ha, both asulam at 2.4 kg/ha and glyphosate at 2.8
kg/ha proved less effective.

Hexazinone at 2.7 and 4.5 kg/ha, picloram at 1.5 and 2.5 kg/ha,
and fosamine at 4.8 kg/ha destroyed the aerial portion of bracken but
in the following year the plant had rapidly regenerated.

Asulam at 4.0 kg/ha initially suppressed the grass sward and
particularly the legumes in it; however, this was not a lasting
effect, and in the following years the stand density and hay yields
exceeded those of the controls. At 4.8 kg/ha, and particularly at 6.0
kg/ha, asulam destroyed the legumes and so reduced the stand density.
At the rate of 4.8 kg/ha, regeneration took place a year later; with
the rate of 6.0 kg/ha, two years later. With either of these rates,
however, hay yields in the second year exceeded those of the controls
(Fig.2).

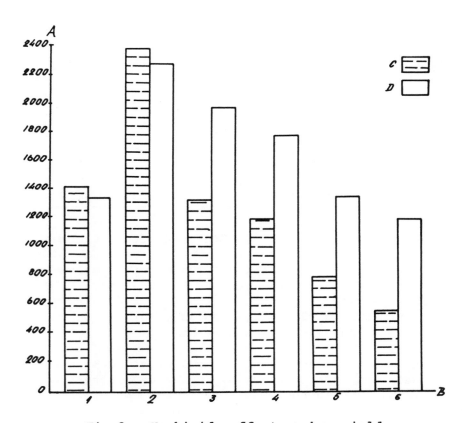

Fig.2. Herbicide effect on hay yield

381

A. Hay yield in kg/ha; B. Herbicides, a.i. in kg/
ha; C. On day 330; D. On day 660
1. Controls; 2. Asulam 4.0 kg; 3. Asulam 4.8 kg;
4. Asulam 6.0 kg; 5. Glyphosate 3.6 kg; 6.
Glyphosate 4.32 kg

Glyphosate at 3.6 and particularly at 4.32 kg/ha has a
blighting effect on the herbage; it thus reduced the stand density by
20% and 50% respectively. With either of these rates, hay yields were
lower in the first year after treatment than those of the controls; in
the second year they were lower only with the higher rate (Fig.2).
    In the year of treatment, hexazinone reduced the grass stand by
50 to 100%. Picloram and fosamine reduced the grass stand by 40 and
50% respectively, and totally eliminated the legumes. The negative
effect of these three herbicides was likewise manifest in the second
year after treatment.

Second experiment

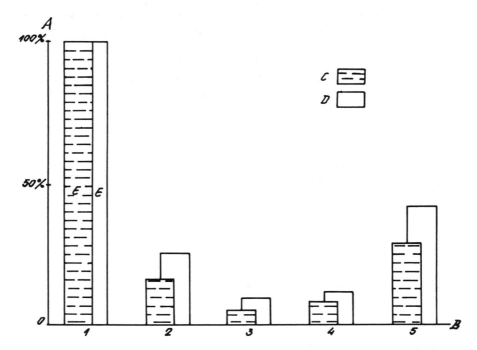

Fig.3. Frond regeneration, 2nd and 3rd year after treatment

A. Bracken canopy, %; B. Treated with asulam at
4.8 kg/ha; C. 2nd year; D. 3rd year; E. 20
plants per m^2
1. Controls; 2. Sprayed on June 15; 3. On July
15; 4. On Aug 15; 5. On Sept 25

In the second experiment, asulam at 4.8 kg/ha was most
effective when applied on July 15, ie. 15 days after complete frond
unfurlment (Fig.3). In the year after treatment, frond regeneration
amounted to 5.2% of that in the controls, and to no more than 9.3% the
next year. Asulam was far less effective when applied on June 15,

before complete frond unfurlment, or in August and September, ie. 45 and 85 days after unfurlment. On day 60, as on day 330 after treatment, the uninfested patches outnumbered those in the controls by 8 and 10% respectively. Two years after treatment, the stand covered 89% of the plot surface, and there were 30% fewer uninfested patches than in the controls; hay yields increased to 2000 kg/ha and exceeded those in the controls by 30%.

Up to day 7 after treatment with asulam at 4.8 kg/ha, its concentration in the fronds rapidly diminished (Fig.4), but levelled off on day 30. During the six hours after treatment, no herbicide was detectable in the rhizomes, but within 12 hours, minute quantities had penetrated to a depth of 20 cm.

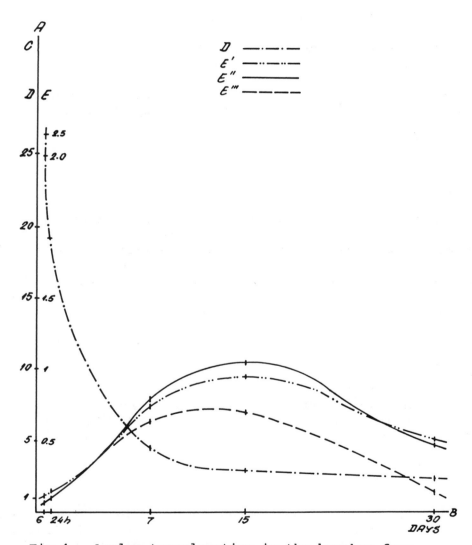

Fig.4. Asulam translocation in the bracken fern

A. Asulam; B. Days; C. Mg/kg; D. Fronds; E. Rhizomes; E'.Rhizomes 0-10 cm deep; E''. Rhizomes 10-20 cm deep; E'''. Rhizomes 20-40 cm deep

With a bracken canopy of 18 plants per m^2, only minute quantities of asulam - up to 0.2 mg/kg in the 0-10 cm layer - were found in the soil, and by day 30 these had diminished to less than 0.1 mg/kg (Fig.5).

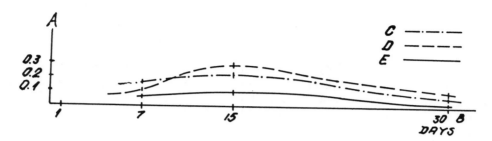

Fig.5.   Residual asulam in the soil

A. Asulam, mg/kg;   B. Days;   C. Layer 0-10 cm deep;
D. Layer 10-20 cm deep;   E. Layer 20-40 cm deep

On day 15 after treatment, residual asulam in the herbage amounted to 2.4 mg/kg, diminishing on day 30 to 0.8 mg/kg. Such levels of residual asulam in the soil and herbage, 30 days after treatment, are well within the 10 mg/kg limit set in Italy.

Third experiment

Applied in concentrated solutions by the rope-wick method after complete frond unfurlment, asulam and glyphosate were highly effective. On days 330 and 660 after treatment, frond regeneration amounted to 6.9 and 9.2% of that in the controls in the case of asulam, and to 8.2 and 11.6% respectively in the case of glyphosate. This method precludes any penetration of herbicide into the grass sward, soil or surface and ground waters.

Fourth experiment

Applied undiluted in water, at 4.8 kg/ha with an ultra-low-volume Micron Ulva 8 sprayer, asulam was highly effective. In the year after treatment, frond regeneration amounted to 5.9% of that in the controls. Two years after treatment the figure was 8.1%.

REFERENCES

1)   Petrov P, Balinova A and Fetvadjieva N (1984) Effectiveness and persistence of asulam, applied at different phases of development of the bracken fern (Pteridium aquilinum L. Kuhn). Presented at the Symposium of the 12th Scientific and Co-ordinative Conference of COMECON, Sofia

2) Petrov P, Fetvadjieva N and Benkov B (1984) Effect on the grass stand of certain herbicides used against bracken (Pteridium aquilinum L. Kuhn). Plant Science, 21, 162-168

3) Fetvadjieva N and Benkov B (1981) Twenty-five years of the Institute of Forage Science, Pleven

4) Fetvadjieva N, Benkov B, Petrov P and Tankov K (1983) A new method of applying herbicides for bracken control. Mechanizing Agriculture, 33, 23-24

5) Brockelsby C H and Muggleton D F In Analytical Methods for Pesticides, Plant Growth Regulators and Food Additives, Vol. 7, ed. G Zweig, 497-508

6) Brockelsby C H (1973) Scientific Report from the Research Laboratories of May and Baker Ltd

385

Bracken and its control in the state forests of Normandy

B Gamblin, P Lamontagne and A Morniche

INTRODUCTION

The Office National des Forêts, a public institution with industrial and commercial interests is in charge of (1) the management of State forests, (2) the running of forestry schemes in Local Authority forests, and (3) through agreements, the execution of various projects related to forests and the environment. In these capacities, it is concerned with 30% of the wooded area in France. In Normandy, the activities of the Office National des Forêts are concerned with 93,000 hectares of forests, mainly owned by the state (92%).

Characteristics of Normandy forests

The climate is a typical oceanic temperate one. It is characterized by relatively abundant precipitation, well spread throughout the year, moderate temperatures and limited seasonal variations of temperature. It is particularly suited to bracken!

The departements of Seine-Maritime, Eure and Calvados are characterized by chalky plateaux, intersected by valleys, some of them large, such as that of the Seine. Soils extend over 3 main formation types: silts and flint formations on the plateaux, more or less marly chalks on the slopes, and alluvia which are often sandy in the valleys. The chalky slopes make up a small area compared to other formations. The departements of Orne and Manche are characterized by hills marked by the presence of crystalline rocks of a more ancient origin (Primary). In both cases, acid substrates predominate. Soils under their influence, combined with the climate, are therefore naturally evolving towards 'sols lessivés' and podzolised soils. In this respect too, the conditions are favourable to the development of bracken.

The forests managed by the ONF in Normandy are 90% full-grown trees and only 10% coppice with standards. Deciduous (hardwood) forests cover 45,000 hectares, resinous (softwood) forests 13,000 hectares and mixed deciduous and resinous forests 17,000 hectares. As a whole, over all the stands, the percentages for the various species are: oak 22%, beech 51%, other deciduous trees 2%, Scots Pine 14%, and other resinous trees 13% (exotics recently introduced).

The Normandy forest stands are characterized by the fact that they are composed of full-grown trees of uniform height and often of the same species (monocultures of beech in Haute Normandie; and in Eawy, Lyons and Eu, plantations of Scots pine). This lack of a second stratum is again a very favourable factor for the development of bracken (la fougère aigle).

This short reminder of the Normandy environment shows that it is perfectly suited to the growth of bracken. Foresters have therefore to deal with the problem of its elimination when its growth threatens the survival of stands.

BRACKEN AND THE FORESTER

The harmfulness of bracken does not manifest itself in the same way throughout the life of a forest stand. It involves at least three aspects:

The long-term problem

Products of the bracken's decomposition contribute to the speeding up of the natural evolution of the soils towards leached and podzolised soils. The decrease in potentiality for forests which may result from this, and which, unfortunately, as far as I know, has never been measured, would probably be a sufficient reason for a more systematic fight against this plant. (This view would not be shared by British ecologists - Ed.).

The immediate problem

This appears mainly at two stages of the life of the stand: during regeneration and during the possible introduction of understorey trees when the stand has reached the stage of being thinned. During the renewal of the stands, the presence of an unbroken canopy of bracken prohibits any germination of seeds or growth of seedlings. Bracken is often not present at the beginning of the renewal operations but it nevertheless nearly always overruns the ground in less than 3 years and can reach heights of 2 or even 3 metres. Seedlings and seeds are then choked, or kept in a state of suppressed growth. In every case they are bound to die sooner or later.

At the thinning stage, in order to avoid the disadvantages of this situation, foresters are led to consider the artificial introduction of an understorey (ie. planting; see below). In the same way as during renewal, bracken is a considerable obstacle to the establishment of introduced saplings and must be destroyed.

An indirect threat

Normandy frequently has periods of dry weather between the end of March and the beginning of July. These coincide with the time when there is a covering of dry bracken before the final growth of the current year's fronds. These coverings are extremely flammable. In the forests visited frequently by tourists they are a very serious problem. 991 ha were swept by fires in the state forest of Rouvray, south of Rouen, between 1926 and 1947, while between 1948 and 1971, 1,785 ha were devastated. The cost of those fires was considerable. The accelerated damage of the soils is added to the loss of the stands! The fight against bracken must be intensified in this field too.

Bracken has nothing but disadvantages for the forester. Moreover, it brings about the disappearance of numerous species of herbaceous and ligneous plants. Foresters have therefore always tried to control it, often, unfortunately, by unsuitable means.

TRADITIONAL MEANS OF CONTROL AND THEIR CONSEQUENCES

The control methods used until recently were all based on mechanical destruction of the aerial parts of the plant. This destruction was done either by hand with a slasher, or, when the density of the plantation allowed it, by machine, with various types of rotary cutters and crushers. This work used to begin around July 15th and went on until December 15th, or even later!

Subsequent analysis of the aftermath shows that far from controlling the bracken, these methods helped to make it denser and more widespread. It also shows that because of the lack of sufficient manpower and equipment, it was necessary to extend the clearing work well beyond the suitable time. The greater part of the saplings and seedlings therefore remained covered by bracken from one year to the next, following August 15th. There resulted retarded growth, malformations, and finally, a total loss of ability to grow normally and produce trees with quality stems. The financial consequences of these practices are incalculable.

The first trials of chemical treatment were only carried out around 1977. The products then used were based on dichlobenil (Casoron - Fidulan) and trials were carried out over more than 200 ha. The amounts used were between 40 kg and 60 kg per ha for applications carried out at the end of April and especially during May. The bracken was destroyed for a single vegetative season and reappeared the following autumn. The treatment had to be reapplied every year.

Example 1

Forêt domaniale du Trait-Maulévrier (Seine-Maritime)
Lot 32 - Area 14 ha
Treatment with casoron at the rate of 60 kg/ha in May 1982.
First year (1982) good results.
Second year (1983) reappearance of a continuous covering of bracken as sturdy as in 1981...A new treatment would have been necessary.

Example 2

Forêt domaniale de Brotonne (Seine-Maritime)
Lots 103 to 105 - Area 27 ha
Treatment with casoron April 1979   60 kg/ha
                        May 1980   50 kg/ha
                        May 1981   50 kg/ha
Bracken was not destroyed, it reappeared in the autumn of 1981. A new treatment had to be applied in 1982.

From what we know about the mode of reproduction of bracken, the evidence shows that one must discard methods of control which consist of grinding, beating down or cutting its aerial parts during the period of growth. They all make the bracken covering denser, more harmful and more difficult to destroy (but see Lowday, herein). Only chemical treatments are efficient but there are marked differences in the results according to the products used. Asulam, for example, gives greatly improved results over dichlobenil.

CHEMICAL TREATMENT WITH ASULAM

One must differentiate between two types of operations, those carried out before planting and those carried out on plantations or established seedlings.

Pre-planting treatment

In numerous cases, for various reasons, foresters are led to consider the renewal of stands by planting. The conditions of light in the stands that have to be renewed, or the period over which cultivation work takes place often lead to the presence in the plot of a covering of well established bracken even before the start of afforestation.
Numerous trials have been carried out, all according to the following scheme:

Periods of operation: Treatment between 14 July and 8 August on bracken having reached at least the three-leaf stage, but especially before the beginning of senescence.

Method of application: Generally by helicopter with 10l Asulox + 20 - 30l water/ha in a single application on strips 15m wide, without overlap.

Additional work: In about 50% of cases, ploughing was carried out in autumn, before planting, to complement the preparation work.

Results: With or without ploughing, the results were (1) the 100% disappearance of bracken the following year (except for a few mistakes made during application), (2) the reappearance of a few scattered bracken plants in the second year, and (3) a covering of 40 to 60% of the ground by bracken after 3 years but with a noticeable decrease in sturdiness (bracken reaching only 60 to 80 cm). These three years of respite give a good start to the saplings and to the establishment of an alternative flora, varying according to each forest.

A second treatment with Asulox in the 4th or 5th year saves the plantation from any further risk. The earliest examples were:

Forêt domaniale de Lyons - Sector 12, lot E.2 and sector 13, lot A.4
   Treatment in 1980 over 30 ha
Forêt domaniale de Montfort (Eure) - lot 64
   Treatment in 1983 over 10 ha
Forêt domaniale des Andaines (Orne) - lots 230-231
   Treatment in 1983 over 11 ha   etc...

Treatment on plantations or natural seedlings

The Normandy landscape and climate is ideally suited to the sylviculture of deciduous trees, in particular Quercus robur, and Fagus sylvatica. The ONF therefore gives the principle allocation to these two species during renewals. Examples of trials with asulam on other species are therefore less numerous.

The method of application is the same as that described earlier, but when the height of saplings is below that of the bracken canopy, treatments are followed by a beating down of the bracken after 6 to 8 weeks. Trials were not carried out according to scientific methodology, so the recordings must only be considered as simple observations.

Toxicity of asulam on saplings and seedlings: Treatments were carried out on developed saplings of common spruce (Picea excelsa), sitka spruce (Picea sitchensis), Corsican pine (Pinus laricio var. Corsicana), beech (Fagus sylvatica), pedunculate oak (Quercus robur), American red oak (Quercus rubra) and sweet chestnut (Castanea sativa). Birch (Betula spp.), wild cherry (Prunus avium), and sycamore (Acer pseudoplatanus) were indirectly concerned. No toxic effects were noted in general. However, in 1984, withering of the terminal shoots of birch, sycamore, wild cherry, pedunculate oak and beech was noted. Sturdy shoots nevertheless developed from the lateral buds. This may have unfortunate consequences for the shape of the future trees and we have not been able to determine its causes (dry weather, heat, terminal shoots of the saplings badly lignified...etc.). Asulam seems also to slow down the growth of broom (Sarothamnus scoparius), another plant which foresters seek to control.

Efficiency of the product on bracken: Generally, when application was correctly done, the product turned out to be effective for 3 to 4 years. In the first year, bracken was 100% absent. In the second year, reappearance of a few fronds was evident. In the third year, recolonization had occurred in patches, while in the fourth year there was nearly a total spread, but by a fern-brake less high than the original one.

Alternative flora: In the context of Normandy forests, the most common alternative flora consists of foxgloves (Digitalis purpurea) and honeysuckle (Lonicera periclymenum) in the first year. In the second year after treatment, honeysuckle can become very troublesome and may necessitate action to destroy it. Sometimes recolonization by bramble (<u>Rubus spp</u>.) or by members of the Graminae (<u>Holcus mollis</u> in particular) have been noted.

In all cases treatment with asulam helps the establishment of ligneous plants, in particular the birch. This last point would appear to be propitious for forestry.

Financial results

The results of chemical treatment with asulam are indisputable and bring about a very important financial benefit in the case of treatments before planting, and are also very satisfactory in the case of treatments on plantations or seedlings <u>in situ</u>. The following study, carried out in the state forest (forêt domaniale) of Croixdalle (Seine-Maritime), provides the following figures:

<u>Stands</u>: plantation of beeches   85%
        natural sowings of oak   5%
        plantation of common spruce   10%
<u>Age</u>: 2 to 6 years
<u>Date of herbicide treatment</u>: first week in August 1980
<u>Application</u>: by helicopter; asulox 101 + water 201 = 301/ha

Financial balance converted to Francs (at 1983 prices)

<u>Sprayed area treatments</u>	<u>Control strip treatments</u> (not sprayed)
1980-One chemical treatment 1150 (105) One bracken clearing 1800 (164)	One bracken clearing 1800 (164)
1981-	One bracken clearing 1800 (164)

1982-One honeysuckle clearing
     combined with one trimming
                2000 (182)
	One bracken clearing 1800 (164)
	One trimming 1200 (109)

1983-	One manual bracken clearing 1800 (164)
1984-	One manual bracken clearing 1800 (164)

1985-One treatment with Asulox will
     have to be carried out in
     July
	In the control strip, further manual clearings of bracken have to be considered for the next 3 or 4 years

In the period 1980-84, the financial gain is therefore:
Cost of control treatments 10,200 F/ha - Cost of sprayed area treatments 4,950 F/ha = 5,250 F/ha (478)
(Figures in parenthesis are £/ha at 11F = £1)

CONCLUSIONS AND PROSPECTS FOR THE FUTURE

The preceeding clearly shows the advantages for the forester of the intensification of the fight against bracken. This fight must consist of three distinct aspects:

(1) Preventative chemical control before planting or establishment of natural sowings.

(2) Development of forestry techniques which restrict growth of bracken during the life of the stand.

(3) 'Curative' chemical control (release) during the development of saplings or seedlings when they are overrun and suppressed by bracken. This category is the most common preoccupation at present.

Asulam is the most active of the phytocide products against bracken that we have tried. We shall therefore go on using it in the form of Asulox (May and Baker) at a dosage of 10 l/ha. However, tests will be carried out to formulate exactly the best methods and times of application, taking into account the conditions of operation specific to Normandy. A recurrence of the incidents which took place in 1984 must be avoided.

Research into forestry techniques enabling the control of bracken will be intensified. This objective should be attained by the selection of mixed stands at two distinct levels which will reduce the quantity of light reaching the ground. Since 1982, only mixed stands have been established, generally as follows, but according to local conditions:

Top Canopy		Understorey
Robur oak	+	Beech
Sycamore maple	+	Beech
American red oak	+	Chestnut
Scots pine	+	Chestnut or red oak

In naturally regenerating forests mixing is systematically encouraged, and suppressed saplings are retained during clearing operations in order to facilitate establishment of a sub-stratum later on. Finally, in pure single-canopy stands which are reaching the thinning stage, sub-stratum components suited to individual forests are artificially introduced.

ACKNOWLEDGEMENT

This paper has been translated from the French original by Catherine Richardson and Richard Smith. The editors accept full responsibility for any minor errors of meaning.

Bracken control in New Zealand forest establishment

D S Preest and N A Davenhill

INTRODUCTION

New Zealand bracken fern (<u>Pteridium</u> <u>esculentum</u>) is probably the most widespread weed of New Zealand exotic forestry. Although it has had some impact on pastoral farming in the past, its relatively low toxicity and low palatability to livestock have meant that control has not generally been the major problem to agriculture that <u>P. aquilinum</u> has been in Europe. Good control is readily achieved with close subdivisional fencing and periodic mob-stocking. Thus, other means of control have not been actively sought by agriculture. However, its vigour, foliar density, and rapidity of growth (1 to 3 m in a matter of weeks) make it a formidable adversary in forest establishment.

Before 1970 there was no reliable means of chemical control. Fire was relied on to achieve the initial clearance of the planting site, followed by pre-plant giant discing on easier terrain, or post-plant slasher releasing on steeper country. Although discing was cheap and effective, slasher releasing was ephemeral and frequently had to be repeated one or more times to ensure sufficient tree survival. Furthermore, the trees often suffered the ill effects of smothering (reduced vigour and spindly growth) before they could be released, or were damaged ("slasher blight") in the process.

Chemicals such as 4-CPA, chlorthiamid, sodium chlorate/borate, karbutilate, dicamba, and picloram had shown some promise overseas. Our experience, based on small-plot and operational trials, was that control was either unreliable at economic rates and/or the chemicals were too residual at effective rates[1,2]. However, the advent of three chemicals, asulam, glyphosate, and hexazinone, in the early 1970s, caused a revolution in our approach to the control of bracken fern in forestry.

HERBICIDES FOR TREE RELEASE

Asulam

Asulam was introduced to New Zealand in 1970 with reports of promising activity on European bracken. Trials soon showed it was also active on New Zealand bracken[3]. It was aerially applied at 5.6 kg in water alone to soft unfurling fronds to safely release young radiata pine (<u>Pinus radiata</u> D. Don) in the spring immediatelly following planting. Advantages included a wide margin of selectivity towards radiata pine and environmental safety. Disadvantages included (1) shortness of control (one season or less); (2) the limited period of bracken susceptibility (ideally asulam should be applied when the lowest pair of pinnae only are unfurled), and (3) the small range of other weeds controlled. The second is the more serious, especially in view of the fickleness of spring weather, and the fact that frond emergence and development often vary greatly according to aspect and microsite. Nevertheless, asulam offered the first real hope of a selective means of bracken control for forestry.

Hexazinone

Trial work with hexazinone (DPX 3674) on bracken fern began in 1975. It showed considerable promise for achieving long-term control[2,4,5,6]. Furthermore, it was well tolerated by radiata pine (but few other tree species), though tolerance is reduced on sites with light sandy or pumice soils low in organic matter, and under warmer (summer) temperature conditions. Considerations of cost and selectivity dictated that its use should be reserved for radiata pine release under circumstances where long-term, pre-plant control by either mechanical or chemical (see later) means had not been possible.

Application rates of 4 to 6 kg are normally required, although in one instance good control was reported from 2 kg. A hot, slow, pre-plant burn to consume as much litter and duff as possible is desirable, as these appear to inhibit hexazinone activity, necessitating higher rates for effective control. Application is best made at the time of early frond emergence (crozier stage), but before soil temperatures get too high. If application is delayed, not only is the risk of tree damage associated with higher soil and air temperatures increased, but the fronds may continue growing until well into January, or even February, forming a dense, tree-smothering canopy before eventually dying and collapsing on the trees.

Although cooler weather (winter) treatments have not generally been successful, in one instance, winter treatment of autumn frond growth arising after a summer burn, showed promise. This may have been due to greater foliar uptake by the newly-emergent, but mature, autumn frond crop.

Radiata pine has been successfully released from 0.5-0.7 m bracken by applying hexazinone by spot-gun as a 1 m diameter spot treatment.

METHODS FOR LONG TERM BRACKEN CONTROL

Asulam and Glyphosate

Glyphosate, introduced shortly after asulam, was also found to be very active on New Zealand bracken[1,2,7] and a large number of other forest weeds, including grasses, herbaceous broadleaves, other ferns, blackberry, pampas, buddleia, and, to a lesser extent, broom and gorse. However, it was not selective to radiata pine. As with asulam, glyphosate, applied at 2.5-3.5 kg on its own to soft unfurling bracken gave good short-term control, but failed to hold back regrowth the following year, or even that autumn.

It was apparent that, although both asulam and glyphosate entered the soft fronds, neither was reaching the underground rhizome system and dormant buds, presumably because at that stage of development there was no effective means of basipetal translocation. However, when applied to mature fronds, when there should have been good basipetal translocation, there was no discernable effect from either herbicide. Apparently, by this stage the well-developed waxy cuticle was preventing uptake. Work was therefore begun on improving the uptake into mature fronds by altering the spray formulation. The addition of diesel oil plus an emulsifier was found to improve dramatically the speed and completeness of frond wetting (and presumably uptake) as well as the length of control achieved by aqueous sprays of both asulam and glyphosate[7]. Unfortunately, the addition of oil destroyed asulam's selectivity, so that, like glyphosate, it could now only be used pre-plant. The treatment schedule recommendations to emerge from this work were:

(1) Apply 5.6 kg asulam or 3.25 kg glyphosate, plus 15 litres of diesel oil and 300 ml of a good quality emulsifier, as a 200-300 litre aqueous aerial spray in summer to the new frond crop once mature.

(2) Burn off not less than 2 weeks later.

(3) Plant trees in the succeeding winter.

Little difference has been observed in the quality of bracken control achieved by either herbicide. However, faster brown-off and desiccation of the fronds and significant control of other weeds on the site are advantages of using glyphosate. Although failures sometimes occur, these treatments have been widely accepted and are still in regular use for long-term (2 years plus) bracken control. Failures appear to be associated mainly with deficiencies in the aerial application - an area of research currently receiving close attention.

Fire

Bracken which has not been burnt for many years usually has sufficient litter to burn freely. In instances where more recent firing has removed the accumulated litter, desiccation of the current frond crop may be desirable to aid burning. This is usually done with paraquat, aerially applied at 1.0-1.5 kg. Sodium chlorate/borate and

397

ammonium sulphammate at 20-30 kg are also effective, but less convenient and/or more expensive to use.

Fire is nearly always used to clear bracken sites for planting. Could it be used in such a way as to extend the control of bracken? Field observation suggested that it might; and so the effect of burn-timing on rhizome starch and frond vigour was investigated[8]. The maximum effect was observed when the new season's fronds were burnt just as they reached maturity; before they had replenished depleted starch reserves. Compared with unburnt plots, rhizome starch reductions of 75% and 50% respectively were measured in the two succeeding winters. This was reflected in reductions of 42% and 51% respectively in fresh frond weight production in the two summers following. Thus, even without chemical or mechanical treatment, there are significant advantages in timing the burn to coincide with frond maturation.

Autumn/winter spraying

A practical difficulty arises with pre-burn summer spraying in many areas of New Zealand. By the time all the new season's spring frond crop has matured (often February or even later), been sprayed, and time allowed for the herbicide to translocate, foresters often run out of good burning weather, and fuel condition is poor. Furthermore, maximum advantage cannot be taken of burning at the optimum, starch-depleted stage as described above.

It has been observed that, in the absence of chemical treatment, one effect of burning the maturing spring frond crop was that the fronds of the subsequent autumn crop were shorter, more numerous, more uniform, and quicker to mature than fronds normally produced in spring by bracken which has not been burnt for several years. Why not burn earlier when burning conditions are more favourable, and then spray the autumn fronds? This would take advantage of the beneficial effects of optimal burn-timing: reduced starch reserves, lower frond vigour, and the stimulation of numerous dormant frond buds, the latter resulting in more herbicide entry points to the rhizomes.

Treatment of the frond crop would be in late autumn or winter once the fronds had matured. Trials have now shown that, provided the fronds have browned-off through frosting, treatment with asulam- or glyphosate-plus-oil as described earlier, appears to be just as effective in late autumn/winter as when applied to the newly-matured spring frond crop in summer (unpublished results). (Only on severely frosted sites are the new fronds of New Zealand bracken killed during winter. In most cases the previous spring or autumn crop lives on until the new spring crop is well-matured).

Summer burning, followed by autumn/early-winter spraying, is currently being promoted, though not widely in use. As well as the advantages already cited, it allows much more flexibility in both burning and spraying, better burns can be expected, and spraying is at a time when there is less pressure on aircraft and local staff; also, because treatment is nearer the planting date, the period of effective control should be increased commensurately. One drawback is the impediment which the newly-sprayed autumn frond crop could offer to planters, mainly on the more fertile sites. In this regard,

398

glyphosate is the better choice because of its quicker knockdown effect.

THE FUTURE

Results from small-plot trials and larger operational trials indicate some possible future developments in the control of bracken.

Diesel oil substitution

The addition of diesel plus emulsifier to asulam and glyphosate spray formulations represents not only an additional (albeit relatively small) cost, but it is a messy nuisance in the field. Trials have shown that if the amount of emulsifier (or, alternatively, a good quality, non-ionic surfactant) is increased 3- or 4-fold to 750-1000 ml/ha, diesel oil may be omitted with little or no loss in effectiveness. This has the advantage that not only are the emulsifiers (or surfactants) freely miscible with the herbicide spray but also the problem of emulsion stability is avoided.

Spray coverage

With highly translocatable, foliar-absorbed herbicides, such as asulam and glyphosate, large numbers of droplets per unit area of foliage may not be essential, provided there is good, large-scale distribution of herbicide over the foliar surfaces. The important criterion for success is that the bulk of the herbicide contacts the fronds. It appears, for instance, that asulam is as effective applied at 160 litres spray volume through foaming nozzles as it is applied at 300 litres through conventional disc-and-core hydraulic nozzles. A significant quantity of asulam is now being applied to bracken through foaming nozzles in New Zealand.

With hexazinone, which is predominantly root absorbed, unless the small foliar absorption component is being enhanced (by the addition of oil or surfactants for instance), spray droplet size is probably unimportant, except for the fact that large droplets are more likely to reach the soil surface. Indeed, granular formulations of hexazinone are proving as effective as soluble powder and liquid concentrate aqueous sprays. Work is in progress on spreading techniques and equipment designed to improve the aerial and ground distribution of granular herbicides.

Spray volume

Most aerial bracken spraying is by helicopter at spray volumes of about 300 L/ha, although hexazinone powder formulation may require volume rates as high as 400 litres because of limited solubility. In one trial, reducing the volume from 220 to 55 litres caused no reduction in the control achieved by asulam, glyphosate, or hexazinone liquid concentrate formulation (unpublished data). Indications from a recent releasing trial with asulam applied at volumes of 220, 55, and

20 litres, are that 55 and 20 litres may be more effective than 220 litres (pers. comm. J. Ray and B. Richardson). Thus it appears likely that reductions in spray volume to about 1/10th of those in current use could be contemplated.

New herbicides

Although the bracken control needs of the forester are well served by asulam, glyphosate and hexazinone, some newer materials show promise. Oxadiazon is very selective to both conifers and hardwoods (including eucalypts) and may be a cheaper, faster-acting alternative to asulam for short-term, post-plant tree release (unpublished results). It affects a wider range of weeds than asulam and has useful residual properties. The pre-burn, pre-plant application of metsulfuron-methyl (DPX-T6376) at rates of 100-400 g shows promise for long-term control, although residues may pose a problem to trees at rates above 200 g.

REFERENCES

1) Chavasse C G R and Davenhill N A (1973) A review of chemical control of bracken and gorse for forest establishment. Proc. 26th N.Z. Weed and Pest Control Conf., Auckland, N.Z., 2-6

2) Preest D S (1975) Review of and observations on current methods of bracken control in forestry. Proc. 28th N.Z. Weed and Pest Control Conf., Hastings, N.Z., 43-48

3) Wasmuth A G (1973) The control of bracken with asulam. Proc. 26th N.Z. Weed and Pest Control Conf., Auckland, N.Z., 7-12

4) Bowers A and Porter J F (1975) Preliminary investigations with DPX 3674 for weed control in forestry. Proc. 28th N.Z. Weed and Pest Control Conf., Hastings, N.Z., 160-164

5) Bowers A and Porter J F (1977) Control of forest weeds with DPX 3674. Proc. 30th N.Z. Weed and Pest Control Conf., Johnsonville, N.Z., 227-232

6) Coackley A and Moore R W (1977) DPX 3674 - a broad spectrum herbicide for weed control in forestry. Proc. 30th N.Z. Weed and Pest Control Conf. Johnsonville, N.Z., 233-237

7) Preest D S (1975) Effect of additives on bracken control by asulam and glyphosate. Proc. 28th N.Z. Weed and Pest Control Conf., Hastings, N.Z., 49-52

8) Preest D S and Cranswick, Andrea M (1978) Burn-timing and bracken vigour. Proc. 31st N.Z Weed and Pest Control Conf. New Plymouth, N.Z., 69-73

Bracken fern in New Zealand and its control with asulam

C Surman

INTRODUCTION

Bracken fern, _Pteridium aquilinum_ var. _esculentum_ is widely distributed throughout the islands of New Zealand. Although no accurate figures are available on the area infested with the plant, it is widely held that its extent exceeds one million hectares in South Island alone. In a postal survey conducted in the South Island by Bascand and Jowett[1], bracken, although widespread, was considered by farmers to be only the eighth most important weed. As in most other countries bracken fern is essentially a problem in hill country, whether utilised for farming or forestry. It is readily controlled by cultivation and thus in lowland areas or tractable country it only presents a problem in amenity areas and alongside roads and railways.

In pastoral areas fire and mob stocking have traditionally been used to progressively reclaim bracken infested land. On land planted to exotic forest, young trees are unable to compete with bracken fern during the establishment phase and measures must be employed during the first two to three years after planting to relieve the competition for light and water. In both these situations the herbicide asulam has found a significant place for controlling bracken. However, work with asulam over the past fifteen years has demonstrated that marked differences between vars. _aquilinum_ and _esculentum_ do occur, necessitating different approaches to its control than those practised in Europe.

THE BRACKEN FERN IN NEW ZEALAND

Few detailed studies of _P. aquilinum_ var. _esculentum_ have been conducted in New Zealand. In her review of the literature, Knowles[2] quotes extensively from European data referring to var. _aquilinum_ and from Australian data on var. _esculentum_[3]. It was concluded that variability within varieties in response to environmental conditions was very great. Although the overall structure of the plant is

401

similar to var. <u>aquilinum</u>, some major differences occur that may markedly affect control strategies. Amongst these are:

Frond emergence and longevity

Fronds generally emerge in late Spring - early Summer. Patterns of emergence vary widely throughout New Zealand, although all areas will experience a strong spring flush. Thereafter emergence may be negligible or continue throughout the season or be restricted to an autumn flush. Climatic factors influence emergence patterns, particularly along the eastern coasts which are more prone to drought. On emergence the young fronds are covered in golden brown scales and these tend to remain on the plant until it is mature. The unfurling process is in marked contrast to that of var. <u>aquilinum</u>. The stipe extends quite markedly and at the same time the midribs of the pinnae unfurl. It is not uncommon for fronds to reach a height of 3-4 feet in this skeletal form before the lowest pinnae begin to unfurl. Thereafter the pinnae unfurl sequentially as in var. <u>aquilinum</u>. It is also common for the stipe to twist as it extends, so that pairs of pinnae are spirally arranged. After unfurling the pinnae rapidly become hardened and a thick wax cuticle develops: by late summer the fronds are quite wiry to the touch.

No definitive studies are available on the life of individual bracken fronds in New Zealand. In areas experiencing low winter temperatures, fronds are frosted off and a more or less annual growth pattern is evident. In most areas, however, a large proportion of fronds will overwinter in the green state: it is generally considered that spring-emerging fronds will die during the following winter or early the next summer, whilst autumn-emerging fronds will overwinter and survive until the next autumn or winter. Immense variability is caused by the local frequency and intensity of frosts. Even when the frond dies or is killed it retains its physical form for at least another twelve months before slowly breaking down. At any one time therefore, the bracken canopy contains both live and dead fronds of a variety of ages so that vigorous stands are very difficult for either humans or animals to penetrate at any time of the year.

It is presumably due to the fact that new fronds have to penetrate through an existing canopy that the above method of stipe extension and unfurling has evolved. Certainly following a burn there is a tendency for fronds to open faster and be shorter than in an undisturbed canopy situation.

Translocation pattern

Early work in the UK with asulam, subsequently confirmed by Veerasekaran[4], indicated that basipetal translocation from a developing frond commenced at an early stage when one or two pairs of pinnae has expanded. It would seem that this may not occur so early with var. <u>esculentum</u> since application prior to full frond expansion does not result in effective control. This may be due to the extended life of the frond.

Toxicity

Var. <u>esculentum</u> does not seem to be as toxic to stock as var.

<u>aquilinum</u>. Although cases are recorded of bracken poisoning in cattle, they are not as common as in Britain. It is therefore common practice for stock to be used to control bracken on land being developed into pasture.

Rhizome structure and dormant buds

O'Brien[3] discussed the rhizome types of var. <u>esculentum</u> in Australia and established that it appeared to carry a high proportion of dormant buds. Clarke[5] also noted in New Zealand that the rhizome tip may be up to 6 feet from the nearest frond. Both these facts render control with translocated chemicals more difficult which is confirmed by experience with asulam.

THE USES OF ASULAM FOR BRACKEN CONTROL IN NEW ZEALAND

Work with asulam in New Zealand commenced in the early 1970s, following the same pattern of usage as in the UK. It rapidly became apparent that differences existed since inconsistent control of bracken was obtained when applications of up to 9.0 kg asulam/ha were made to mature fronds. Applications earlier in the season, however, resulted in substantial desiccation of unfurling fronds. This effect was limited to the season of treatment but it found application in the release of newly planted <u>Pinus radiata</u>. The timing of application was critical. Optimum effects were obtained when foliar sprays of 4.4 - 5.6 kg asulam/ha were made when the majority of fronds had the lowest pair of pinnae almost completely unfurled. Frond development was then halted after 2-3 weeks, the frond becoming necrotic from the tip downward, although only soft tissue was thus affected. Late applications resulted in ineffective tree release.

The variable emergence of bracken - often a fortnight or more difference between north and south-facing slopes - presented problems with the adoption of this technique and except in certain areas its use has largely been supplanted by that of hexazinone, a root-absorbed material that is somewhat more flexible in usage. The above application of asulam utilises the essentially acropetal translocation at this stage of frond development. Complete spray coverage is necessary or only partial effects will occur: application to pinnae on only one side of the frond is likely to result in necrosis of that side alone. Conversely it has been noted that the failure of fronds to emerge later in the season or to develop into distorted skeletal fronds, indicates that some limited basipetal translocation must also be occurring at a relatively early stage. Insufficient material is, however, translocated to prevent frond emergence in the following season.

Various attempts have been made to widen the period of effective releasing by the inclusion of surfactants or other chemicals, but in each case the selectivity of asulam to <u>Pinus radiata</u> was unacceptably reduced. During the mid 1970s Preest[6] confirmed that the activity of asulam could be enhanced and long-term control similar to that achieved in Europe obtained, by the addition of diesel oil and a suitable emulsifier. Since this mixture was not selective to trees, application was restricted to the pre-plant situation in forestry but opened up the possibility of developing control

403

programmes in agricultural situations.

It should be noted that the requirements for long-term control in forestry and agricultural situations vary somewhat. The prime aim of the forester is to prevent the tree becoming swamped during the establishment phase. Although the bracken undoubtedly competes thereafter for water and nutrients this is a secondary consideration. The farmer on the other hand wishes to convert bracken-infested land permanently into pasture and thus his expectations are far higher. Stock can only be expected to effectively contribute to control programmes in spring before fronds have hardened and become unpalatable. During this period stock will trample and eat young fronds. Although var. esculentum does not seem as toxic to stock as var. aquilinum, stock used for bracken control normally suffer some loss of condition.

Application of the asulam/diesel mixture to mature fronds in the late summer/early autumn have no immediate effect on the bracken canopy: only in the following spring are effects evident through the failure of new fronds to emerge. Gradually the canopy becomes necrotic and by 12 months after spraying is completely dead. To enable further development of the treated area to take place, the canopy has to be removed and burning is the most effective method. Early studies showed that asulam was absorbed and largely translocated to the rhizome within a period of two weeks following application and that canopy removal could be entertained (weather permitting) at any time after this without affecting long-term control. Satisfactory prevention of spring regrowth has been obtained from applications of asulam made at more or less any time between full frond expansion (mid summer) right through to very early spring. However, the later the applications the more likely that fronds would die naturally, be damaged by frost or stock or be less efficient at absorbing and translocating the chemical. The most suitable time for treatment is late summer and this has become the standard recommendation. Mature bracken stands are treated with a mixture of asulam 5.6kg/ha, diesel 14 L/ha and Emulsifier X-45 (Rohm and Haas Ltd, USA) 750 ml/ha: some three weeks later the area is burnt prior to re-seeding with grass or planting trees.

Despite an absence of regrowth in spring and gradual necrosis of the canopy, burning in the following summer or autumn frequently results in substantial autumn regrowth. This suggests that a large proportion of dormant buds do exist and survive treatment, and also that the treated and dying fronds exert dominance over the dormant buds for a considerable length of time. Additionally it is known that asulam is not extensively translocated throughout the rhizome system and once absorbed may be translocated to and concentrated in active meristematic areas closest to the site of absorption. The treated frond, undamaged by treatment, may thus be capable of continued metabolism leading to further bud formation in areas of the rhizome remote from the site of treatment. In an attempt to reduce the number of dormant buds present at spraying, areas have been burnt in the spring and matured autumn regrowth treated with asulam and diesel. In some areas, particularly in the milder areas of the North Island, this appears to be more successful than treating undisturbed stands but presents other problems, particularly in relation to access for subsequent development.

A further approach that assists control in this latter

situation is to add small quantities of either paraquat or activated amitrole to the spray solution. This causes a slow desiccation of the fronds within three to four weeks, without apparently interfering with the absorption and translocation of asulam. This therefore makes access easier, removes the competitive effects of the canopy and young trees or grass and also prevents further metabolism by the treated fronds. The use of such combined treatments on undisturbed canopies is, however, less successful, which is indicative of chemical antagonism.

In the majority of situations, treatment of the undisturbed canopy is the method preferred and most widely used by both foresters and farmers. It has been very successfully used, particularly in the South Island but conversely some failures suggest that the burn prior to spraying may prove to be more consistently effective. It is the consistency of effect that is difficult to predict: seemingly identical treatments on adjacent blocks in succeeding seasons may produce widely differing results.

APPLICATION AND ADDITIVES

During the early years of asulam usage in New Zealand some very variable results were obtained, frequently as a direct result of poor application. Inadequate attention was paid to such factors as slope correction, removal of obstructions, proper treatment of gullies, flying height, etc. Much of the country that is treated for bracken fern is very steep and broken. Slopes invariably exceed 30° and uniform chemical coverage cannot reliably be achieved. Helicopters are the only suitable means of application: increased experience with and understanding of the mode of action of asulam have enabled both pilots and users to obtain the best possible results.

A number of different types of nozzles have been evaluated and most appear suitable for the application of asulam. However, the tendency for large droplet nozzles (Delavan Raindrop or Delafoam nozzles) to narrow the swath and make swath edges more defined have made their use in hill country more liable to produce patchy results through mis-matching. Conventional hydraulic nozzles, employing large swirl plates, produce very acceptable results when utilized in a half overlap technique. High water volumes (200-500 litres/ha) have traditionally been utilized by aerial operators for brush and scrub control operations. Volumes of 220 L/ha have been used for bracken but these are being reduced gradually, with the current recommendation at 110 L/ha (two passes at 55 L/ha). Work is continuing to reduce volumes further, and Micronaire equipment, currently used by the N.Z. Forest Service for application of copper sprays for Dothistroma control at 20 L/ha offers some promise.

The inclusion of diesel oil as a component of the spray mixture is unpopular with helicopter pilots: spray deposited on windshields presents a major visibility hazard in hill country in early morning light. Alternatives to diesel plus emulsifier have thus been examined and the silicone copolymer Silwet L-77 (Union Carbide Corpn. USA) has proved a most effective alternative and is now in the final stages of development. Used at 0.1% of the total spray volume, 100 ml of Silwet L-77 has effectively replaced 14 litres of diesel and 750 ml of Emulsifier X-45.

Because of the factors mentioned previously it is apparent that foliar-applied, translocated chemicals such as asulam or glyphosate cannot always be relied upon to give complete, long term control of var. esculentum. A method of breaking bud dormancy would enhance reliability, but given the terrain in which control is attempted, even greater assistance is required for total control.

REFERENCES

1) Bascand L D and Jowett G H (1982) Scrubweed cover of South Island agricultural and pastoral land 2. Plant distribution and managerial problem status. N.Z. J. Exptl. Agric. 10 : 455-492

2) Knowles B (1966) The autecology of bracken. Part 1: A literature review and discussion. N.Z. For. Res. Inst. Forest Products Report No. 189 (unpublished)

3) O'Brien T P (1964) Problems in the control of the bracken fern of Victoria J. Aust. Inst. Agric. Sci. : 30 (2) 199-127

4) Veerasekaran P, Kirkwood R C and Fletcher W W (1977) Studies on the mode of action of asulam in bracken. I. Absorption and translocation of ^{14}C - asulam. Weed Res. 17: 33-39

5) Clarke E W (1960) Fern control. N.Z. J. Agric. 101 (5)

6) Preest D S (1975) Effect of additives on bracken control by asulam and glyphosate. Proc. 28th New Zealand Weed and Pest Control Conf. 43-48

Investigation of wiping methods for applying chemicals to control bracken fern in pasture

J Winkworth and L Hamilton

INTRODUCTION

Bracken fern, Pteridium aquilinum var. esculentum is a highly competitive inhabitor of pastures on the well-drained soils of the higher rainfall areas of south eastern Australia. Mechanical methods such as cultivation, slashing or rolling of fronds were the only means of controlling this weed prior to 1975. Chemical treatment of bracken using the foliar-absorbed herbicide asulam showed promise for the short term control of bracken when applied to soft unfurling fronds[1]. Further work indicated that the most effective time to use this herbicide was at frond maturity. Asulam was said to be an effective treatment for the control of bracken fern when applied by spray boom, knapsack sprayer or knapsack misting machine[2], but it had also been reported that mature fronds were resistant to the entry of normal aqueous spray herbicides[3]. It was later found that the addition of diesel plus emulsifier to asulam increased chemical uptake by mature fronds[4], where a significant reduction in frond numbers resulted. After registration of the mixture of asulam with diesel and emulsifier for control of bracken fern, some resistance to its use was encountered. This resistance partly originated from damage caused to pastures by drift of the mixture onto adjacent land. In addition, the cost of the mixing was high in comparison to the value of the pastures.

The use of a 'rope-wick' application system has previously been shown to be effective for the direct application of herbicides to target weeds protruding above desired plant species[5,6]. In Australia, it was demonstrated that the use of rope-wicks required doubled application (the second pass being in the opposite direction to the first) to achieve effective control of erect weeds with glyphosate[7]. Subsequently, Ruzic (pers. comm.) demonstrated that multistrand rope wicks significantly improved control of weeds compared to simple rope-wicks. Following preliminary work in autumn 1982, Hamilton (unpublished) indicated that asulam could be applied by rope-wick to control bracken and additional experiments were started in the autumn of 1983. The aim of this work, which is reported here, was to further investigate these initial results.

METHODS AND MATERIALS

Site

The selected site for the trial was a well drained, sandy loam soil at Sarsfield, near Bairnsdale, Victoria. It had a pasture which was based upon subterranean clover (<u>Trifolium subterraneum</u>) and ryegrass (<u>Lolium perenne</u>), to which some serradella (<u>Ornithopus compressus</u>) had been introduced. However, the effect of the dense stand of bracken (25 fronds/sq.m) on this pasture understorey had markedly affected the grazing value of the pasture.

Mechanical slashing was carried out in November 1982. This is in line with recommended treatment practice for chemical Bracken control currently used in south eastern Australia. Treatment of the stand in this way has two functions. Firstly, all fronds in the resultant regrowth are of known age, and secondly, the number of fronds, and therefore the entry points to the rhizome system, are maximized due to the immediate regrowth following slashing, plus the normal autumnal growth-flush. The experimental design was a randomised complete block utilizing four replications. Each block measured 20 m x 4 m.

Application Techniques

Two wiping devices were employed. The first was a pipe-wiper, similar to that described by Dale[5]. This unit was 2 m wide and mounted on the front of a small 4-wheel drive vehicle. Two passes were made along the length of each plot, one in each direction. The amount of chemical used was checked after the application of each treatment. The second applicator was a carpet wiper. This device was similar in design to the multi-rope wiper described by Wiese and Lavake[8]. However, in place of rope, hollow, perforated PVC tubing was coated with rubber foam-backed carpet. The details of this applicator and its calibration have been published by Hamilton[9,10]. The carpet wiper was propelled behind an agricultural motor cycle, with a single pass being used for each treatment.

Treatments

The chemicals used were: asulam as 'ASULOX' (May and Baker Ltd) 400 g/l and glyphosate as Roundup (Monsanto Co. USA) 360 g/l. The mixtures used for the trials were:

a) 'ROUNDUP' in a mixture with water at a ratio of 1 part 'ROUNDUP' to 2 parts water.

b) 'ASULOX' in a mixture with water at a ratio of 2 parts 'ASULOX' to 1 part water.

c) 'ASULOX' in a mixture with water plus diesoline and emulsifier in a ratio of 2 parts : 3 parts : 1 part.

d) 'ASULOX' in a mixture of 2 parts : 1 part water plus Ulvapron (equal portions). (Ulvapron is a self miscible spraying oil supplied by BP Oil International.)

All treatments were applied in early June 1983 and are summarised in Table 1.

TABLE 1

Treatment Number	Applicator Type	Chemical	Dose in L/ha Product	Oil Additives + or -	Mixture Ratios
1		No treatment			
2	Pipe	Glyphosate	2.5	-	1:2
3	Pipe	Asulam	2.5	-	2:1
4	Pipe	Asulam	2.5	+	2:3:1
5	Pipe	Asulam	5.0	-	1:2
6	Carpet	Asulam	5.0	+	2:3:1
7	Carpet	Asulam	10.0	+	2:1

RESULTS

Australian bracken is evergreen, and treated fronds tend to persist for up to 18 months before senescence. Therefore, to enable accurate assessment of chemical effects the remaining fronds are removed by slashing and a count of newly emerged fronds made. The site was slashed in October 1983 and counts of emerged fronds were made in December 1983 and May 1984. The data is summarised in Table 2.

TABLE 2

Treatment Number	Total fronds in 4 x 1 sq.m quadrats per treatment	
	December 1983	May 1984
1	90.5	141.25
2	47.75	125.75
3	68.25	128.0
4	27.5	104.5
5	36.25	101.75
6	0.75	1.25
7	1.0	5.75
LSD P < 0.05	33.844	13.167
P < 0.01	46.312	18.018

The results in Table 2 demonstrate that no pipe wiper treatment was capable of producing long term control of bracken at a density of 25 fronds/sq.m. Although some control was obtained at the six month assessment, this had largely disappeared after eleven months. The two carpet wiper treatments were significantly different from all other treatments except the pipe wiper/asulam - diesoline and emulsifier (P < 0.05) after six months. At the eleven month assessment the two carpet wiper treatments were, however, significantly better than all other treatments (P < 0.01). At no time was there a significant difference between the two.

As the effect of asulam in diesoline plus emulsifier has been recorded as causing severe damage to pasture species, an assessment of pasture botanical composition was made 16 months after application. The results of this assessment are shown in Table 3 where an increase in useful pasture species is seen.

TABLE 3

% Composition of pasture species						
Pasture species	Trifolium subterraneum	Ornithopus compressus	Vulpia spp	Lolium spp	Dry fern	Green fern
Untreated	10	9	53	0	13	12
Treatment 6	48	16	16	18	0	0

Eighty-two percent of the botanical composition was regarded as useful pasture species compared to 19% in the untreated areas.

DISCUSSION

The results obtained in this trial indicate that it is not possible to obtain long term control of bracken fern (at a density of 25 fronds/sq.m) with asulam or glyphosate using a pipe-wiper. On the other hand, carpet wipers of the design used give excellent results. This variable control was believed to be due to the limited application area of the rope in pipe wipers which is unable to deliver sufficient chemical to the target surface. Carpet wipers on the other hand are capable of a much greater throughput of chemical, so in order to prevent chemical wastage, the wiper should be correctly calibrated before use.

The substitution of Ulvapron for the diesoline and emulsifier additive currently registered in Australia, appears justified, but additional work is needed to confirm this.

Overall, the results indicate that the quantity of asulam needed per hectare to control bracken fern could be considerably reduced fron 12 L/ha 'ASULOX' currently registered for conventional spraying techniques, such as boom sprays, to around 5 L/ha through a carpet wiper as described. This represents a saving of 58%. Furthermore the use of carpet wipers would avoid damage to desirable pasture species which occurs when conventional spraying techniques are used.

ACKNOWLEDGEMENTS

The authors wish to thank F H Winstone Pty for the loan of a pipe-wiper, and BP Australia Pty Ltd for the samples of Ulvapron used in these trials.

REFERENCES

1) Chavasse C G R and Davenhill N A (1973) A review of chemical control of bracken and gorse in forest establishment. Proc. 26th NZ Weed and Pest Contr. Conf. 2-5

2) Combellack J H (1976) Some biological aspects of bracken in Victoria. Proc. 4th Austr. Weeds Conf. 3: 18

3) Veerasekaran P and Kirkwood R C (1972) The effect of stage of frond development on the absorption and translocation of asulam in bracken. Proc. 11th Brit. Weed Contr. Conf. : 17-23

4) Preest D S (1975) Effect of additives on bracken connrol by asulam and glyphosate. Proc. 28th NZ Weed and Pest Contr. Conf. : 49-52

5) Dale J E (1979) A non-mechanical system of herbicide application with a rope wick. PANS 25 (4) 431-436

6) Messersmith C G and Lym R G (1981) Roller and wick application of picloram for leafy spurge control. Down to Earth 37 (2) 9-12

7) Campbell D J, Fulton R G, Ruzic I M and Somervaille A J (1981) Selective application of glyphosate to erect weeds in pastures. Proc. 6th Aust. Weeds. Conf. 1 : 109-112

8) Wiese A F and Lavake D E (1980) Experiences with a rope wick applicator. Co-operative investigation of Texas Agric. Exptl. Stn. and Agric. Sci. and Ed. Am. A.R., US Dept of Agric 262

9) Hamilton L J (1984) Rope wick applicators. Town and Country Farmer Aust. 1(1) 52-53

10) Hamilton L J (1985) Making and using a weed wiper. Vic. Dept. Ag. Note (in press)

Preliminary screening of asulam and glyphosate – surfactant formulations for control of bracken (Pteridium esculentum)

R E Gaskin, N A Davenhill and J A Zabkiewicz

INTRODUCTION

New Zealand bracken, <u>Pteridium esculentum</u>, is a problem weed in forestry operations second only to gorse in economic costs and third overall in terms of land area treated[1]. Not only does bracken need to be removed prior to tree planting, but the methods used previously were such that further post-planting treatments (either hand or chemical releasing) were frequently required[2]. The most commonly used chemicals, asulam, glyphosate and hexazinone, were all introduced in the early to mid-70s. Experience has shown that, although maximum uptake is obtained when young fronds are sprayed with solutions of asulam and glyphosate, translocation, and hence longer term control, is inadequate. Further, the results are frequently variable and unpredictable from site to site. Better translocation of applied herbicides to the rhizomes should occur following treatment of mature fronds, but uptake would be reduced unless the herbicide was formulated to enhance cuticle penetration. Preest[2], using diesel oil plus emulsifier additives in asulam and glyphosate sprays, applied in late summer, showed significant reductions in frond numbers and biomass produced in the season following treatment and burning-off of the bracken. Since a surfactant (Triton X-45) had been used with the diesel additive, the option existed of testing spray formulations consisting of herbicide plus surfactant only. Studies[3,4] have demonstrated increased uptake of asulam into bracken if surfactants were part of the spray formulation.

Studies on the selection of spray formulations for gorse control[5] suggested the use of contact angle (CA) values as a screening method for surfactant selection and concentration. However, this is only a measure of the potential foliage wetting; selected formulations then have to be further evaluated by radiolabelled herbicide uptake or field trials of the spray formulation.

In this work, commercial formulations of asulam and glyphosate were screened for use on bracken by the CA method with the intention of selecting spray additives superior to the diesel formulations.

Surfactants and concentrations selected by this technique were then tested in field trials to confirm the initial screening and to find the most cost-effective and herbicidally-effective combination.

METHODS AND MATERIALS

Contact angle determinations

Cuticular wax was extracted from mature bracken fronds using a 30 sec chloroform wash. A 10 ul portion of the chloroform wax extract (1% w/v) was spread over the surface of a cleaned glass slide (3 x 80 mm) to give an even wax film on drying. Droplets of individual formulations (3 ul) were applied to the waxed glass surface and the CA calculated from the projected image of the droplet[6]. A minimum of 20 droplets per formulation were measured and mean CA and SD values calculated. The asulam concentration used was 4 kg a.i./300 litres water (equivalent to 10 litres Asulox solution); the glyphosate concentration was 2.52 kg a.i./300 litres, (equivalent to 7 litres Roundup formulation). The additives tested represented several different chemical classes and were: Diesel oil (local supply); Triton X-45 (Rohm and Haas); Bardac 22 (Lonza, USA); Whirlaway Booster (Diversey Wallace, NZ); Cide-kick SA-77 (JLB Chemicals, USA); Butyl oleate (Croda Chemicals NZ); Multifilm X-77 (Ivon Watkins Dow, NZ) and Silwet L-77 (Union Carbide). All these additives are non-ionic with the exception of Bardac 22 which is cationic.

Field trials

TABLE 1 Field trial conditions and operational parameters

	Rotorua	Thornton
Plot size	4 x 10 m	4 x 10 m
Replication	3	3
Bracken size	1-2 m	0.75-1.5 m
Condition	Mature, hardened	Soft, plus mature fronds
Application date	July 1981 (winter)	April 1982 (early autumn)
Fronds cut	September 1981	May 1982
Burn	Yes	Not possible due to environmental hazard
Assessment	March 1982	February 1983
Method	Frond count 30% area sample	% bracken cover, 100% area sample, 3 assessors
Weather at spraying	Calm, overcast	Fine, sunny, light wind

Small plot trials were conducted at two sites in the North Island of New Zealand in successive years using a randomised block design. A CO_2 boom sprayer (with 730077 flat fan nozzles operated at 276 kPa) was used at 1 metre above the canopy in a double pass to give the required 300 L/ha volume. Further experimental details are given in Table 1 for the two simulated operational trials. All data were analysed for significance using analysis of variance. Treatment means were compared by the least significant difference test.

RESULTS AND DISCUSSION

Representative CA values obtained with the asulam and glyphosate spray formulations are listed in Table 2. Both of these herbicides have high CA values at recommended operational dosages (100.5° and 79.5° respectively). In general, addition of any surfactant at 0.1% or above, reduced the CA value of the spray formulation. However, it was considerably more difficult to reduce CA values of the glyphosate formulation than of the asulam. This effect is attributed to some interaction with additive(s) already present in the Roundup formulation.

From past experience, formulations with CA values of 50° or less are considered to have good wetting properties, while complete foliage wetting should be possible if the CA value is 20° or less. Using these criteria, Cide-kick, Butyl oleate and Multifilm X-77 failed to qualify as useful additives for the asulam herbicide spray. For glyphosate, Bardac also fails to qualify. Of the surfactants tested the best additives for both asulam and glyphosate were all non-ionic (although at differing concentrations); these were Triton X-45, Whirlaway Booster, Silwet L-77 and diesel plus Triton X-45 (though far higher concentrations of the last combination were required). Accordingly, selected additives were tested in small-plot spray trials in combination with asulam or glyphosate in comparison with 5% diesel plus surfactant which earlier had given best results for late season spraying[2]. The objective was to find a combination of herbicide and surfactant which was both better and more cost-effective than diesel plus surfactant.

Inspection of the results of the first field trial, at Rotorua, shows that all combinations except for the Bardac were equal to or better than the standard diesel combination for both herbicides (Table 3). Bardac was included because of its CA value with asulam and because it was the only cationic surfactant in the group. The results of the statistical analysis have some apparent inconsistencies, for example glyphosate plus Triton X-45 (0.5%) is significantly different from glyphosate plus diesel, while glyphosate plus Whirlaway Booster or plus Silwet L-77 (0.25%) are not, although they have lower total frond counts.

Generally, differences between herbicides (as indicated by the percentage improved control) are not substantial, as each can work well with the appropriate amount of additive. A point of interest is that bracken control decreased with increasing amounts of additive in two instances. Glyphosate plus 0.25% Silwet L-77 was significantly more effective than with double the amount of additive. Similarly, asulam formulations appeared to give better control with 0.01% than with 0.05% Silwet L-77, although this result was not statistically

TABLE 2   Contact   angles (and S.D.) of Asulox and Roundup formulations
(at 10 and 7 litres/300 litres water respectively) with
various additives

Additive	%	Asulox		Roundup	
		CA(°)	SD(°)	CA(°)	SD(°)
Nil		100.5	(2.0)	79.5	(1.7)
Triton X-45	0.1	41.4	(2.0)	60.5	(1.5)
(octylphenoxypolyethoxy	0.5	41.9	(1.7)	42.8	(2.8
ethanol polymer)	1.0	42.1	(1.8)	39.8	(1.6)
Whirlaway Booster	0.01	90.5	(5.1)	75.1	(2.3)
(50% active surfactant/	0.1	59.5	(1.8)	75.1	(2.2
solvent mixture)	1.0	47.8	(2.0)	60.5	(1.9)
	2.0	50.5	(2.1)	49.8	(1.3)
	10.0	42.1	(1.6)	37.4	(1.9)
Bardac 22	0.1	42.0	(1.8)	68.9	(2.5)
(C-10 quaternary ammonium salt)					
Silwet L-77	0.005	73.4	(1.8)	-	-
(organosilicone block	0.01	43.9	(2.1)	72.8	(2.5
copolymer)	0.05	total wetting		-	-
	0.10	-	-	55.2	(1.8)
	0.25	-	-	35.2	(1.9)
	0.50	-	-	total wetting	
Cide-Kick SA-77	0.5	55.6	(3.2)	70.8	(1.4)
(limonene plus emulsifiers)					
Butyl Oleate	20.0	62.3	(2.1)	56.1	(2.9)
(fatty acid ester)					
Multifilm X-77	0.1	54.4	(2.4)	-	-
(non-ionic polyoxyethylene	0.5	54.7	(1.4)	71.6	(2.4
polymer)					
Diesel + 0.1% X-45	2.0	50.8	(3.1)	71.1	(3.0)
	5.0	46.9	(2.8)	63.4	(2.6)
	10.0	46.6	(2.1)	58.7	(2.0)
	16.0	42.6	(2.1)	52.4	(1.8)

significant.   Obviously complete   wetting of   the   foliage by the
formulation (as indicated by the CA values for these combinations) is
not   desirable at high spray volumes as control is decreased, probably
due to spray run-off.

Selected   spray formulations   were   retested in a second trial
(Thornton, Table 4) at an earlier bracken growth stage (early autumn
instead of early winter).   All asulam surfactant combinations were
more effective than the unformulated spray but not significantly

TABLE 3   Field assessment of bracken control by asulam and glyphosate formulations plus additives at Rotorua

Additive	%	Mean frond count		% improved control	
		Asulam	Glyphosate	Asulam	Glyphosate
Nil		-	-	-	-
Triton X-45	0.1	78^r	102^{xy}	20	23
	0.5	36^P	49^x	63	63
Whirlaway Booster	2.0	33^P	33^{xy}	66	75
Bardac 22	0.1	953^S	236^Z	-883	-79
Silwet L-77	0.01	57^{pq}	-	41	-
	0.05	97^{qr}	-	0	-
	0.1	-	-	-	-
	0.25	-	28^{xy}	-	79
	0.5	-	125^Z	-	5
Diesel (+ 0.1% X-45)	5.0	97^r	132^{yz}	-	-
Control (nil treatment)		-	-	-	-

Treatments with same superscript letters indicate no significant difference at P = 0.05

% Improved control = $\dfrac{\text{Diesel-Treatment}}{\text{Diesel}}$ x 100   - Not evaluated

better than the diesel formulation.   The glyphosate combinations containing Whirlaway and 0.5% Silwet formulations were best and superior to the diesel combination; again the results overall were not substantially different from the asulam treatments in herbicidal effectiveness.   In this trial the fronds were cut sooner after spraying than in the first trial, and not burned, so some further enhancement of herbicidal effectiveness might have been possible.   It is interesting to note the relative lack of difference between treatments in this trial.   This may be due to spraying the bracken at an earlier growth stage when the fronds were less hardened, so that the choice of additive was not so critical.   There may also have been less root-directed translocation of assimilates.   The result with the unaltered glyphosate formulation was therefore the same as that with the diesel combination.

TABLE 4 Field assessment of bracken control by asulam and glyphosate formulations plus additives at Thornton

Additive	%	% Ground cover		% Improved control	
		Asulam	Glyphosate	Asulam	Glyphosate
Nil		43.3[d]	26.1[c]	-120	2
Triton X-45	0.1	12.5[ab]	27.2[c]	37	-2
	0.5	-	-	-	-
Whirlaway Booster	2.0	9.2[a]	8.1[a]	53	70
Bardac 22	0.1	-	-	-	-
Silwet L-77	0.01	-	-	-	-
	0.05	-	-	-	-
	0.1	18.9[abc]	-	4	-
	0.25	-	-	-	-
	0.5	-	8.9[a]	-	67
Diesel (+ 0.1% X-45)	5.0	19.7[abc]	26.7[c]	0	0
Control (nil treatment)		60.7[e]	60.7[e]	-208	-127

Treatments with same superscript letters indicate no significant difference at P = 0.05

% Improved control = $\dfrac{\text{Diesel-Treatment}}{\text{Diesel}} \times 100$ - Not evaluated

Given these results it remained to be seen if the alternative additives were cost-effective. Current New Zealand prices are given in Table 5 for max/min quantities required for the different additive combinations tested. With one exception, costs are equivalent or much lower than those incurred with the diesel additive. The cost (in 1981 terms) of field testing an individual formulation was estimated to be $50NZ, with a ten month wait before assessment. To laboratory screen an untried formulation costs approximately $1.50 per spray solution, taking less than one hour to eliminate non-wetting formulations.

CONCLUSIONS

The screening and evaluation trials reported were part of a

TABLE 5   Comparison of additive costs

Additive	%	Litres/ha*	$/litre	Cost $/ha
Triton X-45	0.1	0.3	8.87	2.66
	0.5	1.5	8.87	13.31
Whirlaway Booster	2.0	6.0	2.21	13.26
Silwet L-77	0.01	0.03	30.0	0.90
	0.25	0.75	30.0	22.50
Diesel (+ 0.1% X-45)	5.0	15.0 (0.3)	0.685 (8.87)	12.94
(+ 0.2% X-45)	10.0	30.0 (0.6)	0.685 (8.87)	25.87

* formulation applied at 300 L/ha

preliminary assessment, the results of which need further confirmation. If only the non-ionic type of surfactant tested is considered, then the CA method has value in selecting potentially suitable surfactants and concentrations. It appears that spray formulations which thoroughly wet the surface without causing run-off are the best for enhancing the activity of both asulam and glyphosate against bracken. The relative effectiveness of such formulations is determined by bracken growth stage, the most potent formulation giving herbicidal effectiveness superior to the original diesel formulation when applied to fully-hardened fronds. This relative improvement is decreased if the bracken is sprayed at an earlier growth stage. It is concluded that non-ionic surfactants are essential to realise the full effectiveness of both the above herbicides at specific bracken growth stages.

ACKNOWLEDGEMENTS

We thank B Kirk, H Sanderson and D S Preest for laboratory or field assistance and S O Hong and I A Andrew for assistance with the statistical evaluations.

REFERENCES

1) Chavasse C G R (1976) The use of herbicides in forestry in New Zealand. N.Z. J. For., 21, 68-94

2) Preest D S (1975) Effect of additives on bracken control by asulam and glyphosate. Proc 28th NZ Weed and Pest Control Conf., 49-52

3)   Cook   G   T, Stephen N H and Duncan H J (1982)   Fundamental studies
in   bracken control - the use of additives to enhance herbicide uptake
and translocation.   Proc. Royal Soc. Edinburgh, 81B, 97-109

4)   Kirkwood   R   C, Veerasekaran P and Fletcher W W (1982)   Studies on
the   mode of action of asulam in bracken.   Proc. Royal Soc. Edinburgh,
81B, 85-96

5)   Zabkiewicz   J   A,   Gaskin   R E and Balneaves J M (1985)   Effect of
additives   on   foliar wetting and uptake of glyphosate into gorse.   In
Application and Biology, pp. 127-134.   British Crop Protection Council
Monograph No 28

6)   Fogg   G E (1947)   Quantitative studies on the wetting of leaves by
water.   Proc. Royal Society of London, Series B. 134, 503-522

The contribution of helicopter services to the improvement of bracken-covered land

M Davies

THE RANGE OF USES OF HELICOPTERS

The versatility of helicopters can be capitalised upon in bracken eradication programmes in many ways. Firstly, their ability to carry sophisticated spraying equipment and quite large loads of chemicals is an initial major advantage. Secondly, once the bracken has been sprayed, these loads can then be exchanged for equally sophisticated spreading equipment to allow the aerial application of both lime and fertiliser. This facility is of great importance on the typical, sloping, bracken-covered land, as the slopes are often steep enough to represent a serious danger to the drivers of tractors and other wheeled equipment. Yet, such steep land carries soils with low pH levels and thus requiring the greatest level of lime application. There is no agricultural reason why bracken spraying and lime spreading should not take place in the same year. In fact, it has been claimed that the addition of lime after spraying, strongly inhibits the regrowth of any bracken plants that may have been missed in the spraying operation. Thirdly, as the land, now cleared of bracken, and limed and fertilised, comes into useful production, it will be necessary to integrate what is effectively extra or new land, into the whole farm plan. This will often bring about the need for fencing operations which can be accelerated by use of a helicopter. Quite often, this land will be inaccessible to wheeled vehicles, and could create problems when attempts are made to transport fencing materials into place. Assuming sufficient helicopter work has been generated in the area through spraying and spreading, for only a small additional cost, fencing posts, wire, nails, tools etc. can be transported to the most inaccessible areas, a job which would normally take days of back-breaking labour.

ADVANTAGES OF THE HELICOPTER SPRAYING METHOD

Herbicide spraying from tractors can achieve a reasonable rate of kill in situations where the terrain is uniform, on gentle,

421

consistent slopes, and where the bracken canopy is not too tall and dense. Fixed-wing aeroplanes can also enable a reasonable rate of kill to be achieved, but again on fairly uniform terrain. Both types of operation are cheaper than the helicopter to a greater or lesser extent. However, the level of effectiveness of a properly appointed, properly flown helicopter is streets ahead of either of the above methods, particularly in terms of the return in relation to money spent. It can effectively and efficiently deal with either very large areas, or areas as small as half an acre.

Its work rate is very fast. A suitable landing and loading site can almost always be found within half a mile or so of the spray target area, even in the most mountainous parts of the country. This keeps 'dead' flying time to a minimum, so maximum use can be made of the limited time-envelope available, taking into account also the tricky micro-climatic situations that can occur in valleys and on slopes. A helicopter can be manoeuvered into the most awkward corners of the narrowest valleys. The helicopter can also fly at the optimum speed for thorough chemical deposition (ie. 40-45 mph). The down draught generated at this speed injects the chemical deep into the bracken canopy (a feature neither tractor nor aeroplane can ever match), resulting in a thorough cover, even on the steepest of slopes. All in all, the helicopter offers the most cost-effective way of applying what is a most successful but relatively expensive chemical (ie. a chemical that one cannot afford to waste or not to use to the maximum advantage). A further advantage accruing from the use of the helicopter, is that if, on any occasion, the pilot becomes unsure as to the location of the exact area to be sprayed, he can fly back to the loading site for further directions, or even take the farmer back up with him to check the location. This cannot be done with aeroplanes (only single-seaters operate in this country in any event) and may even be too time-consuming where tractors are being used.

FARMERS INVOLVEMENT WITH THE PRACTICALITIES OF THE OPERATION

This can be summed up as 'very little', and therefore there are only a few points for the farmer to bear in mind. First of all, he must appreciate the need for a suitable landing/loading site as close to the bracken area as possible, and using his local knowledge, be prepared to assist the helicopter operators as survey agent in the selection of such a site. As a helicopter, when heavily laden, cannot take off completely vertically, the area around the landing site must be free of obstructions (eg. farm buildings, forest patches, steeply-rising ground) for several hundred feet, over at least three quarters of the compass. The reason for the need for a relatively open landing site is because, when heavily laden, the helicopter tends to lift off gradually, while travelling forward at increasing speed. Further, it has to do this while flying into wind. However, sites conforming to these requirements are usually fairly easy to find, even in the most hilly and mountainous areas. The farmer should also make sure that he has the right amount of chemical available on site in good time, and ensure that his bracken area has been clearly identified and preferably marked on the ground so there can be no mistakes make, which could result in the wrong area being sprayed!

The farmer should also be briefed on the agricultural aspects of the operation. Firstly, he should never be led to believe that the aerial application of Asulox or any other chemical is some magic operation that is going to rid him, at one 'fell swoop', of all his bracken. Even experienced helicopter operators who have carried out development and trials work over the years, cannot claim that this would be so. However, a properly flown and correctly appointed helicopter will consistently achieve kill rates of between 99.5% and 99.8%, but, please note, even 0.2% of bracken plants surviving on a hill, is an awful lot of plants! Each of these will grow and multiply if nothing else is done to that land, and within 5-8 years the bracken would then be likely to have returned, if not in full strength, then certainly to a significant level. Further, even the best of pilots is going to miss some areas. Sometimes this will be due to the presence of trees, walls, deep gullies etc. or even strong gusts of wind. Sometimes it will be due to the sheer impossibility of flying 100% accurately, 100% of the time over hostile and often featureless areas of bracken-covered mountain. Missed strips will therefore sometimes occur.

These facts must be explained to the farmer before he places his order. We found that all our customers have accepted the situation and their reaction falls mainly into two classes. One group seem to follow the philosophy that, as the land is fairly inaccessible and steep, while it is worth removing the bracken, any form of follow-up would not be cost-effective, and conclude that, if they can just have 6 or 7 years free of bracken, this would be good value for the money spent. Others decide that as the land, though steep, is strategically placed for more intensive utilisation, it will justify the full follow-up procedure. All farmers appear to have grasped the fact that some of the best soil is to be found on bracken-covered slopes, too steep for anything other than aerial application by helicopter.

The intricacies of the full follow-up procedure are covered elsewhere but should include the farmer's cooperation in ensuring the total eradication of any plants remaining in the year following the helicopter spray operation. This, and the application of lime, are probably the two most important facets of follow-up treatment. Land subjected to the full follow-up procedure, and adequately stocked, should then stay free of bracken for a long time and, possibly, for ever.

THE HELICOPTER OPERATORS' TECHNIQUE AND ROUTINE

This, of course, has a tremendous bearing on the overall success of the operation. In order to achieve the high kill rates necessary to justify the high expenditure associated with bracken control, the helicopter operator must have motivation and not regard the operation as just a means of making money. Further, he must infuse in his staff similar 'high thoughts', so that they work together unselfishly as a team. There are a number of points that must be carefully considered if a good job is to result. These are as follows:

Briefing
This means explaining carefully and correctly to the crew, what

the operation is trying to achieve, and why the service is necessary to the farmer.

Flying technique

This part of the operation must not be rushed. For the best work, flying speed should be 40-45 mph and the flying must be very accurate.

Spray boom set-up

The boom must be set up with care, and the setting altered to suit weather conditions, particularly when large changes in relative humidity occur.

Timing

Never be too early; late July is best in British conditions. Most fronds must be fully unfurled. One can spray until the first signs of bronzing appear in the bracken but spraying should never take place with a high degree of frond or stem breakage, sometimes caused by high winds or severe rain or hail storms.

Wind and slope

Never work in high wind conditions, or much of the chemical will be blown away from the target area. In some years, there are more days spent on the ground than in the air during the bracken spraying period. The increase in acreage due to the slope must be taken into account when first assessing the job. On a 45° slope the acreage shown on the map must be multiplied by 1.4; on a 22.5° slope, by 1.2. A poor job would result from trying to 'stretch' 10 acres-worth of chemical over an area shown on the map to be 10 acres, but where the land is on a 45° slope.

Mixing and loading

The ground crew must be scrupulous in ensuring that the correct mixture is prepared, and the pilot given the correct load.

Attention to all the above points by the aerial operator will ensure that a reasonably consistent, good, initial kill-rate can be achieved. Once the helicopter has finished the spray operation, it is then up to the farmer to carry on the good work, with after-care or follow-up treatments.

CONCLUSION

It has been demonstrated over the last few years, that the use of the helicopter is virtually essential, if spraying for bracken control is to be successful and cost-effective. Furthermore, much of the follow-up procedure on the steeper slopes needs to involve the use of this versatile machine.

Speed of implementation of bracken control programmes should be regarded as a priority, as bracken is, in some areas at least, spreading faster in Britain than the rate at which it is currently being killed.

A comparison of methods of control of bracken re-growth following aerial application of asulam in Northern Britain

G B Horsnail

INTRODUCTION

A recent estimate suggests that bracken occupies some 300,000 ha of Britain and is increasing at 6,000 ha per year[1]. Except for the comparatively small area where ploughing and re-seeding is both practicable and economically viable, it is generally accepted that treatment with asulam is an effective method of bracken control[2]. Complete control of bracken with one aerial application of asulam is, however, rarely possible[2,5]; it has been shown that control levels in excess of 98% can result in serious re-infestation by 4-5 years[3,4] and that control levels at 95% are common[6]. Heavy stocking and general sward improvement are recommended to reduce re-growth[2,5] but this is often not possible, in particular on low grade pastures, grouse moors and amenity areas. The alternative method of controlling re-growth is that of knapsack sprayer spot treatment using an ASULOX:water 1:100 mixture. This has disadvantages; the knapsack load is heavy, and constant re-filling is necessary. Much interest has been shown in the use of hand-held 'weedwipes' which are lightweight and cover a comparatively large area with each chemical load.

This paper considers six field trials which compare the effectiveness of knapsack and weedwipe applications and of mechanical methods of control.

METHODS AND MATERIALS

Sites

In 1982 one site was established in N Yorkshire. Five further sites were established in 1983, two in N Yorkshire and three in Scotland. The experimental design consisted of a simple randomised block, replicated twice with an individual treatment plot size of 10m x 10m. Density of re-growth tended to vary considerably over short distances.   Sites were chosen in areas where previous aerial control of bracken had been comparatively poor and thus had higher levels of re-growth than in much of the adjacent area. Basic details of site locations, timings and at-spray populations are given in Table 1.

TABLE 1

SITE DETAILS

Site No.	Location	Main appli-cation date	Late knapsack appli-cation date	date(s) of mechanical treatments	date of final count	Mean no. of fronds/m² at spray*	Year of main aerial application
1	Levisham, N.Yorks.	20.7.82	26.8.82	20.7&26.8.82	28.7.83	3.97	1981
2	Levisham, N.Yorks.	3.8.83	22.9.83	29.6&3.8.83	4.7.84	9.31	1981
3	Spaunton, N.Yorks.	7.8.83	22.9.83	29.6&3.8.83	4.7.84	7.01	1979
4	Lochwinnoch, Renfrew.	2.8.83	22.8.83	1.7&2.8.83	9.8.84	4.40	1980
5	Ettrickdale, Borders.	3.8.83	24.8.83	3.8.83	19.6.84	12.00	1977
6	Kilmelford, Argyll	9.8.83	30.8.83	9.8.83	30.8.84	25.50	1980

* Non-treated control.

Techniques

Chemicals were applied using a "Kestrel" knapsack (Sites 1-3) or a "Solo" knapsack (Sites 4-6) with a solid cone jet, or a "Weedwiper Mini" fitted with a fast flow rope wick. Two wipes were made per bracken frond.   Bracken was cut using a long-handled grasshook and was pulled by hand.

The main application date was when the bracken was at the full open-frond stage prior to obvious senescence and tissue hardening. However, this growth stage is less distinct in re-growth situations where there is generally a wider range of growth stages.

The chemicals used were as follows:

Trade Name	Ingredients	Concentration	Supplier
"Agral"	Alkylphenol ethylene oxide condensate	90%	ICI
ASULOX	Asulam	40%	May & Baker
"Dessipron"	Adjuvant oil plus emulsifier	97%	BP
"Spasor"	Glyphosate	28.8%	ICI
Kenacid Turquoise Dye U. 5898	-	-	Durham Chemical Dist Ltd

Assessments

The number of bracken fronds in the entire area of each plot were counted at various dates and a representative selection have been included in this paper. At each site the number of damaged fronds per treatment plot was recorded at treatment. This damage varied from complete stem break to stem bending with varying levels of vascular tissue damage.

RESULTS

Table 2 summarises the % increase or decrease in frond populations of the treatment plots in the year after treatment, assuming the population at treatment as 100%.

TABLE 2

CHANGE IN BRACKEN FROND POPULATIONS IN THE YEAR AFTER TREATMENT

Application method	Chemical and carrier	Proportions	% Change in Bracken Numbers					
					Site Number			
			1	2	3	4	5	6
Knapsack (recommended timing)	ASULOX:water	1:100	-64	-93	-55	-93	-92	-91
" (late)	" "	"	-88	-91	-60	-58	-97	-87
Weedwipe	ASULOX:oil	11:7	-39	-82	-39	-39	-80	-4
"	" :water	1:1	-15					
"	"Spasor":water	1.25:2	+33	-52	-65	-42	-53	0
Cut x 1			+46				+128	+3
Cut x 2			-2	-38	+1	-49		
Pull x 1			-1					
Pull x 2			-40					
No treatment			+93	-8	+37	-45	-1	+8

Site 1 was established in 1982 with considerable frond emergence after the main treatment timing of 20.7.82 (Table 3). It was necessary to take the 20.7.82 populations as the base 100% in view of the later differing treatment effects on population. This has depressed the levels of control shown in Table 2 and therefore comparisons between treatments for this site are more valid than the population change values. Sites 2-6 were established in the dry year 1983. There was less frond emergence and in some instances an apparent population loss during the season, particularly at Site 4 where cattle damaged the bracken.

Table 2 shows that knapsack ASULOX spot treatments were the most effective method but that the optimum timing was difficult to ascertain. At Site 3 the weedwipe "Spasor" treatment was at least equal to the knapsack spot treatments. This site was the most severely drought affected with poor bracken growth, and re-growth control levels were generally low.

Of the weedwipe treatments, ASULOX:water was included at Site 1 only, with a poor result. The "Spasor":water treatment was superior to the asulam:adjuvant oil only at the drought affected Site 3. The

427

TABLE 3   Change in bracken population of non-treated controls during the season of treatment

	Mean number of bracken fronds/m^2	
Site Number	At main* application	At late knapsack* application
1	3.97	4.61
2	9.31	8.25
3	7.01	6.64
4	4.40	2.40
5	12.00	11.90
6	25.50	27.00

* For individual site dates see Table 1

weedwipe treatments gave very variable results and at Site 6 had little effect.

Of the mechanical treatments, two pullings gave the best effect at Site 1 where the non-treated bracken population had almost doubled in the second year but this treatment was tested at the one site only. In this one season's work, two cuttings (Sites 1-4) gave comparatively poor results with one cutting having little effect except at Site 5 where the population showed a high increase in the second year.

The comparative numbers of damaged fronds at spraying for the most effective ASULOX knapsack spot treatment timing is shown in Table 4. It can be seen that the frond numbers/m^2 damaged at spraying were in excess of the numbers surviving in the second year at Sites 1 and 4 and were approximately equal at Site 2. Only at Site 5 was damage at a comparatively low level.

DISCUSSION AND CONCLUSIONS

The results show that ASULOX knapsack spot treatments are superior to treatment with this particular type of weedwiper but other types, for example pressure-backup weedwipers, may be more effective. However, other weedwiper problems were encountered during the work. The actual wick tended to coat rapidly with a 'tar' from the bracken and required cleaning with a solvent at regular intervals. In addition, the hand-held weedwiper tended to break the bracken stems; use of tractor mounted weedwipers could increase this problem. Only ASULOX:oil mixture left a visible deposit although even this proved difficult to see. This proved psychologically unsatisfactory to the author and fellow-workers and was commented on by an experienced gamekeeper who field-tested the weedwiper during the 1983-84 season[7]. Use of an effective marker dye could resolve this problem.

TABLE 4   Asulox knapsack spot treatments. Levels of bracken frond
           damage at spraying

Mean number of fronds/m^2

Site number	Total at spraying	Damaged at spraying	Total in yr following	% change
1	3.04	0.40	0.36	-88
2	9.24	0.70	0.74	-91
3	5.64	1.40	2.48	-55
4	6.10	0.66	0.42	-93
5	17.00	0.10	1.00	-92
6	27.00	1.40	2.40	-91

Kenacid turquoise dye was tested by knapsack on trial. The dye did not affect the activity of asulam but was not satisfactorily visible to the operator.

Hand-held weedwipes cannot be completely dismissed. Knapsack work can be very onerous to experienced, physically fit staff and weedwipes do offer a method of checking re-growth using inexperienced personnel.

Levels of bracken stem breaks and acute bending up to c.25% of fronds was present at treatment timing. This was caused by wind, stock and on some sites by walkers.   It could prevent or limit herbicide translocation to the rhizomes and may be a reason for bracken surviving follow-up treatments.

The knapsack spot treatment would also be greatly facilitated if an effective marker dye were available. Under-dosing and over-dosing can occur, in particular when the operator is fatigued. A measured dose applicator is currently under evaluation.

Hand-pulling bracken fronds appears more effective than cutting, but this is based on one site only. This method is of course only practicable on small areas or where very high levels of initial control have been achieved. Pulling, cutting or crushing should be carried out over more than one season, while rough terrain will limit the use of tractor-based methods. Observations show that a planned programme of cutting or crushing is not often adhered to and the results from Site 5 (Table 2) indicate that isolated cutting could increase re-infestation.

ACKNOWLEDGEMENTS

The author acknowledges the contribution of Mr J M Drummond to this work and wishes to thank all land owners and tenants, the staff of the North Yorks Moors National Park and the Chairman of the Spaunton Court Leat, Mr Tom Strickland, for their assistance.

REFERENCES

1) Biennial Report 1979-81. Hill Farming Research Organisation

2) Bracken and its Control. Leaflet 190, reprinted 1983. ADAS, Ministry of Agriculture, Fisheries and Food

3) Schofield J B M and Davies T H (1981) Land and Water Service. Report Number RD/LMC/01. Ministry of Agriculture, Fisheries and Food

4) Robinson R C (1984) Systems of bracken control using asulam. Aspects of Applied Biology, 4

5) Crop Protection Products Manual (1985) May and Baker Ltd, Brentwood, Essex

6) Horsnail G B and Robinson R C (1984) Further developments in the use of asulam for the control of bracken. Proc. Crop Protection in Northern Britain, 315-320

7) P Smith, Gamekeeper, Sigsworth Moor, Pateley Bridge, North Yorkshire. Personal communications

The potential control of bracken by sulphonyl-urea herbicides

A K Oswald, W G Richardson and T M West

INTRODUCTION

Bracken, <u>Pteridium aquilinum</u> (L.) Kuhn, has long been regarded as an invasive species capable of spreading rapidly[1]. The area infested in England and Wales has been estimated as 162,000 ha[2] with some 200,000 ha affected in Scotland[3]. It has also been estimated that the annual national loss of land to <u>P. aquilinum</u> in the UK is some 10,400 ha, out of a total of 3.5 m ha which is also under threat of invasion, thus implying a current change in land use[4]. The weed is poisonous to grazing animals and long-term carcinogenic effects have been demonstrated[5], with possible hazards to humans also[6]. The presence of <u>P. aquilinum</u> interferes with utilisation of grass by stock and makes shepherding difficult.

Spraying with asulam has achieved good control but not eradication[7,8,9]. It has caused damage to many grass species, some of which are commonly found in association with <u>P. aquilinum</u>[10,11]. Re-establishment of the sward is essential for successful grass production after such treatment. This can be difficult, if not impossible, in the typically steep terrain involved. There is, therefore, a need to find a herbicide which could provide successful control of <u>P. aquilinum</u> without damaging indigenous grasses.

The early promise of chlorsulfuron, applied at extremely low doses, for the control of a number of perennial broad-leaved species has been reported[12], and applications to <u>Rumex obtusifolius</u> in pasture have demonstrated the resistance of grass species[13]. The present study investigated the efficacy of chlorsulfuron in controlling <u>P.aquilinum</u> present in a grass sward (Experiment 1). Effects on numbers and weight of fronds and weight of rhizome and grass herbage were measured. Metsulfuron-methyl, an analogue of chlorsulfuron, was tested on <u>P. aquilinum</u> (Experiment 2) and on three grass species grown in pots (Experiment 3).

METHODS AND MATERIALS

Experiment 1

The experiment was situated on Rippon Tor, Bovey Tracey, Devon. The moorland sward, which averaged 22 cm in height, had been grazed by sheep and wild ponies and there was no record of fertilizer usage. At the time of spraying in September 1982, the percentage botanical composition assessed by herbage dry matter (DM) harvested was, _Agrostis capillaris_ 56%, _Agrostis stolonifera_ 25%, _Anthoxanthum odoratum_ 15%, with small amounts of various broad-leaved species and _Luzula campestris_. Counts showed that _P. aquilinum_ was evenly distributed, with an average of 21 green fronds/m^2 giving a dense canopy, 77 cm high.

Treatments: The treatments shown in Table 1 were replicated three times in a randomised block design in plots 5 x 2.5 m and sprayed, using an Oxford Precision Sprayer at a pressure of 210 kPa through TeeJets No 8002, giving a volume rate of 300 L/ha. At spraying, the air temperature was 21°C, the relative humidity 82% and there was no cloud. Grass foliage was damp but _P. aquilinum_ fronds were dry.

Assessments: An area of 3 x 1 m in the centre of each plot was divided into m^2 quadrats. _Pteridium aquilinum_ fronds present in these areas were counted before spraying on 15 September 1982 and subsequently on 8 September 1983 and 26 July 1984. Harvests of _P. aquilinum_ were taken from the two outer quadrats on 8 September 1983 and 26 July 1984, with grass harvests on 9 June and 8 September 1983. All herbage was cut to ground level, using hand shears, after which the weed and grass components were separated, weighed fresh, dried at 100°C for 16 h and re-weighed. On 15 November, 1983, _P. aquilinum_ rhizome was excavated from three, 20 x 20 x 30 cm deep areas in the centre of each of the 3 x 1 m^2 quadrats on each plot. After removal of soil, fresh weights (FW) were recorded. The rhizome from each sample was placed in trays containing a 4:1:1 soil, peat, sand mixture and covered at 1 cm depth, then kept in the glasshouse and allowed to regenerate. All emerged fronds from the planted rhizome were counted on July 15 1984, cut off at soil level and weighed.

Experiment 2

Rhizome fragments obtained from a natural population were planted 8 cm deep in 25 cm diameter pots containing a soil, peat, sand (4:1:1) mixture plus added base fertilizer on 11 May 1983. The pots were kept outdoors and irrigated as necessary using individual trickle irrigation pipes.

Treatments: The pots were brought into a covered area on June 7 1983, after which the treatments listed in Table 4 were applied. A laboratory sprayer fitted with a TeeJet No 8001 was used at a pressure of 210 kPa, giving a volume rate of 184 L/ha. Surfactant (Agral 90) was added to all spray solutions at a rate of 0.25% v/v. At the time of spraying, numbers of fronds ranged from 4 to 30 per pot and were 35 to 90 cm high, with a vigorous rhizome system. Twenty-four hours after spraying, the pots were placed outside in three random replicate blocks.

<u>Assessments</u>: The number of surviving fronds per pot were recorded on 25 July 1984, then cut off at ground level and weighed fresh. Dry weights of rhizome per pot were also recorded after removal of soil.

<u>Experiment 3</u>

Seeds of <u>Agrostis capillaris</u>, <u>A. odoratum</u> and <u>Festuca ovina</u> were sown 0.25 cm deep in 9 cm diameter pots containing a sandy loam soil with additional general fertilizer. Pots were kept outdoors until three days before spraying when they were moved to a temperate glasshouse. At spraying the majority of plants bore four leaves and one tiller.

<u>Treatments</u>: The different treatments (Table 5) were applied with additional surfactant (0.2% v/v Agral 90) on 21 December 1983. A laboratory sprayer was used with a TeeJet No 8002 at a volume of 371 L/ha and a pressure of 210 kPa, after which the plants were replaced in the glasshouse in three replicate blocks.

<u>Assessments</u>: Surviving shoots were cut to soil level on 20 January 1984 and fresh weights recorded.

RESULTS

<u>Experiment 1</u>

<u>Effects on bracken</u>: All treatments reduced numbers of fronds one year after spraying (Table 1). The medium and high doses of chlorsulfuron were most effective, with reductions of 76% following 0.015 and 0.025 kg/ha ai alone and 86 and 90% after the same doses with added surfactant, when compared to untreated plots. Regeneration had occurred two years after treatment but reductions of 50 and 74% were still recorded on plots treated with medium and high doses, plus added surfactant. Although all treatments reduced frond DM weight 12 months after spraying, the most successful were again the medium and high doses of chlorsulfuron, with reductions of 85-95% when applied alone, and 95-97%, with surfactant. In the second year the same doses with added surfactant produced the only significant effects (p < 0.05) with the high dose achieving an 80% reduction. The chlorsulfuron + methabenzthiazuron treatment reduced frond numbers by 43% one year after treatment but this fell to 24% following regrowth. Dry-matter yield was reduced by 67% in the year after spraying and 44% one year later. Asulam reduced numbers of fronds by 62% initially but after regrowth only a 32% reduction was measured. Early effects on DM yield were not maintained and a 39% reduction was recorded two years after

spraying.

TABLE 1 Experiment 1. The effects of chlorsulfuron applied 16
September 1982 on the number and weight of bracken fronds

| Treatment | Dose kg/ ha ai | No of fronds/m^2 | | | g DM/m^2 | |
		15 Sep 1982	8 Sep 1983	26 Jul 1984	8 Sep 1983	26 Jul 1984
Chlorsulfuron	0.005	28	13	35	105	349
"	0.015	21	5	24	34	241
"	0.025	22	5	29	11	237
"	0.005*	20	13	35	79	339
"	0.015*	22	3	19	7	161
"	0.025*	18	2	10	11	76
"	0.015	20	12	29	74	210
+Methabenzthiazuron	1.8					
Asulam	4.48	19	8	26	60	229
Untreated control	0	22	21	38	227	378
	SE ±	3.5	2.5	4.4	22.2	75.3

* = Added surfactant (0.25% v/v Agral 90)

A reduction in the amount of rhizome present, 14 months after
treatment, was achieved by the 0.25 kg/ha dose of chlorsulfuron with
added surfactant (Table 2). All other treatments caused non-
significant ($p < 0.05$) reductions. Regeneration from the rhizome was
also affected by chlorsulfuron treatments. The high dose alone, the
medium and high doses containing surfactant, and the mixture with
methabenzthiazuron, all caused significant reductions in numbers ($p <$
0.01) and fresh weight ($p < 0.05$) of fronds. The low dose with
surfactant also reduced frond weight. Reductions following low and
medium doses of chlorsulfuron alone, or asulam, did not reach
significance.

Effects on grass: The yield of grass DM, 9 months after treatment,
was similar on all treated and control plots (Table 3). During the
summer after spraying, significantly higher yields ($p < 0.05$) were
recorded on plots sprayed with all chlorsulfuron treatments, except
0.015 and 0.025 kg/ha alone and 0.005 kg/ha with additional
surfactant, when compared to untreated plots or those sprayed with
asulam. Medium and high doses of chlorsulfron with surfactant
achieved 88 and 110% increases respectively.

434

TABLE 2 Experiment 1. The effects of chlorsulfuron applied 16 September 1982 on the amount and regeneration of bracken rhizome excavated 14 months after treatment

Treatment	Dose kg/ ha ai	15 Nov 1983 Rhizome FW (g/plot)	15 July 1984 Frond No/ plot	Frond FW (g/plot)
Chlorsulfuron	0.005	183	119	492
"	0.015	205	81	511
"	0.025	184	56	194
"	0.005*	195	94	284
"	0.015*	199	31	157
"	0.025*	129	25	112
"	0.015	214	53	253
+Methabenzthiazuron	1.8			
Asulam	4.48	180	106	565
Untreated control	0	264	199	1332
	SE ±	42.0	48.6	282.4

* = Added surfactant (0.25% v/v Agral 90)

TABLE 3 Experiment 1. The effects of chlorsulfuron applied 16 September 1982 on the amount of grass herbage subsequently harvested

Treatment	Dose kg (kg/ha ai)	Herbage yield (g DM/m^2) at 9 June 1983	8 Sept 1983
Chlorsulfuron	0.005	132	319
"	0.015	118	234
"	0.025	122	227
"	0.005*	105	264
"	0.015*	129	304
"	0.025*	122	340
"	0.015	111	278
+Methabenzthiazuron	1.8		
Asulam	4.48	103	160
Untreated control	0	132	162
	SE ±	24.6	37.6

* = Added surfactant (0.25% v/v Agral 90)

Experiment 2

The high dose of chlorsulfuron, both doses of metsulfuron-methyl and the mixtures of both herbicides, resulted in near or complete eradication of aerial growth, with the low dose of chlorsulfuron also causing a significant reduction in frond weight (p < 0.1) (Table 4). All treatments reduced rhizome dry weight, with the high dose of the chlorsulfuron/metsulfuron-methyl mixture being particularly effective.

TABLE 4 Experiment 2. The effects of sulphonyl-urea herbicides applied 7 June 1983 on bracken grown in pots, assessed on 25 July 1984

Treatment	Dose (kg/ha ai)	Fronds No/pot	Fronds FW(g)	Rhizome DM(g)
Chlorsulfuron	0.0075	31	96	74
"	0.015	0	0	19
Metsulfuron-methyl	0.00375	T	T	27
"	0.0075	0	0	27
Chlorsulfuron + Metsulfuron-methyl	0.0075 0.00375	2	2	24
"	0.015 0.0075	0	0	T
Chlorsulfuron + Methabenzthiazuron	0.015 1.8	11	122	66
Untreated control	0	40	302	205
	SE ±	11.6	66.1	30.2

T = Trace

Experiment 3

The shoot fresh weight of all three species was significantly reduced by all treatments (p < 0.1) (Table 5), asulam being the most damaging. Chlorsulfuron was also less damaging than metsulfuron-methyl applied at the same dose.

DISCUSSION

The results of this preliminary study indicate the potential of sulphonyl-urea herbicides for the control of bracken in hill pasture. Reductions in numbers and weight of fronds were recorded even two years after treatment with chlorsulfuron at 0.015-0.025 kg/ha ai.

TABLE 5   Experiment 3.   The effects of sulphonyl-urea herbicides applied 21 December 1983 on the shoot fresh weight (g/pot) of three grass species assessed on 20 January 1984

Treatment	Dose (kg/ha ai)	Agrostis capillaris	Anthoxanthum odoratum	Festuca ovina
Chlorsulfuron	0.01	10.3	8.3	7.3
"	0.02	6.8	8.9	5.0
Metsulfuron-methyl	0.005	7.4	7.9	5.5
"	0.01	4.8	4.5	3.4
Asulam	4.48	1.0	0.7	0.5
Untreated control	0	13.7	13.1	10.2
	SE ±	0.63	1.01	0.54

Reductions in the amount and regeneration of treated rhizome indicated successful translocation of herbicide through the plant. Significant increases in grass DM herbage harvested 12 months after treatment suggest that removal of the dense weed canopy had led to compensatory grass growth. The influence of wetting agent on herbicide effectiveness, particularly at high doses, was suggested, confirming earlier work on other weed species[14]. However, more specific study would be necessary for accurate conclusions to be drawn. The proprietary mixture of chlorsulfuron and methabenzthiazuron was only moderately successful in controlling P. aquilinum but grass DM yield increases were achieved.

These results suggest an advantage over the recommended asulam treatment, which was less effective in reducing frond growth after two years and had less effect on rhizome weight and regeneration, with the result that there was no obvious compensation in grass growth. Furthermore, successful control with chlorsulfuron was achieved by doses which were up to 300 times lower than the recommended asulam treatment, indicating the prospect of handling lower amounts of herbicide concentrate and suggesting, at current costs, financial economy also.

The pot experiments confirm the promise of metsulfuron-methyl indicated by preliminary screening work[15] and suggest the potential of its mixture with chlorsulfuron. Aerial and subterranean growth of P. aquilinum was completely or severely reduced and although damage to the three grass species was recorded, this was less than following treatment with asulam. The application of even lower doses is also a possibility with this analogue.

Thus, potentially effective control treatments for P. aquilinum are indicated, particularly for situations where grass cannot be grazed because of the presence of a dense weed canopy. The efficacy of metsulfuron-methyl alone and in mixture with chlorsulfuron in the field, and the timing of application in relation to weed growth stage, are currently under test at the Weed Research Division of Long Ashton Research Station. However, the need for further work is indicated, including the identification of the optimum dose required for weed control and grass safety, and the relationship between growth pattern and effective translocation of herbicide.

ACKNOWLEDGEMENTS

The authors wish to thank Mr C Whitley for provision of land, Du Pont (UK) Limited and May and Baker Limited for chemicals, and Mr M R Cookson, Miss J M Heritage, Mr P G Smith, Miss S V Williamson and Mr C G Woodhams for assistance with field and laboratory work.

REFERENCES

1) Braid K W and Conway E (1943) Rate of growth of bracken. Nature, London, 152, 751-752

2) Ministry of Agriculture, Fisheries and Food (1983) Bracken and its control. Advisory Leaflet 190

3) Williams G H (1980) Bracken control: a review of progress 1974-1979. Research and Development Publication No 12, The West of Scotland Agricultural College

4) Taylor J A (1980) Bracken: an increasing problem and a threat to health. Outlook on Agriculture, 10, 298-304

5) Evans I A (1976) Relationship between bracken and cancer. Bot. J. Linn. Soc., 73, 247-268

6) Evans I A, Widdop B, Jones R S, Barber G D, Leach H, Jones D C and Mainwaring-Barton R (1971) The possible human hazard of the naturally occurring bracken carcinogen. Biochem. J. 124, 28-29

7) Martin D J (1976) Control of bracken. Bot. J. Linn. Soc., 73, 241-246

8) Veerasekaran P, Kirkwood R C and Fletcher W W (1976) The mode of action of asulam (methyl (4-amino-benzenesulphonyl) carbamate) in bracken. Bot. J. Linn. Soc., 73, 247-268

9) Williams G H and Fraser D (1979) The effects of asulam, frond cutting and ground mineral phosphate on the yield of swards dominated by bracken (Pteridium aquilinum (L.) Kuhn). Grass and Forage Science, 34, 95-100

10) Martin G S (1970) The effect of asulam applied as for dock control (Rumex spp.) on the production of the grass sward. Proceedings 10th British Weed Control Conference, 476-480

11) Soper D (1970) The tolerance of pasture grasses to asulam. Proceedings 10th British Weed Control Conference, 465-475

12) Richardson W G, West T M and Parker C (1980) The activity and post-emergence selectivity of some recently developed herbicides: R 40244, DPX 4189, acifluorfen, ARD 34/02 (NP 55) and PP 009. <u>Technical Report: Agricultural Research Council Weed Research Organization</u>

13) Oswald A K, West T M and Richardson W G (1982) The use of chlorsulfuron for the control of <u>Rumex obtusifolius</u> in grassland. <u>Proceedings British Crop Protection Conference - Weeds</u>, 219-223

14) Turner D J (1985) Effects of surfactants on the activity of chlorsulfuron alone and in mixture with other herbicides. <u>Aspects of Applied Biology</u>, 9, <u>The biology and control of weeds in cereals</u>, 149-158

15) Richardson W G, West T M and White G P (1984) The activity and post-emergence selectivity of some recently developed herbicides: AC 252214, DPX-T6376 and chlorazifop. <u>Technical Report: Agricultural Research Council Weed Research Organization</u>

Bracken control in new forestry plantations using a dicamba based herbicide as a concentrate ribbon

C G Palmer

INTRODUCTION

Work by Hodgson, Nolle, Aldhouse and McCavish during the 1960s with the herbicide dicamba yielded the following information.

1) Dicamba is highly active on bracken (<u>Pteridium aquilinum</u>) when applied between October and May

2) 4.5 kg ai/ha is the minimum rate for long term control, with 6.7 kg ai/ha the optimum (ai = active ingredient)

3) Three years control is achievable

4) Tree planting interval of at least 3 months is necessary after pre-planting treatment

5) Product effective some 0.5 m outside sprayed plots

Dicamba was marketed by Fisons during 1970/71 as 'Bracklene' applied over the proposed tree lines at the rate of 5.5 kg ai/ha as a 1 m strip, or at 4.1 kg ai/ha overall. The high cost of the treatment led to its early withdrawal. A re-appraisal of the use of dicamba in forestry in the early 1980s led to a review of its use for the control of bracken. In particular, it was felt that the high level of soil activity of dicamba could be utilised by applying a narrow band of herbicide midway between newly planted crop rows which would intercept the bracken rhizomes, but not the tree roots. Selectivity would therefore be possible in the period between planting and the time when the crop roots met between the rows. In practise this would mean application either in the year of planting, or the year following planting.

METHOD AND MATERIALS

Formulations

Dicamba applied as Banvel 4S, Banvel 4WS, BanvelCST, Banvel 720 and dicamba + triaryl methane.

441

Application

Through a Cooper Pegular Falcon fitted with a constant pressure valve adjusted to emit 8-10 ml of diluent/second at 1.5 to 2 bars pressure, using Hardi 1553/10 cone nozzle. A walking speed of 1 metre/second is maintained, with the lance end held 10-20 cm from the ground or bracken litter, and directed midway between the crop rows.

Rates

0.25 gm ai/m to 1.65 gm ai/m.

Assessments

These were by cutting and weighing fronds in a 6 sq m area in each replicate in August before the onset of senescence.

Plot size

Two inter-rows per treatment x 25 m, replicated twice where possible. (See Table 1)

TABLE 1   1984 Trial Details

SITE	A	B	C	D	E	F	G	H
CROP	DF	DF	DF	DF	NS	DF	HL	DF
PLANTED	'82	'82	'83	'83	'84	'82	'82	'84
SPACING	2m	2m	1.8m	1.8m	2m	2.5m	2.5m	2m
SPRAYED	11/5*	11/5	5/4	22/5	2/4	2/4	2/4	3/5
SLOPE	10°	30°	0°	0°	0°	0°	0°	0°

A, B   Ribbsford, Wyre Forest, Worcestershire
C, D   Yew tree break, Forest of Dean
E   Wapley, Mortimer Forest, Shropshire
F, G   Bircher Common, Mortimer Forest, Shropshire
H   Bagshot, Berkshire
(* 1983)
DF = Douglas Fir   NS = Norway Spruce   HL = Hybrid Larch

PERFORMANCE

The 1983 trial was not assessed in the year of application due to an unforseen weeding operation. However, visual recordings noted before this indicated that the ribbon concentrate technique has approximately twice the activity against bracken compared with similar rates applied conventionally. In the second year, the plots on this trial out-performed those treated and assessed in 1984. This may be due to:

1) More favourable rainfall conditions in spring 1983 producing a higher herbicide concentration around the bracken rhizomes (Table 2) and/or

2) Increased reaction between herbicide and the bracken in the second year after application reflecting reduced photosynthesis in the previous year.

The 1984 trials indicated a strong rate response from 49% control at 0.25 gm ai/m to 75% control at 0.37 gm ai/m. Little response was then achieved until rates in excess of 0.87 gm ai/m were applied, (Table 3). However, the erratic responses at site B caused by extremely rough and steep terrain may have obscured the mean figures produced, and if this site is ignored a more logical progression of 69% control at 0.37 gm, and 79% control at 0.5 gm ai/m emerges. Virtually no fronds are produced within a half metre of the treated strip, with light frond production 1 m away. At 1.23 m from the treated strip (as on site F), frond production was approximately 50% of the untreated.

TABLE 2   Rainfall Data

	1984	1985
April 1 to May 14	167 mm	0 mm
May 15 to June 4	55 mm	110 mm
June 5 to July 31	84 mm	36 mm

Weather station - Coddington, Herefordshire approximately midway between sites (excluding Bagshot).
30 year average (Rosemaund E H F, Hereford) is 200 mm for the above 3 month period.

TABLE 3   Results.   Percent reduction in frond fresh weights on 6 sq m area, compared with untreated.

SITE	A*	B	C	D	F	H	MEAN
RATE (gm ai/m)							
0.25	42	61	51	43	–	–	49
0.37	87	83	49	69	89	–	75
0.5	–	55	75	80	83	79	74
0.62 – 0.75	–	64	70	–	86	80	75
0.87 – 1.0	97	84	69	85	89	–	85
1.25 – 1.65	–	–	–	87	89	–	88
UNSPRAYED wt (kg)	7.0	19.4	13.4	13.4	26.6	12.2	15.3

* after two growing seasons (all others in year of application).

CROP SELECTIVITY

Trees on sites C, D and E showed various degrees of browning, and on site C, some pockets of reduced leader growth were noted. However, as all these features also occurred outside the treated areas, they were considered to be site effects and not related to the treatments. At the steeply sloping site B, needle epignasty on a few trees occurred both on a 0.37 gm ai/m plot and on a 1.0 gm ai/m plot. The trees on this site were more advanced than elsewhere and it is likely that rooting systems were affected by the treated band - which in itself would not have been uniformly in the centre of the rows due to the difficult terrain.

DISCUSSION

Based on the two years studied, the following tentative conclusions can be made.

1) Optimum rate appears to be between 0.37 and 0.5 gm ai/m, giving in excess of 70% freshweight control in the first year, and with indications that control levels may be higher in the second year.

2) The treatment appears safe to the crop in the year of planting and in the year following. However, in the third year, and on difficult terrain, some damage may occur.

The treatment can be regarded as a low volume technique, with outputs (assuming 2 m rows) of 30-40 litres/ha being applied. While the work reported has been carried out in April and May, it is probable that March applications may be preferable. Of the nine sites sprayed in 1985, seven have been applied in March to confirm this possibility. In terms of selectivity, the treatment has, to date, been safe where crop rows are a minimum of 1.8 m apart. Bracken control in the crop row will be much reduced if planting exceeds a 2.2 m spacing. Grasses and herbaceous broadleaves with roots in the treated band will be affected by the herbicide and some effects may be expected on mature trees with roots in the treated band. Providing the 1985 trials confirm previous findings, this novel approach to bracken control should provide a less arduous and less weather-sensitive bracken control system than those currently practiced.

ACKNOWLEDGEMENTS

The author wishes to thank the Forestry Commission at Alice Holt, Wyre Forest, Mortimer Forest and the Forest of Dean for their cooperation, and to the Velsicol Chemical Co for the supply of Banvel herbicides.

REFERENCES

1) Nolle H N (1966) Experiments with picloram, amitrol and dicamba for bracken control. Proc. 8th Brit. Weed Control Conf.: 141-149

2) Aldous J R (1966) Bracken control in Forestry with dicamba, picloram and chlorthiamid. Proc. 8th Brit. Weed Control Conf.: 150-159

3) Hodgson G L (1964) Sodium 3, 6 - dichloro-2-methoxybenzoate for the control of bracken: Results of preliminary trials. Weed Res. 4: 167-168

4) Fisons Ltd (1971) Bracklene. Technical Leaflet 1971.

Biological control of bracken: plans and possibilities

J H Lawton

INTRODUCTION

If bracken eradication were easy and cheap, the conference which preceeded the present volume would not have been necessary. But bracken is neither easy, nor cheap to control. Moreover, the author doubts whether minor improvements in, or more earnest application of, existing techniques will much improve the current situation. This paper advocates a more radical solution, by developing the case for biological control of bracken in Britain by the use of introduced insects.

The paper firstly explains how the techniques of classical biological control, normally employed against exotic weeds, might be adapted to control a native plant (bracken), using exotic insects. It then asks what the characteristics of a suitable control agent might be, and shows how <u>Parthenodes angularis</u>, a moth from South Africa, meets these criteria. Other possible candidates are also discussed. Finally, the likely impact of Parthenodes is evaluated.

THE DIFFERENCE BETWEEN CLASSICAL BIOLOGICAL WEED CONTROL AND BIOLOGICAL CONTROL OF BRACKEN

Classical biological weed control involves the release of one or more species of insects against an alien weed. Usually, the insects are herbivores of the plant in part of its original range; more rarely, they are taken from closely related plants[1-4]. Here, I am advocating a variant on this well tried and tested technique, namely the use of one or more species of exotic insects to control a native plant. To my knowledge, this variant has been tried only twice before; once on Santa Cruz Island, California, to control Opuntia cacti, where it was successful, and once in Britain to control thistles, <u>Cirsium arvense</u>, where it failed[6]. Plans are afoot, however, to attempt similar exercises with other native weeds[7]. Classical biological weed control has a more impressive record and is now big and successful business in many parts of the world.

Paradoxically, our capacity to adapt the techniques of classical biological control and use them against this native plant may well rest with bracken's phenomenal success. The plant's Achilles heel is a worldwide distribution[9], offering a large pool of potential biological control agents. Even quite limited surveys show that very different insects attack bracken in different parts of the world[11,12]. I see this large pool of bracken herbivores as a 'toolkit' from which, with patience and understanding, we might reasonably hope to select appropriate agents for biological control.

WHY DO NATIVE INSECTS FAIL TO CONTROL BRACKEN?

A companion paper[12] summarises the reasons why native British bracken-feeding insects fail to have any significant impact on the plant. It is not because bracken has few or no herbivores; 27 species of insects regularly feed on the above-ground parts of the plant in Britain. Rather, it is because most of these species are rare, relative to the biomass of plant material available to them. Only very occasionally do native herbivores become common enough to cause heavy defoliation of bracken[13] (Prof M F Claridge, pers. comm.). However, it is possible to generate outbreaks of bracken herbivores by uncoupling them from their own enemies, broadly defined to include predators, parasitoids and diseases[12]. Although we cannot do similar experiments with all 27 core species, a reasonable working hypothesis is that most native, bracken-feeding insects are kept rare, relative to the abundance of the host-plant, by their own natural enemies. Hence, relieved of such control, exotic insects could cause extensive permanent and ultimately debilitating damage.

There is nothing particularly novel about this suggestion. A prime requisite for successful biological control is to uncouple the agent from limitation by its own predators, parasitoids and diseases[1,2,14]. Hence, exotic insects released in Britain against bracken do not have to cause heavy damage to the plant in their own country; at home, they too presumably have specific enemies. What is vital is that agents are established in Britain which are free from constraints imposed by higher trophic levels. Only then can we hope to damage the plant sufficiently to bring it under control.

CHARACTERISTICS OF AN IDEAL CONTROL AGENT

General principles

Ideally[15], potential biological control agents for use against bracken in Britain must (i) come from a cool-temperate, seasonal climate, similar to that in Britain, (ii) exploit the same subspecies of bracken, (iii) feed in a way that is different from any of the native herbivores and (iv) be bracken-specific and capable of causing significant damage to the plant. Climatic mismatch almost certainly rules out the use, in Europe, of the rich and taxonomically varied pool of insects found on bracken in Papua New Guinea[11,16]. Climatic mismatch was probably also responsible for failure of the only other attempt to control a British native weed with an exotic insect, mentioned above[6]. These considerations suggest that cool temperate parts of the southern hemisphere are the most likely sources of suitable control agents for use in Britain.

Bracken has two major subspecies, aquilinum and caudatum[9]. Morphological and biochemical differences between them could[17], though not inevitably[4], make it difficult to establish insects from one subspecies onto the other. In the first instance, it therefore seems sensible to search for control agents on the same subspecies as here; this narrows the search to South Africa, where bracken is not only the same subspecies (aquilinum) but also the same variety as in Britain[9].

Over and above the question of where to look, is the problem of what to look for. There seems little point in introducing insects so similar, taxonomically and ecologically, to existing species as to make the introductions highly vulnerable to native enemies. The best chance of success lies with species that native enemies fail to recognise or exploit[18]. Species with endophagous (gall-forming and mining) feeding stages are least likely to fall victim as larvae to polyphagous predators. Ideally, candidates for introduction should also be taxonomically distinct from, and attack a part of the plant not exploited by, native herbivores in Britain (to avoid 'taxon-specific' and 'site-specific' enemies, respectively). A rachis miner, in the orders Lepidoptera or Coleoptera, fits this bill admirably[10,15].

Parthenodes angularis as a specific agent

At the moment, one insect fulfils all these criteria[15], a moth found on bracken throughout Southern Africa. The species has been tentatively identified by the British Museum (Natural History) as Parthenodes angularis Hampson (Pyralidae). The genus is poorly known taxonomically, and almost certainly requires revision (Dr G S Robinson, pers. comm.). The South African material that we have collected appears to be all one species, which for the moment we can refer to as P. angularis. The adults are rather pretty, small, golden-brown moths with silver marks on their wings. They have a maximum wing span of about 2 cm. Caterpillars live in mines in the rachis, between ground level and the first pair of pinnae, with up to six larvae per stem. Attack by several larvae causes the top of the frond to die, leaving just the first pair of pinnae. Caterpillars pupate outside the mine. The number of generations each year is not yet known with certainty. There is a large spring generation (when bracken is most susceptible to attack and damage; this is why control by rolling and cutting is best done in spring), but larvae have also been found in summer, and, under laboratory conditions, adult moths from the spring generation emerged from pupae within 22-35 days. There appears, therefore, to be at least a partial second generation each year, enhancing the damaging potential of the moth.

Nothing like Parthenodes occurs on bracken in Britain, except a small moth in the family Gelechiidae called Paltodora cytisella[10]. Paltodora caterpillars mine and form swollen galls in the upper part of the rachis and costa of new fronds. Both the site and mode of damage are rather different from that caused by Parthenodes.

Parthenodes is widespread on bracken throughout South Africa and appears to be climatically tolerant. Large populations occur in the Katburg Mountains, where the climate is similar to that in Britain. Not unexpectedly, the caterpillars in South Africa are attacked by unidentified Ichneumonidae parasitoids; yet infestations are often high. Relieved of natural enemies, the potential for Parthenodes to inflict heavy damage on bracken seems high.

Other possible candidates

Bracken is such a vigorous plant that it seems unduly optimistic to expect control by Parthenodes alone. Three additional species, none apparently as ideal as Parthenodes, have so far been identified in South Africa, and there is a fourth candidate from Tasmania (Table 1). All four species attack the pinnae, and hence could be used to complement the action of Parthenodes.

TABLE 1 Other possible candidates for use as biological control agents of bracken in Britain

Species and higher taxon	Origin	Type of damage	Possible disadvantages
Unidentified lepidopteran	Tasmania	Caterpillars mine pinnules of mature fronds, and destroy the entire mesophyll palisade layer, causing severe damage (Prof J A Thomson, pers. comm.)	On subspecies caudatum. Identity of caterpillars still unknown
Eupteryx maigudoi (Homoptera: Cicadellidae)	South Africa	Sucking bug; known to be bracken-specific in South Africa	May not cause sufficient damage
Conservula cinisigna (Lepidoptera: Noctuidae)	South Africa	Chews pinnae; preliminary data from South Africa suggest that damage can be extensive. Not found on other ferns in field in South Africa	May not be bracken specific. External folivore, similar to some British species, and hence perhaps vulnerable to specialist and generalist enemies
Eriophyid mite; species unknown	South Africa	Causes drastic distortion of pinnae	Difficult to work with, because of small size

What must be emphasised is that detailed field surveys have not yet been made on bracken in many parts of the southern hemisphere, including South Africa. A number of other species undoubtedly await discovery. A particularly valuable additional agent would be a rhizome-miner.

IS BIOLOGICAL CONTROL SAFE, AND WILL IT WORK?

Safety

Classical biological weed control has an excellent and enviable safety record[15], wherever standard and well tried screening programmes have been followed prior to release[19]. Biological control of weeds has been practised for more than 75 years, and introductions of control agents have been made against more than 86 weeds in some 20 countries, with no adverse or unpredictable results[3,20]. Work is now underway in South Africa and under quarantine at CIBC in London to put Parthenodes through these standard screening procedures. Preliminary field data are encouraging. So far, three species of ferns growing close to bracken with Parthenodes have been examined for signs of attack; none have been found. Obviously, we will need to be absolutely convinced of the moth's specificity before applying for permission to release it.

Predicting the outcome with Parthenodes

If Parthenodes is safe (ie. bracken specific) and if permission to release it in Britain is granted, will it work? As indicated above, it seems unlikely that one species of exotic insect will be sufficient to control bracken. I would, however, be more than pleased to be proved wrong in this prediction!

Some indication of Parthenodes' potential can be obtained from Table 2, where the moth has been subjected to a scoring system devised for biological control agents by Dr P Harris, modified by Dr R D Goeden[14]. Insufficient data are available to apply Part III of Goeden's scheme, except that climates are reasonably well matched between the mountains of South Africa and Britain. Hence the total score of 33 on Parts I and II should be increased by at least 3.

A preliminary, incomplete score of 36 is very encouraging. Based on previous experience, Goeden notes that candidates scoring less than a total of 20 points will probably be ineffective as a weed control agent. Parthenodes is already well clear of this threshold. Species with complete scores of between 20 and 50 stand a good chance of contributing to control, particularly if complemented by other imported agents. In other words, I believe that Parthenodes, plus one or two other insect control agents, perhaps acting in concert with fungal pathogens[21], offers reasonable prospects for a low-cost, permanent solution to the bracken problem in this country. Certainly, the chances of biological control making a significant contribution to bracken management in Britain now seem better than they have ever been. Moreover, I see no reason why similar biological control programmes should not be initiated in other countries where bracken is a pest. Several British native insects are prime candidates for biological control of bracken in the southern hemisphere.

TABLE 2 R D Goeden's scoring system for potential biological control agents, applied to Parthenodes angularis. Categories are taken from Table II, pp 292-3, Ref.14. Scores are preliminary. No information currently available for categories marked *; further study may raise one or more of these scores above zero. Scores marked ? are greater than zero, but difficult to assign on current information.

I	Initial assessment of destructiveness in native range	Score
1	Direct damage inflicted in field: D. Destruction of vascular or mechanical support tissues as an endophage	6
2	Indirect damage inflicted in field: A. None known	0
3	Phenology of attack: C. Relatively limited but may have two generations a year, and may increase host-susceptibility to competition from other plants	4?
4	Number of generations: B. Possibly two	2?
5	Number of progeny per female per generation: Unknown (would need to be > 500 to score)	0*
6	Extrinsic mortality factors: C. Subject to mortality from specialist enemies (parasitoids)	6
7	Feeding behaviour: A. Solitary in each mine, though several larvae can occur per rachis	0
8	Distribution: B/C. Criteria do not fit exactly. Widespread in southern Africa	3?
	TOTAL SCORE ON INITIAL ASSESSMENT	21

II	Suitability as a Biological Control Agent	
1	Host-plant source of insect: C. Obtained from the target weed	6
2	Ease of culture: Unknown, probably difficult	0
3	Potential safety: C. Unreported as a plant pest; no known plant pest in same genus	6

450

TABLE 2 continued

4   Host-plant specificity:
    Unknown under laboratory conditions   0*

    TOTAL SCORE ON CRITERIA I & II   <u>33</u>

III <u>Potential Effectiveness in Area of Introduction</u>

    Insufficient data are available to apply this part of the scoring
    system, except that dealing with climate (see text).

ACKNOWLEDGEMENTS

    This work is supported by an AFRC Grant. My ideas on this problem
were shaped and nurtured by discussions with Drs D Schroeder, P Harris
and R D Goeden.   The programme is a joint venture between the
University of York, CIBC (Drs D Greathead and M Cock) and the
University of Rhodes (Professor V C Moran and Dr S Compton). To all
these colleagues and organisations I am extremely grateful.

REFERENCES

1) Huffaker C B (1974) (ed.) <u>Biological Control</u>. New York: Plenum/
Rosetta

2) Schroeder D (1983) Biological control of weeds. In W W Fletcher
(ed.). <u>Recent Advances in Weed Research</u>, 41-78. Farnham Royal:
Commonwealth Agricultural Bureaux

3) Kelleher J S and Hulme M A (1984) (Eds.) <u>Biological Control
Programmes Against Insects and Weeds in Canada 1969-1980</u>. Farnham
Royal: Commonwealth Agricultural Bureaux

4) Hokkanen H and Pimentel D (1984) New approach for selecting
biological control agents. <u>Can. Ent.</u> 116, 1109-1121

5) Goeden R D and Ricker D W (1980) Santa-Cruz island - revisited.
Sequential photography records the causation, rates of progress, and
lasting benefits of successful biological weed control. In <u>Proc. 5th
Int. Symp. Biol. Contr. Weeds, Brisbane, Australia</u>, 355-365

6) Baker C R B, Blackman R L and Claridge M F (1972) Studies on
<u>Haltica carduorum</u> Guerin (Coleoptera: Chrysomelidae) an alien beetle
released in Britain as a contribution to the biological control of
creeping thistle, <u>Cirsium arvense</u> (L.) Scop. <u>J. Appl. Ecol.</u>, 9. 819-
830

7) Delfosse E S (1985) (ed.) <u>Proc. 6th Int. Symp. Biol. Contr.
Weeds, Vancouver, Canada</u>, (In press)

451

8) Julien M H (1982) (ed.) Biological Control of Weeds. A World Catalogue of Agents and their Target Weeds. Farnham Royal: Commonwealth Agricultural Bureaux

9) Page C N (1976) The taxonomy and phytogeography of bracken - a review. Bot. J. Linn. Soc., 73, 1-34

10) Lawton J H (1982) Vacant niches and unsaturated communities: a comparison of bracken herbivores at sites on two continents. J. Anim. Ecol., 51, 573-595

11) Lawton J H (1984) Non-competitive populations, non-convergent communities, and vacant niches: the herbivores of bracken. In D R Strong Jr, D Simberloff, L G Abele and A B Thistle (eds.). Ecological Communities: Conceptual Issues and the Evidence, 67-101. Princeton, Princeton University Press

12) Lawton J H, MacGarvin M and Heads P A (1986) The ecology of bracken-feeding insects: background for a biological control programme. In R T Smith and J A Taylor (eds.) Bracken 85 Conference Proceedings. Kirkby Lonsdale: Parthenon Press

13) Lawton J H (1976) The structure of the arthropod community on bracken. Bot. J. Linn. Soc., 73, 187-216

14) Goeden R D (1983) Critique and revision of Harris' scoring system for selection of insect agents in biological control of weeds. Protection Ecology, 5, 287-301

15) Lawton J H (1985) Ecological theory and choice of biological control agents. In Reference 7. In press

16) Kirk A A (1982) Insects associated with bracken fern Pteridium aquilinum (Polypodiaceae) in Papua New Guinea and their possible use in biological control. Acta Oecologica/Oecol. Applic., 3, 343-359

17) Harris P (1984) Euphorbia esula-virgata complex, leafy spurge and E. cyparissias L., Cypress spurge (Euphorbiaceae). In Reference 3, 159-169

18) Goeden R D and Louda S M (1976) Biotic interference with insects imported for weed control. Ann. Rev. Ent., 21, 325-342

19) CIBC (1978) Screening Organisms for Biological Control. Farnham Royal: Commonwealth Agricultural Bureaux

20) Batra S W T (1982) Biological control in agroecosystems. Science 215, 134-139

21) Burge M N, Irvine J A and McElwee M (1986) Fungal pathogens on bracken. In R T Smith and J A Taylor (eds.) Bracken 85 Conference Proceedings. Kirkby Lonsdale: Parthenon Press

The potential for biological control of bracken with the causal agents of curl-tip disease

M N Burge, J A Irvine and M McElwee

INTRODUCTION

One of the contributory factors to the success of bracken as a persistent, invasive weed is its resistance to disease. A small number of fungi succeed in parasitising bracken, and a few of these have caused sufficient damage in the field to have stimulated research into their possible use as biological control agents. Apart from those responsible for curl-tip, fungi that have been examined in this respect include Ascochyta pteridium[2], Ceratobasidium anceps[3,4], Cryptomycena pteridis (Templeton, pers. comm) and a species of Fusarium[5].

The curl-tip syndrome includes dark brown flecks and eyespots on the petioles, larger sunken longitudinal lesions, shrivelling of pinnules and epinasty of frond branches. The distinctive symptom which gives the disease its name is the necrosis of the frond apex which remains curled. Details of the disease symptoms and the widespread occurrence of the disease in Great Britain have been reported elsewhere[1,6,7]. Curl-tip pathogens have been previously studied by Angus[1] who demonstrated that Phoma aquilina Sacc. (Penz.) was the most damaging under greenhouse conditions.

In all the studies on the possible use of fungal pathogens in biological control of bracken, success in the field has been limited. However, the discovery of a stand of bracken severely diseased with curl-tip near Inverness (NH 640453) in 1979 prompted the present studies. We report here on some of our findings regarding the disease cycle and the potential for improving fungal pathogenicity through the agency of chemical adjuvants to the inoculum.

EXPERIMENTAL

Spore release from litter

Ascochyta pteridis Bres. and Phoma aquilina Sacc. (Penz.) are two species of Coelomycetes that are consistently isolated from bracken diseased with curl-tip[1,7]. We have found that the two pathogens can also be readily isolated from bracken litter taken from diseased sites during the winter months. In order to determine the quantities of inoculum that may be released from bracken litter, samples of dead rachis bearing signs of disease from the previous season were collected in May 1984 from a site near West Linton, Peebleshire (NT 126539). Sub-samples of these were thoroughly wetted, drained, and then incubated in plastic bags at 25°C. At intervals of time the samples were agitated in sterile distilled water and the number of conidia of A. pteridis and P. aquilina liberated, were counted. Large quantities of spores of both pathogens were released (Table 1) indicating that the litter harbours a considerable reservoir of inoculum. Spores of A. pteridis were slightly the more numerous. Proof of identity of the spores observed was obtained by platings on malt extract agar.

TABLE 1 The release of conidia of A. pteridis and P. aquilina from bracken litter

Duration of incubation (h)	Spores ($\times 10^8$) released per gram of litter (95% confidence limits)	
	A. pteridis	P. aquilina
0.25	4.2 ($\pm$ 1.4)	2.8 ($\pm$ 1.1)
4.00	7.5 ($\pm$ 2.1)	4.4 ($\pm$ 1.7)
24.00	21.0 ($\pm$ 3.2)	16.3 ($\pm$ 5.6)

Inoculation and penetration

The first symptoms of curl-tip appear on the bases of young petioles as clusters of minute dots or flecks soon after the emergence of the crozier through the litter. Reisolations from these necroses in June 1983 yielded mostly A. pteridis, although P. aquilina and a Septoria sp. were also present[7]. In May 1984, however, 134 individual flecks from twelve croziers were plated on malt extract agar as soon as the necroses became visible. A. pteridis was obtained from 51 of these; nothing grew from the remainder. Slightly older, and larger necrotic spots commonly yielded P. aquilina in addition to A. pteridis; Septoria was rarely isolated.

Application of conidial suspensions of A. pteridis (10^6/ml; 2ml/plant), with an artist's paint brush, to the surface of petioles of six young croziers raised in the growth cabinet, resulted in the production of fleck-like necroses within five days. Control plants remained unmarked. The flecks produced by A. pteridis remained small, and the fronds continued to grow as vigorously as the controls.

These observations suggest that the continued development of the flecks into necrotic lesions observed in the field is due to the presence of P. aquilina which would appear to take advantage of the damage caused by A. pteridis for necrotrophic tissue invasion.

Inoculation trials

Inoculation trials with A. pteridis and P. aquilina have been conducted separately and in combination. Healthy young sporophytes held in a Fisons 'Fitotron 600H' growth cabinet (12 h cycle of 20°C day/15°C night; 14 h photoperiod of 25,000 lux; continuous RH of 90 $\pm$ 7%) were subjected to four inoculation treatments with 12 replicates per treatment: (1) A. pteridis (2) P. aquilina (3) A. pteridis and P. aquilina, and (4) controls with no fungus. The total concentration of spores in each treatment was between 10^6 and 10^7 per ml and adjuvants were supplied in the form of 0.1% each of 'Polycell Regular' wallpaper paste as a sticking agent and malt extract broth as a nutrient source. The inoculum was applied evenly with a 707 portable sprayer (Hills Industries Ltd, Birmingham) at a rate of 20 ml/plant. Damage was recorded according to a 0-5 scale, where 0 = no damage and 5 = plants dead. The position on the scale was estimated by comparison with a photographic record[8]. Table 2 indicates that plants treated with spores of A. pteridis became more damaged than control plants or plants inoculated with P. aquilina alone. The results are significant (P = 0.01) and were subjected to Duncan's test to obtain least significant differences. There is also evidence that the presence of P. aquilina is inhibitory to the effects of A. pteridis.

TABLE 2   Damage to bracken plants treated with spore suspensions supplemented with "Polycell" and malt extract (0-5 scale; see text)

Treatment	Days after inoculation		
	6	12	18
A. pteridis	^{c}1.63	2.13	2.46
P. aquilina	^{ab}0.67	^{a}1.08	^{b}1.25
A. pteridis + P. aquilina	^{bc}1.08	^{a}1.25	^{ab}1.67
Control	^{a}0.25	^{a}0.75	^{a}0.75

Figures with different prescripts vertically are significantly different (P = 0.01)

Enhancement of disease using herbicide and alginates

It was considered that the efficiency of the curl-tip pathogens as potential biocontrol agents may be improved by the addition of certain adjuvants to the inoculum. Herbicides have often been implicated as agents which may enhance disease developments in plants[9,10]. We have examined elsewhere[7] the performance of several contact herbicides which may assist the pathogenicity of the curl-tip fungi; low concentrations of the herbicide ioxynil have been shown to be non-toxic to A. pteridis and P. aquilina, yet cause sufficient damage to bracken to allow colonisation of the foliage.

Alginates have also proved to be useful in biological control of weeds with plant pathogens[11]; their advantages include adhesion of the pathogen to the host surface and protection of the spores from desiccation. The alginate 'Manucol DM' (Kelco/AIL International Ltd, London) has been shown to improve the longevity of spores of A. pteridis and P. aquilina on petioles treated in the field, and also to allow their germination at a relative humidity as low as 32%. In the absence of alginate, spores germinated well at 95% RH but not at all at 81% RH (McElwee, unpublished data).

TABLE 3 Damage to bracken plants caused by spore mixtures of A. pteridis and P. aquilina supplemented with ioxynil (I) and Manucol (M) (0-10 scale; see text)

| Treatment | Days after inoculation | | | |
	7	14	21	28
Spores only	^{a}0.36	^{a}0.64	^{a}0.77	^{a}1.04
Spores + 1% M	^{a}0.27	^{a}0.54	^{a}0.54	^{a}0.50
Spores + 1/50 I + 1% M	^{c}6.59	9.32	9.64	^{b}8.45
1/50 I + 1% M	^{b}5.00	7.00	7.00	6.73
Spores + 1/100 I + 1% M	^{c}6.59	8.23	8.54	^{b}8.09
1/100 I + 1% M	^{b}4.86	6.14	^{b}6.73	5.77

Figures with different prescripts vertically are significantly different (P = 0.01)

In order to investigate the effects of treatments containing various combinations of fungal spores, ioxynil and Manucol on bracken, plants were raised from rhizome buds in the greenhouse and transferred to growth cabinets when the first pair of pinnae were fully expanded. The conditions in the cabinet were as previously described. Eleven replicates were treated with one of six different formulations of inocula (Table 3). Spores of A. pteridis and P. aquilina were mixed in equal proportions to give a total concentration of between 2×10^5 and 2×10^6 spores/ml. Manucol was supplied at a concentration of 1.0% in each formulation, and ioxynil was supplied at 1/50 or 1/100 (200 or 100 ppm active ingredient) of the manufacturer's recommended field strength. The inoculum was applied to all the above-ground parts of each plant with a 1.25 cm paint brush at a rate of 10ml per plant. Plants were examined at intervals of 7, 14, 21 and 28 days, and damage recorded. The 0-5 scale, based on the

456

photographic record (previously referred to), was expanded to a 0-10 scale, since a wider range of damage was apparent and intermediate values could be recorded. The results (Table 3) indicate that spores in the presence of each concentration of ioxynil caused more damage than spores alone for the duration of the experiment. Spores in 1/50 ioxynil caused more damage than that caused by 1/50 ioxynil alone after 7 and 28 days; spores in 1/100 ioxynil caused more damage than 1/100 ioxynil alone after 7, 21 and 28 days. The slight reduction in damage to all plants recorded after 21 days is the result of the production of new healthy shoots from rhizome buds in each pot which were included in the overall damage assessment. Manucol had no significant influence on the amount of damage caused under the conditions of this experiment. Results were subject to analysis of variance and least significant differences were calculated according to Duncan's test (P = 0.01).

DISCUSSION

Curl-tip disease can be severely debilitating to bracken in the field but an epidemic (epiphytotic) does not develop for one or more of several possible reasons, for instance variability of resistance in different bracken stands, variability in virulence of the pathogens, or localised climatic constraints on disease development and availability of inoculum. A major problem is the ability of bracken to regenerate from underground rhizome buds, and the rhizome itself does not appear to be greatly damaged by the pathogens responsible for curl-tip. However, in naturally infected bracken sites, the death of fronds encourages the release from dormancy of secondary buds which themselves become diseased, resulting in a gradual weakening of the whole stand by depletion of rhizome reserves. The bracken is usually noticeably thinned and grass growth is more vigorous than in a healthy stand.

The aim of biocontrol, using indigenous micro-organisms such as Ascochyta pteridis and Phoma aquilina, is to manipulate the organisms in such a way as to overcome the constraints to disease development as far as possible. Details of these constraints in respect to curl-tip are not yet available but knowledge of the disease cycle itself is a valuable starting point. We have elucidated the involvement of the two pathogens in the development of curl-tip and have indicated ways in which the natural resistance of the weed to these fungi can be reduced by the application of adjuvants such as herbicides and alginates to the inoculum. Such techniques can severely damage bracken raised in growth cabinets but have not yet succeeded under field conditions. Continued research into the potential of different combinations of adjuvants and pathogens is necessary to maximise the rate of disease development.

ACKNOWLEDGEMENTS

This work was supported by Studentships from the Agriculture and Food Research Council (J.I.) and the Department of Agriculture and Fisheries for Scotland (M. McE.). The authors are grateful to Kelco/ AIL International Ltd, London, and May and Baker Ltd for the supply of alginates and ioxynil, respectively.

457

REFERENCES

1) Angus A (1958) Note on diseases of bracken (Pteridium aquilinum) in Scotland. Proc. Bot. Soc. Edinb., 37, 209-213

2) Webb R R and Lindow S E (1981) Evaluation of Ascochyta pteridium as a potential biological control agent of bracken fern (abstr.). Phytopathology, 71, 911

3) Gregor M J F (1932) The possible utilisation of disease as a factor in the control of bracken. Scot. For. J., 46, 52-59

4) Gregor M J F (1935) A disease of bracken and other ferns caused by Corticium anceps. Phytopath. Zeit., 8, 401-419

5) Cunningham G H (1927) Natural control of weeds and insects by fungi. N.Z. J. Agric., 34, 3-8

6) Alcock N L and Braid K W (1928) The control of bracken Scot. For. J., 42, 68-73

7) Burge M N and Irvine J A (1985) Recent studies on the potential for biological control of bracken using fungi. Proc. Roy. Soc. Edinb., 85B, 187-194

8) McElwee M (1983) Studies on the influence of selected herbicides on the infection of bracken by the fungal pathogens Phoma aquilina and Ascochyta pteridis. Honours Thesis, University of Strathclyde

9) Kavanagh T (1969) The influence of herbicides on plant disease. I - Temperate fruit and hops. Sci. Proc. R. Dubl. Soc. Ser. B2, 179-190

10) Kavanagh T (1974) The influence of herbicides on plant disease. II - Vegetables, root crops and potatoes. Sci. Proc. R. Dubl. Soc. Ser. B3, 251-265

11) Walker H L and Conick W J Jnr (1983) Sodium alginates for production and formulation of mycoherbicides. Weed Science, 31, 333-338

Bracken clearance and potential for afforestation

D R Helliwell

INTRODUCTION

This paper is an attempt to examine some of the issues that would be involved if areas of bracken-covered land were to be afforested.

Other papers in this volume indicate the sort of land on which bracken occurs. As a general rule, bracken grows on freely-drained, moderately deep, acidic soils at elevations where tree growth of some sort is possible. On such sites bracken would, under natural conditions, be a dominant plant in the field layer of broadleaved woodland or pine forest; and the presence of an abundant growth of bracken usually indicates a site on which it would be possible to grow a reasonably good crop of trees. This is, of course, a very broad statement, and, as noted by Anderson[1], "Bracken grows on a very wide range of fertility-classes and seems to indicate one thing only, and that is a depth of porous, well-aerated soil of at least six inches". It should not, therefore, be used as an indication that the site is suitable for a particular species of tree or as an indicator of the probable rate of growth of such trees.

Having said that, however, it is true to say that much of the land on which bracken grows is above-average in terms of potential for tree growth, and has fewer problems than the more poorly-drained types of land, where early wind-throw of tree crops limits the size of tree that can be grown and places serious constraints on the profitability of timber production. The choice of tree species which can be grown is also likely to be wider, including larch, Douglas fir and some broadleaved trees, eg. birch, rowan or, possibly, oak, ash, sycamore and beech. Additionally, establishment can usually be achieved without ploughing or draining. Bracken presents us with problems for forest establishment, unless it is adequately controlled by cutting or herbicides until the trees are tall enough to avoid being shaded or bent over by the weight of dead bracken. It does not appear to compete as strongly for moisture as a dense stand of grass, or to have any strong allelopathic effects such as that which Calluna vulgaris has on some trees.

CONSTRAINTS ON AFFORESTATION

Possible constraints on the afforestation of bracken-covered land include (i) environmental constraints: effects on wildlife, landscape and public access, and (ii) economic constraints: availability of capital, and costs of fencing and managing small areas of woodland, often on steep slopes.

Nature conservation

Most bracken-covered areas are not very highly rated in terms of nature conservation (though there may be exceptions), and the effects of afforestation are unlikely to be highly detrimental, particularly if deciduous species are used, and if the trees are planted at a fairly wide spacing (ie about 3 x 3m) and thinned early and frequently to avoid closure of the canopy. The effect will be to replace totally or partially the canopy of bracken with a taller canopy of trees. This is likely to encourage a greater diversity of animal species and, in the long-term and under appropriate management, a greater diversity of plant species.

Landscape

The effect on the landscape may be significant, but, if a fairly natural boundary can be followed and planting is on a reasonably small scale, the effect on long-distance views will not be serious, particularly if deciduous species are used, either pure or in mixtures with evergreen trees. At a distance, the replacement of a rough-textured, dark green cover of ferns by a rough-textured dark green cover of trees is likely to make relatively little difference, at least in summer, provided that the planting does not extend beyond the bracken area. There will be some change of course, but the main problem, as far as the landscape is concerned, is likely to be the alteration and closure of views, if planting takes place near to roads or paths, and some care would be needed in such places.

Access

Effects on access could be serious locally, but, in general are unlikely to be very detrimental. Rank bracken is not easy to walk through except on well-trodden paths, and it should be possible to keep at least some of these open after planting. At a later stage, when the trees are approaching maturity, access may in fact be easier than it was before planting took place.

Ecomonics

On the economic front, a shortage of capital for afforestation could be met by grant aid, or by attracting investment from institutions or private investors. A high level of grant aid would be appropriate where afforestation is not economically attractive but where the environmental benefits are appreciable. Elsewhere, a lower level of aid should suffice, it if can be shown that afforestation of an appropriate type is likely to be profitable. We will return to this matter later.

Afforestation will also have some effects on the total run-off from catchment areas, but it seems likely that if there is a reduction, it will be less than that which has been noted when comparing forest with grassland, particularly during the summer months. Moreover, the quality of the water may be improved[2,3].

ECONOMICS OF WOODLAND MANAGEMENT

I have recently attempted to set out a basis for the assessment of the economics of woodland management[4] which I regard as more realistic and more easily comprehended than the conventional method of using "net discounted revenue" over the life of a timber crop.

If one can reach a situation where an owner has a range of trees on his land, from small saplings to mature trees, it is relatively simple to draw up a balance sheet of benefits and costs. The actual figures will vary with the crop, the size of the enterprise, past and present expertise and managerial efficiency, but they are likely to resemble those in Table 1.

TABLE 1   Typical expected annual costs and returns per hectare from afforested land (£)

	1 ha conifer plantation	5 ha broad-leaved woodland	20 ha conifer plantation	50 ha mixed conifer and broadleaves
Average annual expenditure	280	115	200	175
Rental[a]	25	20	25	20
Total	305	135	225	195
Average annual income	200	80	320	300
Other benefits[b]	15	40	10	20
Total	215	120	330	320
Net benefits	-90	-15	+105	+125

461

a   The "rental" figure is intended to be related to a combination of the capital value of the crop and the degree of risk involved in growing that crop on the site in question, rather than to the rent which could be charged to a tenant.

b   "Other benefits" include amenity, conservation, and sporting values.

This Table is a very simplified presentation, and the amenity value, for example, may be much greater in some instances. The extent to which seasonal surpluses of labour can be utilised may also affect these figures. It should, however, be emphasised that small isolated woodlands with poor access are rarely likely to be profitable in purely financial terms. The owner's personal tax liabilities will also be of relevance eg. the levels of income tax and other taxes which vary with individuals, commercial companies and charitable bodies in appreciably different ways. We are, nevertheless, looking for woodland units of 10 ha or more whenever possible.

INTEGRATION OF FORESTRY WITH AGRICULTURE

The integration of woodland management with farming activities is a subject which crops up from time to time. In some countries, notably Scandinavia and, to a lesser extent, New Zealand, there is considerable integration, with farmers growing timber as a normal part of their working lives, just as they rear pigs or grow cereal crops. In Britain, there has been little integration except on the larger estates, many of which have been broken up in recent times, and most farmers and agricultural advisers have no experience in woodland management. This is a barrier which needs to be overcome if afforestation is to take place within the existing social and physical pattern of the hills rather than as an external imposition. The very interesting study by Mutch and Hutchison[5] indicates some of the advantages of true integration, where woodlands can diversify the economic basis of a farm, providing additional gross income, greater financial flexibility, and direct benefits in the form of sheltered, winter grazing. This study also points to the need for advisers to understand the needs of the farmer, rather than giving "pure forestry" advice. For instance, larch might be planted to allow for future grazing within the plantation, rather than spruce which would give a greater volume of timber. Larch also provides a more useful timber for use on the farm, is easier and quicker to establish and is often more acceptable in the landscape, though perhaps less easy to sell on the open market.

The allocation of land for afforestation needs to conform to the needs of efficient stock husbandry and farming. However, it is safe to say that many bracken-covered areas will be eligible, particularly if they are steep and difficult or impossible to traverse by tractor, and if they are currently contributing little or nothing to the farm economy.

One compromise which might be worth applying in some cases would be the planting of a crop of trees on bracken-covered land, followed by thinning fairly heavily once the bracken has been suppressed, and then maintaining a partial tree cover for a number of years, to provide sheltered grazing for sheep and/or beef cattle. This might represent the most effective use of such land, with only minimal effort in controlling the bracken for 3 or 4 years while the trees are very small. This raises questions as to which tree species are most effective in suppressing bracken, and how rapidly it will re-invade when the trees are thinned. Is total suppression necessary, and are there particular levels of stocking trees and livestock which will allow grass to grow but reduce the rate of bracken re-invasion? A fairly small programme of experimental work and survey might answer these questions and arouse sufficient interest in farming circles to persuade some farmers to undertake planting.

Other changes are also needed, in the advisory services, grant aid, and tax allowances available to farmers, as indicated by MacEwen and Sinclair[6]. However, it is my firm belief that valuable timber could be produced from much of our bracken-covered land without any loss of agricultural production, and without significant damage to wildlife or landscape. With due care, these aspects could even be enhanced, together with a strengthening of the social and economic basis of upland areas. This fact was recognised in the discussion document produced by Durham County Council[7], which advocated the planting of an additional 5 to 10 per cent of the eastern part of that County.

Large areas of common land are covered by bracken (see Hughes and Aitchison, and Smith, herein), and changes in their future legal status or management might enable some parts to be planted with trees. This, also, would need to be done with sensitivity and care, if serious damage is not to be done to the landscape and to nature conservation.

At the present time the European Economic Community produces only 50% of the timber that it needs. This is in contrast to its production of most temperate agricultural foodstuffs, many of which are in embarrassing surplus. Again, the United Kingdom produces only 10% of its timber requirements. This figure is expected to rise to about 20%, as young plantations come into production and further afforestation takes place, but there is still a huge market for timber in this country. Timber is a highly versatile raw material, which can be used in the round, sawn, chipped, or as a chemical feed-stock, and if it can be produced at a reasonable cost there will always be a steady market for it. This is particularly true of the better quality saw timber, for which we have, in recent years, drawn heavily on previously unworked forest areas in Canada and elsewhere.

The individual farmer or landowner with a relatively small area of woodland, 10 to 50 hectares, is well placed to give the care and attention that is needed to produce valuable saw timber, particularly if the trees are growing on fertile, well-drained soils on relatively sheltered sites. He may not be able to compete with State forestry or the large commercial companies in the production of cheap pulpwood, which in any event is unlikely to be worth much more than £5 per ton prior to harvesting, but he can compete in the better quality markets, where prices of £30 per ton for standing timber are not uncommon. If he can produce between 10 and 20 tons per hectare per annum of timber, which, allowing for the less valuable thinnings, is worth around £15-£20 per ton standing, this represents an eventual gross annual return of £150-£400 per hectare (£60-£160 per acre) from land which previously produced very little. A woodland acreage of, say, 20 hectares could give an increase in turnover of £3,000 to £8,000 per year - or more, if the farmer fells and extracts the timber himself. On a national basis, if 200,000 hectares were afforested, this could produce over 2 million cubic metres of timber per annum, providing direct employment for about 3,000 people, in addition to a greater number in service and processing industries.

It is, however, essential that the farmer knows what he is doing, has access to sound advice, is committed to the venture, and can work out a comprehensive scheme for the whole farm, whereby, for example, fencing and road construction are useful to both enterprises. There is, however, a need for more working examples and for clearly-written guidance on the management of this proposed type of woodland. Woodland management requires just as much skill as shepherding, grouse management or dairying, especially if high-grade production is to be achieved. Low-grade production has, for various reasons, been the norm in this country, for too long.

REFERENCES

1) Anderson M L (1950) Selection of tree species. Edinburgh: Oliver and Boyd

2) Evans I A (1986) The carcinogenic, mutagenic and terratogenic toxicity of bracken. Presented at Bracken 85, Leeds (herein)

3) Galpin O P and Smith R M M (1986) Bracken, water supplies and stomach cancer - is there a link? Presented at Bracken 85, Leeds (herein)

4) Helliwell D R (1984) Economics of woodland management. Chichester: Packard

5) Mutch W E S and Hutchison A R (1980) The interaction of forestry and farming. Edinburgh: East of Scotland College of Agriculture

6) MacEwen M and Sinclair G (1983) New life for the hills. London: Council for National Parks

7) Durham County Council (1984) The future of the Durham Dales. A discussion document